ACOUSTICS

ACOUSTICS

By

JOSEPH L. HUNTER

PROFESSOR OF PHYSICS
JOHN CARROLL UNIVERSITY

Englewood Cliffs, N.J.

PRENTICE-HALL, INC.

Library of Congress Catalog Card Number: 57-8466

Second printing......June, 1962

PRINTED IN THE UNITED STATES OF AMERICA
00275-C

To the memory of
Father Francis E. Fox

PREFACE

The first part of this book, consisting of Chapters 1 through 4, covers the fundamentals of wave and vibration theory, including an introduction to mathematical methods, terminology, and notation peculiar to the science of acoustics. The remaining eight chapters form the second part, being an introduction to those applications of acoustics which appear to be of greatest importance, both historically and from the point of view of current research and development. My choice of topics for the latter chapters has been guided by the plan used by the Acoustical Society of America in the classification of its publications.

Three important objectives guided the organization and writing: First, to give the reader a solid introduction to fundamental acoustics, which is really equivalent to a study of wave propagation in material media. Second, to acquaint him with the operation and design of modern acoustic apparatus and the problems of present-day acoustics. Third, to provide the reader with the background and technical proficiency necessary to understand acoustical writing as found in the *Journal of the Acoustical Society of America;* for this reason, topics in applied acoustics have been treated to stress the major problems that engage the interest of investigators in the special fields of acoustics, and the type of thinking which they bring to bear on these problems. My intention has been to develop acoustical insight and intuition, rather than attempt an exhaustive presentation in any subfield.

Liberal use is made of fully worked-out illustrative problems. These include several typical design problems in the chapters on applied acoustics. Throughout, equivalent circuits are used as a basis for design problems, so as to show in detail how these arise from the physical statement of the problems.

Prerequisites are courses in general physics and calculus, including some partial differentiation. A course in electric circuit theory would be advantageous, because of the widespread use in acoustics of electroacoustic analogies and the similarity of the mathematical approach. Mathematical techniques of special importance to acoustic theory are explained in sufficient detail to make the treatment relatively self-contained.

The eight chapters devoted to applied acoustics are relatively independent: Chapters 5, 6, 7, and 10 are concerned primarily with acoustic apparatus and measurements; Chapter 11 with physical acoustics; Chapters 8 and 9 with intelligibility, including the influence of environment; and Chapter 12 with underwater sound.

Joseph L. Hunter

ACKNOWLEDGMENTS

It is impossible to acknowledge properly all of the assistance which I have received during the preparation of this book. The texts and journal articles contained in the end-of-chapter references have been invaluable, as have been the contributions of several manufacturing organizations specializing in acoustical equipment. Special thanks must be given, however, for permission to reproduce many excellent figures which have appeared previously in texts, journals, and manufacturers' literature. Below is a list of sources of these figures, together with their figure numbers in this text.

Vern Knudsen and Cyril Harris, *Acoustical Designing in Architecture*, John Wiley, New York, 1950: Figs. 9.11, 9.21, 9.61, 9.72, 9.102

Vern Knudsen, *Architectural Acoustics*, John Wiley, New York, 1932: Fig. 9.101

Harry F. Olson, *Elements of Acoustical Engineering*, 2nd ed., Van Nostrand, New York, 1947: Figs. 5.41, 5.42, 5.43, 5.103, 5.111, 6.51, 7.41, 7.71, 9.131, 9.132

Harvey Fletcher, *Speech and Hearing in Communications*, Van Nostrand, New York, 1953: Figs. 8.31, 8.32, 8.41, 8.51, 8.52, 8.61, 8.62, 8.74, 10.72

Clevite-Brush Co., Cleveland, Ohio: Figs. 6.41, 6.43, 6.44, 6.45, 7.31, 7.62, 8.22, 8.81, 10.52, 10.53, 10.62

L. L. Beranek and A. G. Petersen, *Handbook of Noise Measurement*, General Radio Co., Cambridge, 1953: Figs. 9.121, 9.122, 10.61, 10.71; Tables 8.111, 8.112, 8.113

Bell Telephone Laboratories, New York City: Figs. 6.26, 6.34, 8.21

Allen B. Dumont Laboratories Inc., Clifton, New Jersey: Figs. 7.21, 7.22

Fairchild Camera and Instrument Corporation, Jamaica, New York: Fig. 7.72

J. J. Markham, R. T. Beyer and R. B. Lindsay, *Revs. Mod. Phys.* **23**, 353–411 (1951): Figs. 11.12, 11.32, 11.51, 11.52, 11.53, 11.54, 11.55

French and Steinberg, *J. Acoust. Soc. Am.*, **19**, 90 (1947): Figs. 8.82, 8.83, 8.91, 8.92, 8.93, 8.94, 8.95

M. J. Sheehy, *J. Acoust. Soc. Am.*, **22**, 24 (1950): Fig. 12.11

R. L. Wegel and C. E. Lane, *Phys. Rev.*, **23**, 266–285 (1924): Figs. 8.51, 8.52

R. J. Evans, *Electronics*, August, 1946, pp. 88–93: Figs. 12.21, 12.62

Lanier and Sawyer, *Electronics*, April, 1946, pp. 99–103: Figs. 12.51, 12.52, 12.62

Shortley and D. Williams, *Elements of Physics*, 2nd ed., Prentice-Hall, Inc., 1955: Fig. 8.11

H. Fletcher and R. H. Galt, *J. Acoust. Soc. Am.*, **22**, 95 (1950): Fig. 8.32

H. Fletcher and W. A. Munson, *J. Acoust. Soc. Am.*, **5**, 82 (1933): Fig. 8.31

W. B. Snow, *J. Acoust. Soc. Am.*, **8**, 14 (1936): Fig. 8.41

L. S. Goodfrient, *Audio Engineering*, May, 1950, p. 20: Fig. 9.52

E. Toth, *Audio Engineering*, February, 1952, p. 31: Fig. 9.111

A. B. Wood, *A Textbook of Sound*, G. Bell and Sons Ltd., London, 2nd ed.,
    1941: Fig. 11.63 (after Payman, Robinson, and Shepherd)

I was assisted greatly in the preparation of the manuscript itself by
Mrs. Jane McDonald, faculty secretary at John Carroll University, and by
Joseph Trivissonno, former graduate student in Physics at John Carroll
University, now at the Case Institute of Technology. In addition, graduate
students Thomas Mercer and Robert Coerdt gave valuable aid.

CONTENTS

3. Plane Sound Waves   82

4. Spherical Waves and Radiation   132

5. Loudspeakers   167

Chapter 1

OSCILLATION

Acoustics is an art and a science. It was an art with the Greeks, as mechanics was an art with the medieval builders of Gothic cathedrals. Both Grecian amphitheaters and medieval vaulting demonstrate the same intuitive grasp of scientific principles, though the latter antedated Newton by several centuries, and the former were constructed ages before acoustics became a science. The physicist, of course, is interested in the science as it exists today, but he will find that it has never lost its artistic nature. It is perhaps the most gregarious of physical sciences, overstepping the bounds of physics, and dealing with anatomy, psychology, music, architecture, and other branches of human endeavor not limited by the cold objectivity characteristic of physical science.

However, the subjective element in acoustics should not be over-emphasized. Once the connection between audition and acoustic waves had been established, physicists undertook the development of the physical theory of such waves—guided in part by auditory experiment, but also following basic physical laws with regard to the nature of waves, to conclusions independent of experiment. Indeed, it was once remarked that the science of acoustics was distinguished by the grandeur of its theory and the poverty of its observations. Because of the rudimentary nature of early acoustic apparatus and the meagerness of energy present in acoustic waves, many of the fundamental findings of the acoustic science were exploited with far greater success in other branches of physics.

The vacuum tube and the microphone have changed this picture completely, and the applications that have come about since their invention make full use of the unified theory which preceded them. Not that the theory has been static—new devices call for new theoretical developments, and for a change in the emphasis previously given to various segments of the over-all theory. The oscillation and the wave remain the theoretical bases of acoustics, but the treatment changes with the applications of the particular era. Therefore, before a formal exposition of acoustic theory and its modern applications is undertaken, it is beneficial to consider, in a broad way, those who occupy a place in the field of acoustics.

The musician and the instrument maker are engaged in the production of tones and tone combinations that are pleasing to the human ear. The tools

1

of their trade are strings, membranes, bars, plates, and air columns, which are struck, bowed, blown, or somehow excited to vibrate in a desired way. The volume and richness of the tone may be enhanced by resonating chambers, as in the violin. This is the field of primary sound production; and though the examples given are primarily of cultural interest, all these have been applied to more utilitarian branches of acoustics. By far the most important primary source, which dwarfs all others in dignity of purpose and excellence of structure and function, is the human voice box. It is true that no knowledge of the operation of this marvelous device is needed for its use by the individual. Nevertheless, the mechanics of speech and hearing have been subjected to the most searching scrutiny within recent times. Physiologists and psychologists have applied basic physics to the vocal cords and the hearing mechanism with striking success. Telephone engineers have also been active in this field because of their interest in the transmission of intelligence.

Where the ultimate goal of the telephone engineer is a maximum of intelligibility compatible with the extreme complexity and expanse of the telephone network, the radio engineer strives for perfect *fidelity* of reproduction. His purpose is achieved when the vibrations of loudspeakers in millions of homes are exact facsimiles of those originating in the vocal cords of speakers and singers, or in the strings, brasses, woodwinds, and percussion instruments of the symphony hall.

The design of the auditorium itself is the province of the acoustic architect. Echoes and excessive reverberation must be prevented, lest speech be unintelligible, and music a confused mass of sound; yet controlled reverberation must exist, for, like the resonating chamber of the violin, it is essential to the volume and richness of the sound. Indeed, present-day acoustical engineers consider the auditorium as having an intimate part in the production of orchestral tone; for its resonances enter into the totality of tone production just as truly as the individual resonances of the instruments themselves. The acoustic architect, like the radio engineer, must know how to take advantage of amplification, for the acoustics of the enclosure may be greatly improved by the judicious placement of microphones and loudspeakers. The deadening and isolation of sound may also be considered within the sphere of architectural acoustics, both in auditorium architecture and in the design of special structures to house engines such as jets, which develop tremendous acoustic powers.

The naval tactician has become acutely aware of acoustics. A quiet ship is not so likely to be picked up by enemy listening apparatus, and conversely, a sensitive sound receiver may give advance warning of the presence of enemy craft. Further, so that noise reduction in ships may proceed in a scientific manner, the Navy has become vitally concerned with accurate instrumentation for the measurement and analysis of sound. Similar applications of acoustic measurements could be given for each of the fields of acoustical engineering noted in this introduction.

The physicist is interested in sound as such because it is a wave propagation in a material medium. By studying it, he can get important clues to the structure and characteristics of the medium which propagates it. Perhaps he alone studies sound as sound. To go a step further, he is often content to study the wave as a wave. For example, he shows no preference for audible, as against ultra-audible sound. Since waves and their properties are of such far-reaching importance in his field, much of his work is independent of acoustics in the popular sense of the term. Yet this sort of investigation is often invaluable in the everyday applications of the science.

To some, the all-important mathematical foundations of acoustics are un-inspiring. But there is a unity, an order, an intricacy of structure and development in the logic of acoustic theory that is an art in itself. This artistry may not be readily apparent, any more than great music is necessarily appreciated when first heard. Yet the theoretical progress from the vibration, the source of sound, on through the wave in the string (the simplest form of wave), to the propagation of the general sound wave, is a sparkling example of mathematical and physical reasoning; and it is accomplished with such economy of thought and directness of purpose that, to many, the journey has been more exciting than the destination. This, of course, is a mistake. The mathematics is only a means to an end. But it is equally a mistake to attempt to achieve the end without the means. To reverse a familiar quotation, there is only one road to Rome. An understanding of the wave and vibration theory of the first four chapters of this text is the irreducible minimum for effective work in acoustics.

1.1 Oscillation in General

Sound may be defined either as a stimulus which brings about the psychological reaction of hearing, or as the mechanical phenomenon which results in this stimulus. Although attempts have been made to confine the term "sound" to one or the other of these meanings, it must be admitted that the word is used in both senses. For the purpose of this chapter, we may start with the definition recommended by the American Standards Association:

> Sound is an alteration in pressure, stress, particle displacement, or particle velocity, which is propagated in an elastic material, or the superposition of such propagated vibrations.

The above definition is purely physical, and completely general in specifying the type of physical alteration which is propagated. That is, it may be in the form of a single pulse, an irregular though repetitive variation, a complex periodic change, or a simple periodic change. The alteration, or "disturbance," as it is often called, has its origin in the motion of some material body. Since, in most cases, the alteration is at least repetitive, the study of *vibrators*, or *oscillators*, has traditionally been the starting point for the study of sound.

Vibration is governed by purely mechanical laws, and thus acoustics may be considered a subfield of mechanics. Still, within the special field of acoustics, the terms "mechanical" and "acoustical" have different connotations; thus we have "acoustical" as distinguished from "mechanical" oscillations. Oscillations are also important in the field of electricity, and because of the progress that has been made in the study of the electrical oscillations, it is very beneficial in the study of acoustics to consider analogies involving circuits. Indeed, modern acoustics is indebted not only to the development of such electric devices as the microphone, loudspeaker, and amplifier, but also greatly to the mathematical theory of electric circuits and electric wave propagation.

The type of motion on which the fundamental concepts of mechanical, acoustical, and electrical oscillation are based is known as simple harmonic motion. It is characterized by a sinusoidal change of a physical quantity as a function of the single variable, time. Though most sounds are not simple harmonic in nature, practically all of them may be represented as a *superposition* of simple harmonic oscillations. Moreover, a large class of electric circuits is characterized by strictly sinusoidal variation; and a large body of important concepts, based on the supposition of sinusoidal variation, particularly the *impedance* concept, has been carried over from electricity into acoustics. The importance of the impedance concept can hardly be overemphasized. Little improvement in earphones took place from their invention by Bell in 1876 until the introduction of the motional impedance concept by Kennelly and Pierce in 1912. Rapid development followed almost immediately.

The simplest electric system is called the *circuit*. Circuit electricity may be defined as a study of the cause-and-effect relation between voltage and current.* Similarly, mechanical oscillation theory may be considered the cause-and-effect relation between force and velocity, and acoustical oscillation theory may be considered the cause-and-effect relation between *pressure* and *volume velocity*. The succeeding articles of the first chapter will be based more on the study of mechanical oscillation than on the other two types; yet if space permitted, practically the same discussion could be followed for electrical and acoustical oscillation.

1.2 Vibration and the Vibration Equation

Elementary dynamics is based on Newton's equation, $\mathscr{F} = ma$, in which a force $\mathscr{F}$ acts on an *isolated* particle of mass m, and produces a resulting acceleration a. This equation also holds if the particle is part of a *mechanical system*, provided that $\mathscr{F}$ is understood to be the *net* force acting on the particle. For instance, if the motion of the particle gives rise to a frictional force proportional to its velocity, $\mathscr{F}$ in the above equation is the vector sum of the external applied force and the frictional force. If, in addition, the particle is

---

* The current should be measured in amperes.

subject to elastic constraint, there will be a reaction force which in most important instances is linearly proportional to the displacement (x) of the particle from some equilibrium position. The complete force equation for this particle will be

$$\mathscr{F} = f - R_m \frac{dx}{dt} - sx = m \frac{d^2x}{dt^2}$$

or
$$m \frac{d^2x}{dt^2} + R_m \frac{dx}{dt} + sx = f \tag{1.21}$$

where the velocity and acceleration are written as first and second derivatives of the displacement, and f as the *externally applied* force. The resulting equation contains only the first power of the displacement and its derivatives, and for this reason, it is called a linear differential equation. Nonlinear differential equations arise in instances where the damping force is proportional to the square or higher powers of the velocity, or where the elastic force is proportional to higher powers of the displacement. Such variation is the rule for high velocities and large displacements, such as might occur in explosions, supersonic flight, and shock waves produced by missiles of high velocity. Nonlinear differential equations are usually difficult of solution, and it is advantageous if a linear approximation can be made. The situation in acoustics is such as to make the linear approximation justifiable in most important cases, and the resulting simplification adds greatly to the unity and coherence of acoustic theory. It will therefore be assumed hereafter, unless specifically noted, that the displacements and velocities are such that there is a negligible departure from linearity. In Eq. (1.21), R_m is defined as the *mechanical resistance*, and s as the *stiffness constant*.

The simplest vibratory system consists of a single mass particle restrained in a position of equilibrium by a linear elastic force, with zero external and frictional forces. In this special case,

$$m \frac{d^2x}{dt^2} + sx = 0 \tag{1.22}$$

or
$$\frac{d^2x}{dt^2} = -\frac{s}{m} x \tag{1.22a}$$

Figure 1.21 shows examples of such a system. In (a), the stiffness constant is assignable to a single spring, while in (b), it is a constant of the *system*. In both cases, however, the stiffness of the system is the ratio between the force on the mass and its static displacement from the equilibrium position. Elementary dynamic analysis shows that the mass particle will *oscillate* about the center of equilibrium with a frequency of oscillation determined by the mass and the stiffness, and an amplitude determined by the initial conditions, namely, the initial displacement and velocity of the particle. We show this by a solution of Eq. (1.22). This equation may be solved by a method which is commonly used in mathematical physics; that is, by assuming for the solution a mathematical form which seems likely to fit the equation, and then proving it correct. Since the differential equation presents a simple relation between

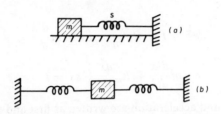

Fig. 1.21. Systems composed of mass and springs. In (b) the stiffness constant s applies to the system and *not* to the individual springs. With this qualification, the systems are mechanically equivalent.

a variable and its second derivative which is true of both the sine and the cosine, we shall assume a sinusoidal solution. If

$$x = A \cos \omega t + B \sin \omega t \qquad (A,\ B \text{ constants}) \quad (1.23)$$

then $\qquad \dfrac{d^2x}{dt^2} = -\omega^2 (A \cos \omega t + B \sin \omega t) = -\omega^2 x$

Equation (1.23) is thus a solution to the differential Eq. (1.22a), the only condition being that ω^2 have the value s/m. The constants A and B are purely arbitrary. The *general* solution of a differential equation of the second order requires two arbitrary constants, and is compatible with any possible motion of the physical system which it describes. When the arbitrary constants have special values, the solution describes a particular motion of the system. Thus, if $B = 0$, so that

$$x = A \cos \omega t \qquad (1.24)$$

we have simple harmonic motion (abbreviated SHM), in which the particle has its maximum value at the initial instant ($t = 0$), where A is the numerical value of this maximum displacement. If we differentiate Eq. (1.24) and allow t to become zero, we may show that the velocity is zero at the start.

Similarly, $x = B \sin \omega t$ (Eq. 1.25) is a particular solution in which the particle has zero initial displacement and maximum initial velocity. We may show by differentiation that $B\omega$ gives the value of this velocity maximum. The terms *displacement amplitude* and *velocity amplitude* are also used for maximum values.

Physical interpretation of the solutions follows readily. For definiteness, consider Eq. (1.24). The particle will *oscillate* about a center of equilibrium with a *frequency* of *oscillation* determined by the physical constants s and m, and a displacement amplitude determined by the *initial conditions*, namely, the initial displacement and velocity of the particle. Since the derivation in

Eq. (1.23) is valid only if the argument ωt is measured in radians, the displacement completes a *cycle* of its motion each time the argument increases by 2π. If we take T, the *period*, as the time during which a cycle of motion takes place, we have

$$\omega T = 2\pi, \quad T = \frac{2\pi}{\omega} \tag{1.26}$$

The inverse of the period is called the frequency, f_0. Since ω, and therefore f_0, are related to the physical constants of the system s and m, we have for the frequency of vibration,

$$f_0 = \frac{\omega}{2\pi} = \frac{1}{2\pi}\sqrt{\frac{s}{m}} \tag{1.27}$$

Let us now investigate the *general solution* (Eq. 1.23) of the differential equation. This solution may be given an alternate expression,

$$x = C \sin (\omega t + \delta) \tag{1.28}$$

by the trigonometric indentity

$$\sin (\omega t + \delta) = \sin \delta \cos \omega t + \cos \delta \sin \omega t$$

A comparison of the two equivalent forms shows that the following relations must hold:

$$A = C \sin \delta, \quad\quad C = \sqrt{A^2 + B^2}$$
$$B = C \cos \delta, \quad\quad \delta = \arctan (A/B) \tag{1.29}$$

From the form of Eq. (1.28) we note that $C \sin \delta$ is the initial value of the displacement, and by differentiation we find the initial velocity to be

$$\omega C \cos \delta$$

The argument in Eq. (1.28) is called the "phase" of the oscillation. The constant δ is thus the "initial phase" or the "initial phase angle."

Equation (1.21), which has been developed for a mechanical system, has analogues in acoustical and electric systems. Since the object, in this chapter, is to study the broad subject of oscillation, rather than purely mechanical vibration, we shall develop the corresponding acoustical and electrical equations. In a later chapter, we shall dwell at greater length on the quantities which comprise the acoustical equation, but a less detailed treatment will suffice for the present.

Consider the system shown in Fig. 1.22, consisting of an air-filled cavity

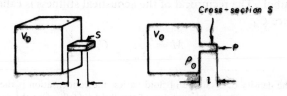

Fig. 1.22. Helmholtz resonator.

joined to the open air by a short neck of small cross section, and exposed to a small varying excess external pressure. In the absence of this excess external pressure, we may assume that the internal and external pressures and densities are equal. Any variation in the external excess pressure p will ultimately cause variation in the internal excess pressure p_i, according to the law $p_i = Bs$, where B is the bulk modulus, and s is the condensation.* For small variations, we may assume that the mass of air in the neck moves as a unit, and therefore this air mass will have an instantaneous acceleration proportional to $p - p_i$. Furthermore, since the compression of the air in the chamber is proportional to the inward motion of the air in the neck, the cavity acts as an elastic element. We shall also assume, without detailed investigation, that there may exist a reactive force proportional to the velocity of motion, which therefore has the characteristics of a damping force. The source of this damping will be discussed in a later chapter.

The mass of the air in the neck is ρSL, where ρ is the instantaneous density of the air, S is the cross section of the neck, and L is the length of the neck. If x is the displacement of the concentrated mass of air in the neck, a mass of air ρSx will enter the cavity, and raise the density by the amount $\rho Sx/V$ which, compared with the original density, gives Sx/V for the condensation, and BSx/V for the internal excess pressure. The pressure difference acting on the air in the neck is thus $p - BSx/V$. The dynamic equation is

$$\rho L \frac{d^2x}{dt^2} + R'_A \frac{dx}{dt} + \frac{BS}{V}x = p \tag{1.210}$$

where R'_A is a damping constant.

This is an equation comparable in every respect with the equation for mechanical vibration. A slight modification is usually made for acoustical applications. It is preferable to use the concept *volume displacement*, $X = Sx$, rather than the linear displacement x in dealing with extended systems such as gases and liquids. Thus the equation is usually written

$$\frac{\rho L}{S} \frac{d^2X}{dt^2} + R_A \frac{dX}{dt} + \frac{B}{V}X = p \tag{1.211}$$

In this form, the coefficient of the acceleration term is called the *inertance*, M; the coefficient of the velocity term, the *acoustical resistance* R_A. The coefficient of X is called the *acoustical stiffness*, for which there is no commonly used symbol. The reciprocal of the acoustical stiffness is called the *acoustical compliance* C_A.

$$M = \frac{\rho L}{S}, \qquad C_A = \frac{V}{B} \tag{1.212}$$

---

* If the density of a sample of fluid varies, the condensation is the relative change in density, $s = d\rho/\rho$. The bulk modulus of the fluid is defined as the ratio of the pressure change and the resulting condensation.

We shall not discuss the solution of this equation, other than to point out that the natural frequency is

$$f_0 = \frac{1}{2\pi\sqrt{MC_A}}$$

which is identical in form to the expression for the natural frequency of the mechanical oscillator. Substituting for inertance and acoustical compliance

$$f_0 = \frac{1}{2\pi\sqrt{\rho LV/SB}}$$

Last, we discuss the third member of the analogy, and set up the equation of electrical oscillation. The voltage-current relation in an electric system is determined by the three electrical parameters: inductance, resistance, and capacitance. If we take the charge q as the variable rather than the current i, it is possible to express these relations without the use of an integral sign, and at the same time to make the electrical equation resemble more closely the mechanical and acoustical equations which have been derived. Thus in an inductor we have the relation $e_L = L_E(di/dt) = L_E(d^2q/dt^2)$; in a resistor $e_R = R_E i = R_E(dq/dt)$; and in a capacitor, $e_C = (1/C_E)q$. If these three elements are connected in series and a voltage e is applied across the series circuit, the following relation will exist between the applied voltage e and the voltages across the elements

$$L_E \frac{d^2q}{dt^2} + R_E \frac{dq}{dt} + \frac{1}{C_E} q = e \qquad (1.213)$$

Although the science of mechanics is older than that of electricity, and the fundamental electrical quantities can be given a mechanical foundation, oscillation problems have been investigated in greatest detail in electricity. Certainly the action of inductors and capacitors is more widely known than that of inertances and acoustic compliances. It is a fact that there is a wide-spread tendency to predict the operation of an acoustical system from that of its known electrical analogue. The relations of this article show that a short narrow tube in an acoustical system will have an effect corresponding to that of an inductor in an electric system, while a cavity will have an effect corresponding to that of a capacitor. Below is shown in tabular form the other corresponding terms in the analogy.

Mechanical	Acoustical	Electrical
Force	Pressure	Voltage
Displacement	Volume displacement	Charge
Velocity	Volume velocity	Current
Mass	Inertance	Inductance
Mechanical compliance	Acoustical compliance	Capacitance
Mechanical resistance	Acoustical resistance	Electrical resistance

The remainder of the first chapter will consist mainly of the solution of the equation of mechanical oscillation, and the interpretations arising from this solution, with occasional allusions to electrical principles, where it is felt that these principles are generally familiar.

1.3 Simple Harmonic Motion

Equations (1.22), (1.23), (1.24), and (1.25) define SHM (simple harmonic motion) from the dynamic viewpoint as the motion of a mass particle attracted to a center of equilibrium by a linear force. However, there is an equivalent definition of SHM which is purely kinematic. Lest it be thought redundant to treat two equivalent definitions in detail, let us state that certain methods of treating vibration problems can be traced back to the kinematic definition for their origin, and a thorough understanding of these methods is very helpful in the study of acoustics. SHM can be defined kinematically as follows:

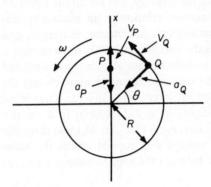

Fig. 1.31. Point in simple harmonic motion.

If point Q moves on the circumference of a circle at constant speed, and if point P is the projection of the point Q on any diameter, the point P moves with simple harmonic motion.

If we take the vertical diameter as the path of motion of P and assign Cartesian axes, we have (Fig. 1.31)

$$x_P = R \sin \theta, \quad v_P = v_Q \cos \theta, \quad a_P = - a_Q \sin \theta \qquad (1.31)$$

where a_Q is toward the center.

Now if we let ω_0 be the angular velocity of point Q, then $\theta = \omega_0 t + \delta$, where θ is the phase angle and δ is the initial phase angle. Also $v_Q = R\omega_0$ and $a_Q = R\omega_0^2$. Thus, substituting in Eq. (1.31),

$$x_P = R \sin (\omega_0 t + \delta)$$

$$v_P = \frac{dx_P}{dt} = R\omega_0 \cos (\omega_0 t + \delta)$$

$$a_P = \frac{d^2 x_P}{dt^2} = - R\omega_0^2 \sin (\omega_0 t + \delta) \qquad (1.32)$$

We note

$$\frac{d^2 x_P}{dt^2} + \omega_0^2 x = 0 \qquad (1.33)$$

Comparison of Eq. (1.32) and (1.33) with Eq. (1.22) to (1.24) makes it obvious that the point P is in SHM.

One gains valuable insight into the relations between displacement, velocity, and acceleration by plotting x, dx/dt, and d^2x/dt^2 as functions of time (Fig. 1.32). We note that the velocity maxima occur one-quarter cycle before the displacement maxima, and the acceleration maxima lead the velocity maxima by one-quarter cycle. We express this by saying that the displacement and the velocity are in *time quadrature*, with the velocity leading.

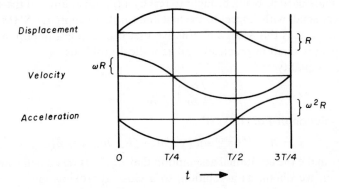

Fig. 1.32. Graph of displacement, velocity, and acceleration as functions of time.

The period might also be divided into 360 equal parts called degrees, whereby the velocity *leads* the displacement by 90 degrees. This is equivalent to $\pi/2$ radians. It is important to note that ω_0 gives the ratio of the velocity amplitude to the displacement amplitude, and also the ratio between the acceleration amplitude and the velocity amplitude.

A thorough knowledge of the fact that phase differences exist in simple harmonic motion is important to a comprehension of forced vibration. It is natural to expect that some property representative of motion should be at its maximum when the force causing the motion is at its maximum. But displacement, velocity, and acceleration are' all representative of motion; therefore, which of the three shall it be? We shall find in the subsequent study of forced vibration that under special conditions, any one of the three may be exactly in phase with the force, but that under general conditions it is unlikely that any of the three will be exactly in phase with the force.

1.4 Free Damped Oscillation

A mass on a spring, if given an initial displacement and left to its own resources, will vibrate for several minutes, perhaps an hour. But its amplitude of vibration will gradually decay, and the mass, for all practical purposes, will eventually come to rest. In this free, damped motion, the external force is zero but the mechanical resistance nonzero. The vibration Eq. (1.21) becomes

$$m\frac{d^2x}{dt^2} + R_m\frac{dx}{dt} + sx = 0 \tag{1.41}$$

It is not important, for acoustical applications, to solve this equation for all combinations of the mechanical constants m, R_m, and s. If the third term is very small compared with the first and the second, we approach the limiting case of a mass particle being brought to rest by a frictional force; if the second term is very small with respect to the first and third, we approach SHM as the limiting case. It is this second alternative that is of greatest importance, for the damping is small in practically all acoustical problems.

If the inequality

$$\left(\frac{R_m}{2m}\right)^2 < \frac{s}{m} \tag{1.42}$$

holds, a solution of Eq. (1.41) is*

$$x = Ae^{-(R_m/2m)t}\sin\left[\sqrt{s/m - (R_m/2m)^2}\,t + \delta\right] \tag{1.43}$$

If we now make the additional assumption that $R_m/2_m$ is *very* small compared with $\sqrt{s/m}$, we obtain as a solution, to a close approximation,

$$x = Ae^{-(R_m/2m)t}\sin(\omega_0 t + \delta) \quad (\omega_0^2 = s/m) \tag{1.43a}$$

This solution indicates that the particle oscillates with a frequency equal to that of an undamped oscillator of the same mass and stiffness, but with gradually decreasing amplitude. The quantity $R_m/2m$ is called the *decay rate a*. Over a small number of cycles the motion is indistinguishable from SHM, but over a large number of cycles the very gradual decrease of the amplitude becomes apparent. The *decay curve* $x = Ae^{-(R_m/2m)t}$ is the locus of the maxima of the oscillation curve.

Closely related to the decay rate are the *time constant* τ, the *logarithmic decrement* Δ, and the *quality factor* Q. These terms are described in the succeeding paragraphs.

It is often useful to know the time during which the amplitude will decay to some arbitrary fraction of its original value. Since the decay curve is exponential, it is convenient to choose the value $1/e$ for the fraction. This period of time is defined as the *time constant* τ. Reference to Eq. (1.43) will show that it has the value $\tau = 2m/R_m$.

The logarithmic decrement is defined as the natural logarithm of the ratio of two successive displacement maxima. From the equation for the envelope of the oscillation curve, if A' is the value of any maximum displacement, the next maximum will have the value $A'e^{-(R_m/2m)T}$. Thus

$$\Delta = \ln\frac{A'}{A'e^{-(R_m/2m)T}} = \frac{R_mT}{2m} = \frac{T}{\tau} = aT$$

---

* This may be checked by substitution; however, it is a laborious, though straightforward, task.

The Q is inversely proportional to the logarithmic decrement. It is defined as the quantity $m\omega_0/R_m$. For the relation between Q and Δ we have

$$Q = \frac{m\omega_0}{R_m} = \frac{2\pi f_0 m}{R_m} = \pi \frac{2m}{R_m T} = \frac{\pi}{\Delta}$$

There is no convenient physical interpretation of Q in terms of the theory so far advanced. However, subsequent articles will show it to be a quantity of great importance in oscillation theory.

Figure 1.41 shows the curve of oscillation, the envelope of decay, and the quantities defined above.

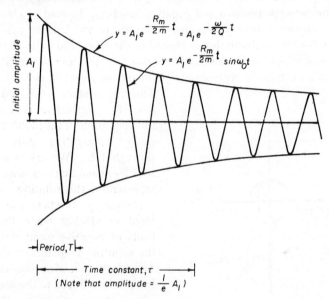

Fig. 1.41. The damped free vibration. Damping constants are: decay rate $a = R_m/2m$; time constant $\tau = 2m/R_m$; logarithmic decrement $\Delta = R_m T/2m$; $Q = \omega m/R_m$.

The study of free damped oscillation is very important in the theory of galvanometers, and in the design of high-quality reproducers, where the effect of *transients* must be considered. The decay rate and the time constant are important in the study of architectural acoustics. The logarithmic decrement is used in systems with large damping, whereas the Q is more likely to be used in systems with small damping. Since acoustical systems in general have extremely low damping (in fact, the damping is neglected in many applications) the logarithmic decrement is seldom mentioned in acoustical treatments. On the other hand, the Q, which is the least useful in the study of free damped oscillation, has an important place in the study of driven oscillation and in applications involving energy and power. Driven oscillation is the next topic of discussion. Before we undertake this study, however, it will be appropriate to develop certain mathematical forms which simplify the solution of the equation and the interpretation of the solution. These forms are the complex variable and the rotating vector.

1.5 Complex Numbers

Early in the history of mathematics, there was no clear concept of either zero or negative numbers. We interpret them without difficulty today, however, by considering the real number system as a series of points on a line, the integers being separated by equal spaces, and zero being the point of separation between positive and negative numbers. Instead of identifying a negative number with a displacement directly to the left, we may use the following system: each number is plotted to the right, and a line drawn from the origin to the point. If the number is negative, this line is rotated through 180°, and its extremity represents a point on the negative part of the axis.

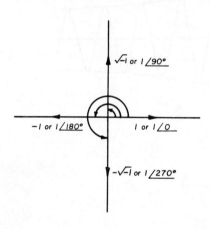

Thus the number −6 is looked upon as (−1) × 6, the 6 units representing the magnitude of the number, and the (−1) representing pure rotation through 180°. We say in mathematical language that −1 is an *operator* representing this rotation.

Imaginary numbers are encountered in algebra when the square roots of negative numbers occur in the solution of quadratic equations. The square root of any negative number can be reduced to the square root of a positive number times the square root of (−1), so that it is necessary only to interpret this square root ($\sqrt{-1}$) to be able to handle imaginary numbers in general.

Fig. 1.51. Positive, negative and imaginary numbers interpreted as rotations.

Since −1 has already been identified as an operator, it is quite logical to treat $\sqrt{-1}$ in the same manner. We therefore define the effect of this number as follows:

Multiplication of a number by $\sqrt{-1}$ corresponds to the rotation of this number through 90°, counterclockwise (Fig. 1.51).

For convenience we replace $\sqrt{-1}$ by the symbol j. We now define addition of imaginary numbers:

$$aj + bj = (a + b)j \qquad (a, b, \text{real})$$

Multiplication is defined as follows:

$$(a)(bj) = (ab)j; \qquad (aj)(bj) = -ab$$

The addition of a real number to an imaginary number cannot be further reduced. Such a sum is called a *complex number*. The following example shows the multiplication and addition of complex numbers:

$$(10 + 5j) + (8 - 3j) = 18 + 2j$$
$$3 \times 4j = 12j$$
$$(10 + 5j)(8 - 3j) = 80 + 10j + 15 = 95 + 10j$$

Division of complex numbers follows from multiplication through the process of rationalization. This is shown in the following example:

$$\frac{3 + 4j}{2 + 3j} = \frac{3 + 4j}{2 + 3j} \cdot \frac{2 - 3j}{2 - 3j} = \frac{18 - j}{13} = \frac{18}{13} - \frac{1}{13}j$$

It is important to note that any operation on a complex number by a complex number gives a complex number as a result (the real and pure imaginary numbers are of course special cases of complex numbers).

The complex number is plotted as a point in the x-y plane, the real part of the number being plotted as the abscissa of the point, and the imaginary part as the ordinate of the point. This method follows interpretation of j as representing rotation through 90°.

When the ordinate and abscissa of a point are given, we have its *cartesian* or *rectangular* representation. The same point, however, has an equivalent *polar* representation in terms of its distance from the origin (or radius vector) and the angle between the radius vector and the x axis (Fig. 1.52). This angle is closely related to the *phase angle* which appears in the theory of harmonic vibrations.

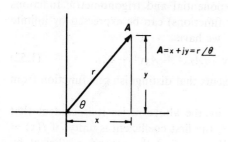

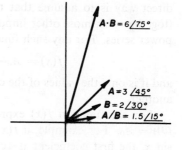

Fig. 1.52. The complex number in rectangular and polar form.

Fig. 1.53. Multiplication and division of complex numbers.

To write a complex number in its polar form, we write the magnitude of the radius vector followed by the angle. Thus the complex number $2 + 2j$ has a magnitude $2\sqrt{2}$ and an angle 45°, and is written $2\sqrt{2}\underline{/45°}$ in polar form.

Multiplication and division are easily performed when complex numbers are in their polar form, by the following rule:

To multiply two complex numbers, multiply the magnitudes and add the angles. To divide two complex numbers, divide the magnitude of the dividend by that of the divisor and subtract the angle of the divisor from that of the dividend (Fig. 1.53).

As an example of multiplication and division, we have the following:

$$5\underline{/23°} \times 3\underline{/4°} = 15\underline{/27°}$$
$$3\underline{/10°} \times 6\underline{/-3°} = 18\underline{/7°}$$
$$12\underline{/23°} \div 3\underline{/4°} = 4\underline{/19°}$$
$$3\underline{/-20°} \div 6\underline{/-23°} = \tfrac{1}{2}\underline{/3°}$$

Complex numbers can be transformed from one representation to another by the following transformation equations (Fig. 1.52):

Rectangular to Polar	*Polar to Rectangular*
$r = (x^2 + y^2)^{1/2}$	$x = r \cos \theta$
$\theta = \arctan \dfrac{y}{x}$	$y = r \sin \theta$

The following is an example of their use:

$$1 + j = \sqrt{2}\underline{/45°}$$
$$6\underline{/30°} = 3\sqrt{3} + 3j$$

Finally, we have the equation of Euler:

$$e^{j\theta} = \cos \theta + j \sin \theta \qquad (1.51)$$

This relation is so important for the mathematics of vibration theory that we shall give at least some of the background of its proof. Perhaps the most direct way is to assume that the exponential and trigonometric functions (together with most other important functions) can be expressed by infinite power series. For any such function, we have

$$f(x) = A_0 + A_1 x + A_2 x^2 + A_3 x^3 + \ldots \qquad (1.52)$$

and it is only the values of the coefficients that distinguish one function from another.

For the function $f(x)$ expressed by the above series it is evident that $f(0) = A_0$. For example, if $f(x) = e^x$, the first coefficient is unity; if $f(x) = \sin x$, the first coefficient is zero. We may find the second coefficient by differentiating the series and allowing the variable to become zero (that is $f'(0) = A_1$). By a series of similar steps, additional coefficients can be found, although after a limited number of steps the law of formation of coefficients becomes evident and obviates any further steps. This law of formation can be expressed by the equation

$$A_n = \frac{f^n(0)}{n!} \qquad (1.53)$$

where $f^n(0)$ is the nth derivative of the function with the variable made zero.

The series for e^x, cos x, sin x, and e^{jx}, evaluated in this fashion, are given below:

$$e^x = 1 + x + \frac{1}{2!}x^2 + \frac{1}{3!}x^3 + \cdots$$

$$\sin x = x - \frac{1}{3!}x^3 + \frac{1}{5!}x^5 - \cdots$$

$$\cos x = 1 - \frac{1}{2!}x^2 + \frac{1}{4!}x^4 - \cdots \qquad (1.54)$$

$$e^{jx} = 1 + jx - \frac{1}{2!}x^2 - j\frac{1}{3!}x^3 + \cdots$$

$$= \left(1 - \frac{1}{2!}x^2 + \frac{1}{4!}x^4 + \cdots\right) + j\left(x - \frac{1}{3!}x^3 + \frac{1}{5!}x^5 + \cdots\right)$$

Comparison of the series for cos x, sin x and e^{jx} shows Euler's equation to be true. As an extension of this theorem we have

$$e^{x+jy} = e^x \cdot e^{jy} = e^x(\cos y + j \sin y) \qquad (1.55)$$

Further, since

$$\cos y + j \sin y = \sqrt{\cos^2 y + \sin^2 y} \left/ \tan^{-1}\frac{\sin y}{\cos y} \right. = 1 \underline{/y}$$

then e^{jy} is a complex number *of magnitude unity and angle y* (Fig. 1.54).

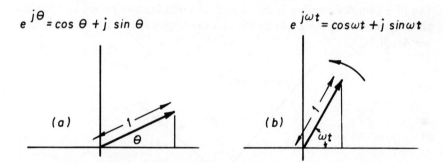

$e^{j\theta} = \cos \theta + j \sin \theta \qquad\qquad\qquad e^{j\omega t} = \cos \omega t + j \sin \omega t$

(a) $\qquad\qquad\qquad\qquad\qquad$ (b)

$\theta \qquad\qquad\qquad\qquad\qquad \omega t$

Fig. 1.54. Complex numbers of unit magnitude. In (a), $e^{j\theta}$ (θ constant) is a complex constant of magnitude unity and angle θ. In (b), $e^{j\omega t}$ is a complex variable of unit magnitude and angle ωt.

If the angle y is a variable, say $y = \omega t$, then the complex number $e^{jy} = e^{j\omega t}$ is of unit magnitude but variable angle, rotating about the origin with frequency $\omega/2\pi$. If A is a real constant, the complex number $Ae^{j\omega t}$ is of magnitude A and of the same rotational frequency. Both these complex numbers start from a position on the axis of reals.

It is only a minor generalization to consider the effect of making the multiplying constant a complex number. Let us write it in the polar form:

$$A = A\underline{/\delta}$$

Then the complex number $Ae^{j\omega t}$ is of amplitude A, of initial angle δ, and

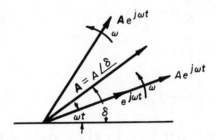

Fig. 1.55. The complex numbers $Ae^{j\omega t}$ and $Ae^{j\omega t}$, where $A = A\underline{/\delta}$ (δ constant).

of rotational frequency $\omega/2\pi$. The complex constant may be written in any of the three forms*

$$A, \quad A\underline{/\delta}, \quad Ae^{j\delta}$$

The time derivative of a variable complex number is interpreted as follows:

Let

$$x = Ae^{j\omega t}$$

Then

$$dx/dt = j\omega \, Ae^{j\omega t} = j\omega x$$

These complex numbers are plotted in Fig. 1.56. Thus, taking the time derivative of a complex number is equivalent to multiplication by $j\omega$, and has the effect of increasing the angle by 90° and the magnitude by the factor ω (also see Art. 1.3).

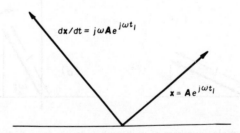

Fig. 1.56. Derivative of the complex number $Ae^{j\omega t}$, showing rotation through 90 degrees.

Before leaving the subject of complex numbers, we note a method of solving the differential equation of SHM formally by the complex exponential.

---

* In electrical engineering notation, the complex voltage vector E includes the variable $e^{j\omega t}$; i.e., $E = E_0 e^{j\omega t}$.

To solve

$$\frac{d^2x}{dt^2} + \omega_0^2 x = 0 \tag{1.56}$$

Let x be generalized to a complex number so that

$$\frac{d^2\mathbf{x}}{dt^2} + \omega_0^2 \mathbf{x} = 0 \tag{1.57}$$

If

$$\mathbf{x} = A e^{j\omega_0 t} \tag{1.58}$$

then

$$\frac{d^2\mathbf{x}}{dt^2} = -\omega_0^2 A e^{j\omega_0 t} = -\omega_0^2 \mathbf{x}$$

That is, Eq. (1.59) is a solution of Eq. (1.58a). An interpretation of this solution will be given in Arts. 1.6 and 1.7.

From Euler's equation we can obtain expressions for the sine and cosine in terms of exponentials that have numerous applications in mathematical physics:

$$e^{jx} = \cos x + j \sin x$$
$$e^{-jx} = \cos x - j \sin x$$
$$\cos x = \frac{e^{jx} + e^{-jx}}{2}, \qquad \sin x = \frac{e^{jx} - e^{-jx}}{2j} \tag{1.59}$$

1.6 Rotating Vectors

We have already noted that the complex number $A e^{j\omega t}$ may be considered a *rotating vector*, with constant angular velocity, while in Art. 1.3 we have associated uniform circular motion with SHM. It is clear, therefore, that the projection of the end point of a rotating vector moves on the vertical axis with SHM, and that complex numbers in the exponential form can serve for the expression of SHM.

Often in the theory of mechanical vibration, and in the solution of a-c electric circuits, it is necessary to add two sinusoidally varying quantities having the same frequency. Examples are the addition of the two particular solutions in Art. 1.2 to obtain the general solution, and in electricity, addition of voltages across several circuit elements in series to obtain the circuit voltage. At the moment, we are not so much interested in the origin of the sinusoidal waves to be added as in the method of addition. Two such waves and their sum are shown in Fig. 1.61, together with a *vector diagram* with the vectors oriented so that their vertical projections give the *initial* values of the two *component* sine curves, the length of the vectors being determined by the values of the maxima of the sine curves. If these vectors are supposed to be in counterclockwise rotation, their vertical projections will always give the instantaneous values of the corresponding curves. We can see this by tracing one of the vectors and its corresponding sine wave through one complete cycle.

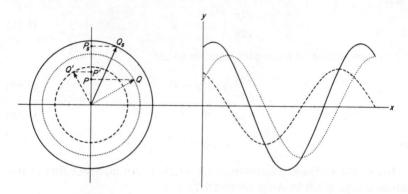

Fig. 1.61. Addition of two sine waves. The sine curves are plots of the vertical projections of the points Q, Q', and Q_s against time. The radii of the circles equal the maximum values of the respective sine waves. The orientation of the radius vectors of Q, Q', and Q_s determine projections of these points which equal the initial values of the sine waves. At every instant, the instantaneous displacement of P_s is the algebraic sum of P and P'.

There is a theorem, often used in elementary mechanics, that the sum of the vertical projections of two vectors equals the vertical projection of the vector sum. Forming the vector sum by the parallelogram rule, and projecting onto the vertical axis, we can find the initial value of the sum of the two sine curves. As time goes on, the two component vectors will rotate like a rigid system, with the sum vector rigidly attached. If we hereafter *understand* that all vectors on a vector diagram are rotating at constant frequency, then we must see that complete information on the three variable quantities is given by the cluster of three vectors, for this cluster determines the magnitude of each, their relative phases, and their initial values. The three vectors are, in a sense, equivalent to the three sine curves.

Initial values of varying quantities are not usually of importance. For instance, in Fig. 1.61 the essential items are the amplitude of each component sinusoidal curve, their *relative phases*, and the resultant sum curve. All these can be found from our rigid trio of vectors, *regardless* of its orientation. For instance, if the framework as a whole were initially rotated clockwise to bring the vector Q to the horizontal axis, the quantity represented by this vector would have an initial value of zero. Such a vector is termed a *reference vector*, since the initial phase of the second vector is the phase difference of that vector *referred to Q*.

The relations shown in Fig. 1.32 for the displacement, velocity, and acceleration in free, undamped SHM can be more concisely shown on a vector diagram (Fig. 1.62). The diagram may be interpreted as follows: (1) the lengths of the vectors give the peak values of the respective quantities; (2) the angles between pairs of vectors give mechanical angles of lead or *lag*; (3) *either* the velocity has an initial value of zero, or the diagram is to be interpreted on a *steady-state basis*, with velocity taken as the reference vector.

So far we have used vectors for *adding like* quantities, two displacements, two velocities, two currents, and so forth. We should note that the result is similar to that which would be obtained with complex numbers. In electric circuits, addition of voltages or currents is usually a preliminary step, the ultimate problem being the solution of the equation $E = IZ$, where E is the voltage, I is the current, and Z is a function of the circuit constants called the

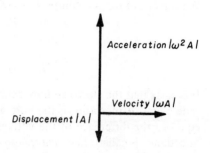

Fig. 1.62. Vector displacement, velocity and acceleration.

impedance. Let us say that we know the exact time variations of both current and voltage in an a-c circuit, and that we have plotted both of them vectorially. We again have two vectors of definite length, rotating at equal frequencies, with a fixed angle between them. However, the relation between the voltage and current vectors is not one of addition or subtraction, since they are not the same type of quantity. We define the *ratio* of the voltage vector to the current vector as the *complex impedance* of the electric circuit, and upon investigation, this impedance is found to be a function of the resistance, inductance, and capacitance of the circuit. For division, we use the rule defined for division of complex numbers. Thus, if the voltage vector of

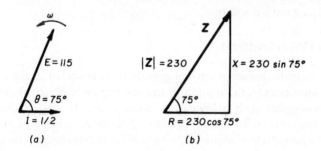

Fig. 1.63. (a) Vector diagram. (b) Impedance triangle.

magnitude 115v leads the current vector of magnitude $\frac{1}{2}$ amp by a phase angle of 75°, we have for the impedance the complex constant $230/\underline{75°}$. All the essentials of this circuit are shown in the vector diagram of Fig. 1.63.

For comparison, let us use complex notation to treat a similar circuit. The complex voltage will be represented by

$$E_0 e^{j\omega t} \quad \text{or} \quad E_0 e^{j\delta_1} e^{j\omega t}$$

Likewise, the current will be written

$$I_0 e^{j\omega t} \quad \text{or} \quad I_0 e^{j\delta_2} e^{j\omega t}$$

We thus have for the complex electrical impedance,

$$Z_E = \frac{E_0 e^{j\omega t}}{I_0 e^{j\omega t}} = \frac{E_0}{I_0} = \frac{E_0 e^{j\delta_1}}{I_0 e^{j\delta_2}} = \frac{E_0}{I_0} e^{j(\delta_1 - \delta_2)}$$

$$= \frac{E_0}{I_0} \underline{/\delta_1 - \delta_2}$$

It is clear that the electrical impedance is a complex constant having a magnitude equal to the ratio of the voltage and current magnitudes and an angle equal to the difference of the voltage and current angles. This angle of the impedance is called the *circuit phase angle*. Note that the impedance, though a complex number, is not a rotating vector, since the variable factor $e^{j\omega t}$ cancels.

Having illustrated both addition and division of complex quantities and rotating vectors, we shall undertake the solution of the complete vibration Eq. (1.21) by these methods. The investigation will be limited to that of a sinusoidally varying impressed force, and it will be assumed that such a force gives rise to sinusoidal displacement, velocity, and acceleration. (Actually this assumption can be quite readily checked.) We can treat the equation as signifying the vector addition of three forces to equal the applied force. The problem can be stated in a manner similar to that of the electric circuit: given the mechanical constants of the system, and the value of the force, find the displacement. The solution involves finding both the magnitude of the displacement and its phase with respect to the force. The complex, or vector, solution accomplishes both magnitude and phase solutions as component parts of one unified solution.

1.7 The Driven Oscillator

If a variable-frequency current generator is connected to the voice coil of a large loudspeaker, the motion of the coil can be made great enough to be easily observable with a low-power microscope. It will be observed that though the current, and hence the driving force, is maintained at a constant value, the amplitude of motion varies greatly with frequency. The loudspeaker contains mass, stiffness, and mechanical resistance, and to a close approximation can be considered a simple vibrator. Therefore the theoretical solution of the motion of the driven loudspeaker can be obtained by the solution of the complete vibration equation. The loudspeaker is only one example of a source of sound. Wherever a vibratory system is set into motion by a vibratory force, this equation must be employed. The formal mathematical solution of this equation is the subject of this article.

The general vibration equation (Eq. 1.21) is a relation between instantaneous values of the displacement (and its derivatives) and the driving force. We solved this for free vibration in Arts. 1.2, 1.3, and 1.4, finding that oscillation occurred at a definite frequency $(1/2\pi) \sqrt{s/m}$, and that, if friction is present, the amplitude decreases exponentially to zero.

If a sinusoidal force were to be suddenly applied to an oscillator, the initial motion would be a superposition of the damped motion and a sinusoidal oscillation at the frequency of the driving force. The former is called the *transient*, the latter is called the *steady-state* solution. Although the transient is not without importance, we shall at present direct our efforts to finding the steady-state solution—that is, that part of the solution which is purely sinusoidal, and in which the frequency is that of the driving force. We have already shown in Eq. (1.58) that a complex exponential form will satisfy a differential equation if the solution is known to be sinusoidal in time. We shall therefore employ this method to find the steady-state solution of the equation of driven vibration. Writing the equation in the complex form, we have

$$m\frac{d^2x}{dt^2} + R_m\frac{dx}{dt} + sx = F_0 e^{j\omega t} \tag{1.71}$$

Since the displacement will vary with the frequency of the driving force, it must be of the form

$$x = A_0 e^{j\omega t} \tag{1.72}$$

where the complex constant A_0 indicates that both the amplitude and phase of the displacement must be determined.

By differentiation,

$$\frac{dx}{dt} = j\omega A_0 e^{j\omega t} = j\omega x \tag{1.73}$$

$$\frac{d^2x}{dt^2} = -\omega^2 A_0 e^{j\omega t} = -\omega^2 x \tag{1.74}$$

On substitution in the differential equation, we obtain

$$(-m\omega^2 + j\omega R_m + s)\, x = F_0 e^{j\omega t} \tag{1.75}$$

We have for the solution:

$$x = \frac{F_0}{(s - m\omega^2) + j\omega R_m} e^{j\omega t} \tag{1.76}$$

The interpretation of this equation is as follows:

1.   The displacement has the frequency of the driving force.

2.   The displacement amplitude equals the force amplitude divided by the amplitude of the complex number $(s - m\omega^2) + j\omega R_m$.

3.   The phase of the displacement lags the phase of the force by the angle θ' of the complex number $(s - m\omega^2) + j\omega R_m$; that is, by the angle

$$\theta' = \arctan\frac{\omega R_m}{s - m\omega^2}$$

Actually, the relation between force and velocity is more useful than the relation between force and displacement. We can readily find the expression for the velocity from that of the displacement by differentiation:

$$V = \frac{dx}{dt} = \frac{j\omega F_0 e^{j\omega t}}{(s - m\omega^2) + j\omega R_m} = \frac{F_0}{R_m + j(\omega m - s/\omega)} e^{j\omega t} \tag{1.77}$$

This ratio between the driving-force vector and the velocity vector is called the *mechanical impedance* of the oscillator. The mechanical impedance is seen to be a complex constant which is a function of the driving frequency and the circuit constants m, R_m, and s. The real part of the complex impedance is called the mechanical resistance, and the imaginary part is called the *mechanical reactance*. In polar form, the mechanical impedance has a magnitude $\sqrt{R_m^2 + (\omega m - s/\omega)^2}$ and an angle $\theta = \arctan[(\omega m - s/\omega)/R_m]$. The magnitude is the ratio of the force amplitude to the velocity amplitude. As such, it has the dimensions g sec^{-1}, which are defined as *mechanical ohms*.

We can also solve Eq. (1.71) in a manner completely analogous to that used in electric circuit theory by writing the equation in the form

$$ma + R_m v + sx = F \tag{1.78}$$

If each term is understood to be a rotating vector and the magnitude and phase relations between displacement, velocity, and acceleration are recalled, the graphical solution shown in Fig. 1.71(a) is obtained.

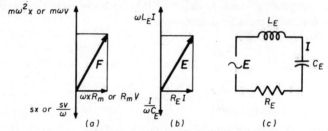

Fig. 1.71. Vector solution for a driven oscillator, and an electric circuit which has a similar vector solution.

For comparison, we show the vector solution of the analogous electric circuit, Fig. 1.71(b), which has the equation

$$E_L + E_R + E_C = E \tag{1.79}$$

We have several times drawn an analogy between mechanical and electric systems, basing the analogy on the *form* of the *differential equations*. This analogy does not extend to the physical make-up of the systems. The mechanical system which gives rise to Eq. (1.71) is shown in Fig. 1.72(a). In this system, the mass, spring, and friction elements are attached to a rigid weightless bar, constrained to remain parallel to the rigid wall which serves as an immobile point of attachment for the spring and friction elements. The three reaction forces acting to the right thus combine to oppose the applied force acting to the left. This system, in appearance, more closely resembles a parallel than a series electric circuit.

This analogical difficulty has been recognized by those who have pursued the subject of *dynamical analogies*, and as a result, an alternative scheme of analogy has been proposed. In contrast to the impedance analogy used by Olson, Massa, and Mason, in which force is paired with voltage, and velocity with current, an admittance analogy has been suggested by Firestone, in

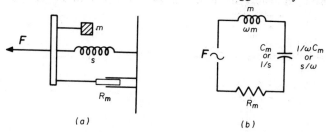

Fig. 1.72. Pictorial and symbolic diagrams for a driven mechanical oscillator.

which force is paired with current, and velocity with voltage. It is beyond the scope of this text to discuss the relative advantages and disadvantages of the two schemes. We can only state that we shall use the *impedance analogy*, and give an example of its use in representing the equivalent circuit of a mechanical system, and comparing this to an analogous electric circuit.

Figure 1.71(c) shows an actual connection diagram of a coil, capacitor, resistor, and generator, and Fig. 1.71(b) shows the impedance diagram, the vector voltages across the elements adding to equal the applied voltages. Now the mechanical system shown in Fig. 1.72(a) gives a mechanical impedance vector diagram similar in every way to Fig. 1.71(b). Therefore when we draw the equivalent circuit we show the impedance elements *in series*—that is, we make it conform to the electric circuit of Fig. 1.71(c). Furthermore, it is modern practice to use the analogous electrical symbols for the impedance elements. We thus obtain Fig. 1.72(b) for the mechanical impedance diagram. The parameter is written above the element and the impedance below.

The chief disadvantage of this system is that the circuit diagram cannot be drawn from direct examination of the mechanical system. Taking everything into consideration, however, this scheme appears best suited for our purposes.

Sometimes, in problems of forced motion, the force is not directly given. As an example, referring to Fig. 1.72(a), the displacement of the support (the wall) may be given. The problem is then to find the displacement of the mass in terms of displacement of the wall. It is not difficult, however, to remold the problem so that the displacement of the support constitutes an effective force acting on the mass of the system through the medium of the stiffness and damping elements, which constitute a coupling member between the support and the mass. Looked at in this manner, the combination of stiffness and damping elements may be said to constitute a *resilient mount*.

Let x_0 be the instantaneous displacement of the support. We then have

$$x_0 = Ae^{j\omega t}, \quad \frac{dx_0}{dt} = j\omega Ae^{j\omega t} = j\omega x_0, \quad \frac{d^2 x_0}{dt^2} = -\omega^2 Ae^{j\omega t} = -\omega_0^2 x_0$$

The compressive force in the spring will be $s(x - x_0)$, and the damping force in the dashpot will be $R_m(d/dt)(x - x_0)$. The vibration equation will therefore have the form

$$m\frac{d^2 x}{dt^2} = -R_m\frac{d}{dt}(x - x_0) - s(x - x_0) \qquad (1.710)$$

$$m\frac{d^2}{dt^2}(x - x_0) + R_m\frac{d}{dt}(x - x_0) + s(x - x_0) = -m\frac{d^2 x_0}{dt^2} = m\omega^2 Ae^{j\omega t}$$

By Eq. (1.74) this has the solution

$$[x - x_0] = \frac{\omega^2 Ae^{j\omega t}}{(s - m\omega^2) + j\omega R_m} \qquad (1.711)$$

In vibration insulation, the object of the resilient mount is to secure a small value of the ratio $|x/x_0|$. We can obtain this ratio from Eq. (1.711). We have

$$x - x_0 = x - Ae^{j\omega t} \qquad (1.712)$$

Combining Eqs. (1.711) and (1.712) we obtain

$$x = Ae^{j\omega t}\left(1 + \frac{m\omega^2}{s - m\omega^2 + j\omega R_m}\right) = \left(\frac{s + j\omega R_m}{s - m\omega^2 + j\omega R_m}\right)Ae^{j\omega t}$$

If a is the amplitude of x, we have for the amplitude ratio

$$\left(\frac{a}{A}\right)^2 = \frac{s^2 + \omega^2 R_m^2}{(s - m\omega^2)^2 + \omega^2 R_m^2} \qquad (1.713)$$

From the last equation, it is evident that the motion of the mass will be greater than that of the support at the resonant frequency, but the damping is helpful in preventing it from becoming infinite. For frequencies below the resonant frequency the motion of the mass will always be greater than that of the support. The proof is left as an exercise for the student. We shall assume this to be true, and find the influence of the mounting on frequencies far enough above the resonant frequency that the system is effectively mass-controlled.

The expression for the ratio of the displacements then becomes approximately

$$\left(\frac{a}{A}\right)^2 = \frac{s^2 + \omega^2 R_m^2}{m^2\omega^4 + \omega^2 R_m^2}$$

This equation shows that both the stiffness and the damping should be low if the amplitude of the mass is to be much less than that of the support. As a matter of fact, the motion of the mass will approach zero if the vibration frequency of the support is well above the natural frequency of the system and both the damping and stiffness approach zero. However, where there is a possibility that the support will have frequency components in the neighborhood of the resonant frequency, it is advisable to permit a certain amount of damping to prevent abnormal rise of amplitude at resonance. In general we may conclude that an isolation mount should have as small a stiffness as possible, that it should be heavily loaded ($m \gg s$), and that the amount of damping required depends on how close to the resonant frequency unwanted vibrations may occur.

1.8 Energy of the Oscillator

Energy is perhaps the most basic, if intangible, of all physical quantities. The physicist regards several physical concepts as so many useful tools, but he takes energy with great seriousness. Several atomic models have been employed since the origin of the atomic theory, and few have been looked upon as anything approaching ultimate reality, but atomic energy levels persist despite all changes in atomic model. Likewise, in acoustics, energy is a concept of fundamental import. The energy density of a sound wave has been called the most fundamental property of the wave. In the acoustics of enclosures, the expression for energy density within the enclosure is the goal of all investigations. Acoustic radiation is measured by the energy radiated. Since all energy concepts in acoustics go back to the energy of the oscillator, one cannot overemphasize the concept of the energy of the oscillator.

The mechanical energy of the oscillator is made up of potential and kinetic energy, the potential energy residing in the elastic element, and the kinetic energy in the mass. Whatever energy enters the frictional element is dissipated, and therefore is not considered a part of the energy of the oscillator. If the oscillator is in free, undamped vibration, or is being driven by a force which supplies energy at a rate equal to that at which energy is being dissipated in the mechanical resistance, the amplitude is constant with time, and the *steady-state* condition exists. This condition is assumed in the derivation.

The kinetic energy of the system is simply $\frac{1}{2}mv^2$, where m and v are the mass and velocity of the mass particle. The potential energy is found as the work put into the spring in stretching it. Since the stress for any displacement x is sx, the element of work is $sx\,dx$, and the expression for potential energy when the mass particle is at a distance x from its center of equilibrium will be

$$E_P = \int_0^x sx\,dx = \tfrac{1}{2}sx^2 \tag{1.81}$$

The total energy is the sum of the kinetic and potential energies. We can obtain it simply as the maximum value of the potential energy, $\frac{1}{2}sA^2$, or the maximum value of the kinetic energy, $\frac{1}{2}m\omega^2A^2$. We shall, however, derive the total energy in a more general manner to show expressly that it is constant.

Let

$$x = A \sin (\omega t + \delta)$$

Then $$\frac{dx}{dt} = \omega A \cos (\omega t + \delta)$$

$$E_P = \frac{sx^2}{2} = \frac{s}{2}A^2 \sin^2 (\omega t + \delta) = \frac{mA^2\omega^2}{2} \sin^2 (\omega t + \delta)$$

$$E_K = \frac{m}{2} \left(\frac{dx}{dt}\right)^2 = \frac{m\omega^2 A^2}{2} \cos^2 (\omega t + \delta)$$

$$E = E_P + E_K = \frac{s}{2}x^2 + \frac{m}{2}\left(\frac{dx}{dt}\right)^2 = \frac{1}{2}m\omega^2 A^2 \tag{1.82}$$

For a fixed frequency, the energy is proportional to the square of the amplitude, whereas for a fixed amplitude the energy is proportional to the square of the frequency.

There is an important practical aspect to this relation. Vibration "pickups" are widely used in industrial, scientific, and engineering fields to measure the strength of vibration of structures. The pickups must be calibrated for use, and the absolute method of calibration is to attach the pickup to a "shaking table" whose amplitude of vibration may be observed directly. The electric output of the pickup may then be recorded as the frequency is varied, and a frequency calibration curve drawn.

As the frequency rises, the energy necessary to preserve a significantly large amplitude for observation rises with the square of the frequency. At about 200 cycles, in the present state of the art, it becomes a difficult engineering problem to build shaking tables of sufficient capacity to produce the necessary amplitudes. For instance, the energy requirement at 1,000 cycles is 100 times that required for the same amplitude at 100 cycles.

Having discussed the energy of an oscillator, we can now gain a better physical picture of the significance of the decay constants introduced in Art. 1.4. In that article it was possible only to discuss these constants from the point of view of decay of amplitude. Their relation to decay of energy is equally important in the practical applications of acoustics. Let us assume that an oscillator maintains its frequency constant despite a decay in amplitude. We can then treat the amplitude as the single dependent variable in the expression for energy:

$$E = \tfrac{1}{2}m\omega^2 A^2 \tag{1.82a}$$

The rate of loss of energy will then be

$$-\frac{dE}{dt} = -m\omega^2 A \frac{dA}{dt} \tag{1.83}$$

The time equation of the amplitude may be written

$$A = A_0 e^{-R_m t/2m} \tag{1.84}$$

If we differentiate this expression we obtain

$$\frac{dA}{dt} = -\frac{R_m}{2m}A_0e^{-R_mt/2m} = -\frac{R_m}{2m}A \tag{1.85}$$

The quantity $R_m/2m$ has been defined as the decay rate (for amplitude). From Eq. (1.85), it is seen that an equivalent (and often preferable) definition for the decay rate is

$$a_A = -\frac{dA/dt}{A} \tag{1.86}$$

where a_A is now the decay rate for amplitude. That is, the decay rate is the ratio of the rate of loss of amplitude to the instantaneous amplitude. A constant ratio between the rate of change of a quantity and its instantaneous value is characteristic of many physical processes. As an example, rate of loss of mass of a radioactive substance is proportional to the mass of the substance.

Equation (1.82a) can also be written in the form:

$$E = \tfrac{1}{2}m\omega^2A_0^2e^{-R_mt/m} = E_0e^{-R_mt/m} \tag{1.87}$$

$$\frac{dE}{dt} = -\frac{R_m}{m}E_0e^{-R_mt/m} = -\frac{R_m}{m}E \tag{1.88}$$

If we now define the decay rate for energy similarly to the decay rate for amplitude in Eq. (1.86a)—that is, as the ratio of the rate of change of energy* to the instantaneous energy, we have

$$a_E = -\frac{dE/dt}{E} = \frac{R_m}{m} \tag{1.89}$$

The energy decay rate therefore is twice the amplitude decay rate. Expressions of the form of (1.86) and (1.89) give physical meaning to the decay rate.

1.9 The Power Concept in the Oscillator

Closely allied to the concept of energy, or work, is that of power, which is defined as the time rate of doing work, the rate of energy consumption, the rate of energy flow, or more generally, the quantity which has the dimensions of energy divided by time. The power concept must be well qualified, lest there be misunderstanding. First, the power concept has no application in the free, undamped oscillator, since, as we have shown, the total energy is constant. Second, although there is a rate of change of mechanical energy in the free damped oscillator, this is usually regarded as an energy change within the oscillator, rather than a power flow, although it must be admitted that the difference is conceptual rather than real. It remains that the most important cases of power flow are in the driven oscillator, in steady state, in

---

* This rate of change of energy is the average over a cycle. Strictly, the instantaneous rate of energy loss is proportional to the instantaneous velocity.

which there must be a steady flow of power from some external source to supply the power lost in the frictional resistance of the oscillator.

A distinction must be made between *instantaneous power*, which can be defined from elementary mechanics, and *average power*, which is the quantity of importance in applications. Instantaneous power p_i is defined as follows:

$$p_i = fv \cos \phi \tag{1.91}$$

where f is the instantaneous value of the force on a particle, v is the instantaneous value of the velocity of the particle, ϕ is the geometrical angle between the line of action of the force and that of the velocity.

It is evident that in the linear oscillator, the factor $\cos \phi$ will be either 1 or -1, the positive value occurring when the velocity of the mass particle is in the direction of the external driving force. At such an instant the external force is said to be delivering power to the oscillator. At other times the instantaneous power is negative. Thus an oscillation of power occurs in a driven vibrator. In general, the curve of instantaneous power is not *purely sinusoidal*, though it may be shown to be the superposition of a constant and a sinusoid. In power considerations, vector and complex notation must be used with great caution, if at all. For instance, the product of the vector force and the vector velocity does *not* give a power value, either instantaneous or average. We shall forego vector notation entirely, and work from instantaneous power throughout.

If we take θ to be the phase angle between the force and the velocity, the following is the general expression for instantaneous power:

$$p_i = (F_0 \sin \omega t)[V_0 \sin (\omega t - \theta)] \tag{1.92}$$

By a simple trigonometric identity, this may be changed to the more useful form

$$p_i = \frac{F_0 V_0}{2} [\cos \theta - \cos (2\omega t - \theta)] \tag{1.93}$$

The instantaneous power expression thus consists of two terms, one constant and one sinusoidal, as stated above, the sinusoidal term varying with a frequency twice that of the force. Since the variable cosine term has an average value of zero, the average power is quite clearly the value of the constant term

$$P_{Av} = \frac{F_0 V_0}{2} \cos \theta \tag{1.94}$$

A somewhat more conventional method of deriving the expression is to define average power as the energy flow per cycle divided by the period. Although in essence it differs very little from the above development, it is worthy of illustration, because it is typical of the *averaging* process, which we shall use in other articles.

$$P_{Av} = \frac{1}{T} \int_0^T p_i \, dt = \frac{F_0 V_0}{2T} \int_0^T [\cos \theta - \cos (2\omega t - \theta)] dt$$

$$= \frac{F_0 V_0}{2T} \left[(\cos \theta)t - \frac{\sin (2\omega t - \theta)}{2\omega} \right]_0^T = \frac{F_0 V_0}{2} \cos \theta$$

Since $\cos \theta = R_m/Z_m$, the power expression can also be written

$$P_{Av} = \frac{F_0 V_0}{2} \cdot \frac{R_m}{Z_m} = \frac{V_0^2 R_m}{2}$$

This is an important expression since it shows that, regardless of the phase angle, the power can be found if the velocity and the mechanical resistance are known.

1.10 Mechanical Impedance

The fundamental problem of the driven oscillator is the solution of the equation $F = Z_m V$. Any of the three factors may be the unknown. It has already been ascertained that the mechanical impedance is a function of a single variable ω, the other elements being mechanical constants. The impedance function is therefore usually shown by a frequency plot, which is the subject of this article.

Once a plot of impedance against frequency has been obtained, one can readily find the force necessary to provide a constant velocity, since by the above equation, the force magnitude will be directly proportional to the impedance magnitude, and the phase angle of the impedance gives the angle between the phase of the force and that of the velocity.

The converse problem, finding the velocity at various frequencies when the force is held constant, involves division by the impedance. For this reason, the *mechanical admittance* Y_m has been defined as the reciprocal of the mechanical impedance. Once the curve of $|Y_m|$ for an oscillator has been drawn, a change of scale gives the curve of $|V|$. The angle of Y_m is the negative of the angle of Z_m.

If we write the impedance in its complex form,

$$Z = R_m + jX_m$$

where X_m is the *mechanical reactance*, we have for the admittance,

$$Y_m = \frac{1}{Z_m} = \frac{1}{R_m + jx_m} = \frac{R_m}{Z_m^2} - j\frac{X_m}{Z_m^2}$$

$$= G_m + jB_m$$

where $G_m \equiv R_m/Z_m^2$ and $B_m \equiv -X_m/Z_m^2$.

We define G_m as the *mechanical conductance* and B_m as the *mechanical susceptance*.

Since both the impedance and the admittance are complex numbers, they are best shown by plotting separately their real and imaginary parts (Fig. 1.101). We shall simplify the plotting of these curves by first noting the values of R_m, X_m, G_m, and B_m, at critical points, the variation between these points being fairly obvious.

1. Where ω has the value $\omega_0 = \sqrt{s/m}$, $X_m = 0$, and therefore $G_m = 1/R_m$ and $B_m = 0$. (R_m, of course, is constant with frequency.) Therefore R_m is

the entire impedance, and $1/R_m$ is the entire admittance. The phase angle is zero (that is, the velocity is in phase with the force), and the oscillator is said to be resistance-controlled. This condition is also called resonance, and ω_0 is called the resonant frequency. The power flow into the oscillator from an external force of amplitude F_0 will be $F_0V_0/2 = F_0^2/2R_m$, the energy being dissipated in the mechanical resistance. If the impressed force is constant with frequency, the power is a maximum at the resonant frequency.

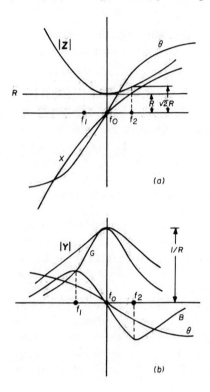

Fig. 1.101. (a) Impedance, resistance, and reactance; (b) admittance, conductance, and susceptance.

2. At the two frequencies for which X_m is numerically equal to R_m, G_m will equal $1/2R_m$, and B_m will equal G_m. The magnitude of the impedance will be $\sqrt{2}R_m$ and the magnitude of the admittance $1/\sqrt{2}R_m$. The phase angle will be 45°, and will be either lagging or leading, depending on the sign of the imaginary term. The power flow will be

$$\frac{F_0V_0}{2}\cos 45° = \frac{F_0^2}{2\sqrt{2}R_m}\cdot\frac{1}{\sqrt{2}} = \frac{F_0^2}{4R_m}$$

This is seen to be half the power flow from an equal force at the resonant frequency, and for this reason these frequencies are called the *half-power* frequencies.

3. At frequencies far above the resonant frequency, X_m becomes approximately ωm, and makes up practically the entire impedance. The phase angle of the impedance approaches 90°, B_m becomes approximately $1/\omega m$ and G_m approaches the value R_m/ω^2m^2, while the phase angle of the admittance approaches the value $-90°$. Because the mass term supplies almost the entire impedance, the oscillator is said to be mass-controlled. The power is given approximately by $F_0^2R_m/\omega^2m^2$.

4. At frequencies far below resonance, X_m becomes approximately $-s/\omega$ and $|Z_m| \approx X_m$. The phase angle of the impedance approaches $-90°$, and that of the admittance approaches 90°. The value of B_m approaches ω/s, while G_m approaches $R_m\omega^2/s^2$. The oscillator is said to be *stiffness-controlled*, and the displacement is in phase with the force. The power flow is given approximately by $F_0^2R_m\omega^2/s^2$.

The frequency difference $f_2 - f_1$ between the two half-power frequencies is called the *band width* of the oscillator. Closely related to the *band width* is the relative band width, which is defined as the ratio of the band width to the resonant frequency. From the definition of the Q given in Art. 1.4, we may show that the relative band width is the reciprocal of the Q.

Illustrative Example: Show that the relative band width $= 1/Q$.

Solution: At the half-power frequencies, $\dot{\omega}_2$ and ω_1,

$$\omega_2 m - \frac{s}{\omega_2} = R_m, \qquad \omega_1 m - \frac{s}{\omega_1} = -R_m$$

$$\frac{\omega_2}{\omega_1} m - \frac{1}{\omega_2 \omega_1} s = \frac{1}{\omega_1} R_m, \qquad \frac{\omega_1}{\omega_2} m - \frac{1}{\omega_2 \omega_1} s = -\frac{1}{\omega_2} R_m$$

Subtracting,

$$m\left(\frac{\omega_2^2 - \omega_1^2}{\omega_1 \omega_2}\right) = \left(\frac{\omega_2 + \omega_1}{\omega_1 \omega_2}\right) R_m$$

$$m(\omega_2 - \omega_1) = R_m$$

$$\frac{\omega_2 - \omega_1}{\omega_0} = \frac{R_m}{m\omega_0} = \frac{1}{Q}$$

from the definition of Q in article 1.4.

1.11 Root Mean Square Values of Oscillating Quantities

A constant force acting on a system in which the mechanical impedance is purely resistive produces a velocity:

$$V = \frac{F}{R_m}$$

and for the constant power,

$$FV = \frac{F^2}{R_m} = V^2 R_m$$

When alternating quantities are considered, we seek some means of comparing these with constant values from the viewpoint of equal power consumption in equal mechanical resistances. Clearly, the average power in the alternating case will be equal to the constant power in the case of steady velocity and force if the *average square* of the alternating velocity equals the square of the constant velocity, or the *square root of the average square* or *root mean square* velocity is equal to the constant velocity.

We find the root mean square of a sinusoidal velocity as follows:

$$V_{rms}^2 = \frac{1}{T} \int_0^T V_2^0 \sin^2 \omega t \, dt$$

$$V_{rms}^2 = \frac{V_0^2}{2T} \int_0^T (1 - \cos 2\omega t) \, dt = \frac{V_0^2}{2T}\left(t - \frac{\sin 2\omega t}{\omega}\right)_0^T = \frac{V_0^2}{2}$$

and therefore

$$V_{rms} = \frac{1}{\sqrt{2}} V_0$$

By a similar process, we can prove that the same relation exists between the peak value of the force and the root mean square (rms) value.

It is becoming conventional to give rms values of oscillating quantities rather than peak values. Hereinafter, in this text, scalar symbols without subscripts will refer to rms values. The use of rms values simplifies the writing of many equations, and brings out their close relation to equations found in electric circuit theory, where rms values are the rule. It is immaterial whether vector diagrams are drawn for peak values or rms values of quantities, since only a change of scale is involved. Similarly, the definition of impedance as the ratio of force to velocity is unaltered, since the ratios of the rms values are the same as the ratios of the peak values. It should be noted that the instantaneous power flow is not constant in the *steady-state* condition of an oscillator, but the *average* power flow from cycle to cycle remains the same. The term "constant" is also used to refer to alternating quantities. We may speak of a constant force generator, meaning that the force *amplitude* does not change with frequency, or with the passing of time. The terms "constant" and "steady" in most of the remaining context of this book are used in the latter sense.

1.12 Coupled Oscillators

Coupled oscillators are important in both theoretical and applied acoustics. From the viewpoint of fundamental acoustic theory, the study of coupled oscillators has importance because it represents a transition from the simple harmonic oscillator to systems of oscillators—the first step in the progression from the harmonic vibration to the harmonic wave. In applied acoustics, the isolation of vibration, such as machinery vibration, is based on the theory of coupled oscillators. We have already seen a simple example of vibration insulation in Art. 1.7, but more complex systems require further consideration. For theoretical purposes, it is sufficient, and indeed, advantageous, to assume that the coupled system is homogeneous, that is, that the coupled masses are equal, and that the coupling members are similar. For example, if they are springs joining the masses together, one can assume that they are of equal length and of equal stiffness. The reason for that is that material media are relatively homogeneous, or at least that the propagation of waves in homogeneous media must be established before the problem of propagation in inhomogeneous media can be attempted. The mathematical treatment is also simplified. On the other hand, the problem of machinery vibration demands a more general treatment. Here the designer, in a sense, chooses the coupling himself, and therefore he must know how the coupled system reacts to different couplings, and also the effect of differences in the masses. The present article will first consider the problem of a symmetric system consisting of two masses and three springs, but will later generalize so as to make the theory applicable to vibration insulation, and other problems.

Consider the system shown in Fig. 1.121, consisting of two masses sliding in a frictionless groove, each mass attached to a rigid support with a spring, while the two masses are coupled together with a third spring. We shall first assume that the two particles are of equal mass, and that the springs are of equal stiffness and of equal length. Even this rather simple system can have a very complicated

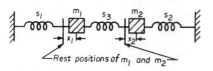

Fig. 1.121. Coupled oscillators.

motion, and we will be concerned chiefly with the concept of *normal coordinates*, by which we can grasp the fundamental characteristics of the motion of the two masses despite the superficial complexity of their individual motions.

Let us suppose that at a certain instant the mass m_1 is displaced a distance x_1 from its rest position, while at the same instant the mass m_2 has a displacement x_2 from its rest position. We then have the elastic forces acting on m_1,

$$- sx_1 - s(x_1 - x_2)$$

and for the forces acting on m_2,

$$s(x_1 - x_2) - sx_2$$

The dynamic equations of the two masses are thus

$$m_1 \frac{d^2x_1}{dt^2} = - 2sx_1 + sx_2$$

$$m_2 \frac{d^2x_2}{dt^2} = sx_1 - 2sx_2$$

$$(1.121)$$

This pair of simultaneous differential equations in the two variables x_1 and x_2 can be solved directly for the individual motions of x_1 and x_2, respectively. However, it turns out that an indirect solution is much more useful, particularly so in this case, where we have the simplicity of equal masses with equal stiffness constants.

Dividing by the common mass, and successively adding and subtracting Eqs. (1.121), we obtain

$$\frac{d^2}{dt^2}(x_1 + x_2) + \frac{s}{m}(x_1 + x_2) = 0$$

$$\frac{d^2}{dt^2}(x_1 - x_2) + \frac{3s}{m}(x_1 - x_2) = 0$$

$$(1.122)$$

Equations (1.122) are similar to the differential equation of undamped free simple harmonic motion for both the *sum* and *difference* of the displacements of the two masses. These new variables $(x_1 + x_2)$ and $(x_1 - x_2)$ are called the *normal coordinates* of the coupled system. The idea of a *coordinate* being the sum or difference of two displacements is likely to be confusing when first encountered, since in elementary work, a coordinate, though it may represent a displacement, a velocity, an acceleration, or some other quantity, is almost always associated with a *single* variable. Let us, however, solve Eqs. (1.122) for the normal coordinates of the system. We obtain:

$$x_1 + x_2 = A \cos(\omega_1 t + \delta_1) \qquad \omega_1 = \sqrt{\frac{s}{m}}$$

$$x_1 - x_2 = B \cos(\omega_2 t + \delta_2) \qquad \omega_2 = \sqrt{3}\sqrt{\frac{s}{m}} = \sqrt{3}\,\omega_1 \tag{1.123}$$

The phase angles can be ignored, since only the steady-state solution is desired. The equations then have the simpler form,

$$x_1 + x_2 = A \cos \omega_1 t$$
$$x_1 - x_2 = B \cos \omega_2 t \tag{1.124}$$

These equations may then readily be solved for the individual displacements, yielding

$$x_1 = \tfrac{1}{2}(A \cos \omega_1 t + B \cos \omega_2 t)$$
$$x_2 = \tfrac{1}{2}(A \cos \omega_1 t - B \cos \omega_2 t) \tag{1.125}$$

Before discussing the solutions represented by Eqs. (1.125), we shall consider two special cases in which the motion of the system as a whole may be simple harmonic; that is, a motion in which each mass may execute SHM with a common frequency. Such a motion occurs if either of the normal coordinates is identically zero; it is called a *normal mode* of the system, and the associated frequency of vibration is called a *normal frequency* of the system. Thus, if

$$x_1 - x_2 = 0$$

that is, if both displacements are equal at all times, we have the first single Eq. (1.122):

$$\frac{d^2}{dt^2}(x_1 + x_2) + \frac{s}{m}(x_1 + x_2) = 0$$

which may be written

$$\frac{d^2 x}{dt^2} + \frac{s}{m}x = 0$$

where x is the common displacement. In this first normal mode, the two masses vibrate in phase with a normal frequency $\sqrt{s/m}$, which is equal to that of a simple harmonic oscillator of mass m and stiffness s. To generate this normal mode, the masses must be given initial displacements of equal magnitude and in the same direction.

The second normal mode is defined by the condition

$$x_1 + x_2 = 0$$

in which the masses have instantaneous displacements equal in magnitude but oppositely directed. The equation for the common displacement is

$$\frac{d^2x}{dt^2} + 3\frac{s}{m}x = 0$$

It indicates that the second normal frequency is $\sqrt{3}\,\sqrt{s/m}$. To generate the second normal mode, the masses must be given equal and opposite initial displacements.

The general solution for the individual displacements of the masses Eq. (1.125) shows each to be composed of a superposition of two sinusoids, each of a frequency which has been defined as a normal frequency; i.e. it is composed of two normal modes, where the strength of either normal mode is completely arbitrary. Definite initial conditions determine the relative strength of the normal modes. As an example, let us suppose that m_1 is given an initial displacement C, while m_2 is given an initial displacement of zero. Since $x_1 + x_2 = x_1 - x_2$ at $t = 0$, the two normal modes are of equal strength, Eqs. (1.124) show that $A = B = C$. The equations of motion become

$$x_1 = \frac{C}{2}(\cos \omega_1 t + \cos \omega_2 t)$$

$$x_2 = \frac{C}{2}(\cos \omega_1 t - \cos \omega_2 t) \tag{1.126}$$

Figure 1.122 shows the motions of the two coupled masses for this special initial condition. The motion of each mass is actually acyclic, since the two normal frequencies are incommensurable. The main purpose of this figure is

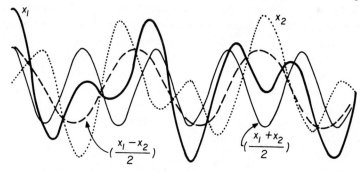

Fig. 1.122. The normal modes for the coupled system of Fig. 1.121, and the instantaneous motion for the individual masses, where m_1 started from rest with an initial displacement and m_2 started from rest with zero initial displacement.

to demonstrate that the very complex curves representing the individual motions of the masses are composed of the two simple sine curves representing the normal coordinates of the system.

Equations (1.124) can be used to solve for the motion for any initial condition in which both masses are at rest. The constant A is then given by the sum of the initial displacements, and the constant B by their difference. This requires only a minor generalization of Fig. 1.122 in which the amplitudes of the sine curves are made proportional to the constants A and B.

The motion can also be pictured by supposing two rotating vectors, proportional in length to the strength of the normal coordinates, and rotating at the normal frequencies. The projection of the sum vector on the vertical axis gives the motion of one of the masses, while the projection of the difference vector gives the other. From Art. 1.6, the equations of motion can therefore be written

$$x_1 = Ae^{j\omega_1 t} + Be^{j\omega_2 t}$$
$$x_2 = Ae^{j\omega_1 t} - Be^{j\omega_2 t}$$

$$(1.127)$$

We shall use this exponential solution in the analysis of a more complex system in Art. 1.15.

Let us now take a somewhat more general view of the problem. If the spring s_3 were absent (or equivalently, if its stiffness were negligible) the system $s_1 - m_1$ would represent a simple harmonic oscillator with a natural resonant frequency determined by the ratio s/m, and an energy determined by these same parameters and the amplitude of motion. The system $s_2 - m_2$ would constitute a similar system. We can now suppose that the system $s_1 - m_1$ is given an oscillatory motion by some cause which is of no interest in the immediate problem, and inquire as to the motion which will be transmitted to the second vibratory system if the spring s_3 has a stiffness, which, though small, is other than zero. It cannot be ignored, however, that there will be reaction back upon the first system once motion occurs in the second system. Therefore the problem is fundamentally similar to the problem of the simpler system, except that the unequal parameters make the mathematical forms more complicated. In this view, however, there is a subtle difference in outlook. Here we are considering, in effect, not a single system consisting of two masses and three springs, but rather, two systems coupled together by a stiffness element.

In order to keep the mathematical complexity within bounds, we shall introduce the following simplifications:

$$\frac{s_1}{m_1} = \frac{s_2}{m_2}, \quad s_3 \ll s_1, \quad s_3 \ll s_2$$

These conditions are such as to make the resonant frequencies of the coupled systems equal in the absence of coupling, and second, the coupling element is much weaker than the stiffness of the individual oscillators. The second condition means, in effect, that there exist two systems, rather than one, each slightly influencing the other, because of the coupling element. It is regrettable that the more general problem cannot be attempted, for there are points that could be illustrated with regard to insulation of vibration if the masses and stiffness of the two systems could be made completely general.

The simultaneous differential equations of the system are

$$m_1 \frac{d^2x_1}{dt^2} = -(s_1 + s_3)x_1 + s_3x_2$$

$$m_2 \frac{d^2x_2}{dt^2} = s_3x_1 - (s_2 + s_3)x_2$$

It is known that the normal coordinates of this system are

$$X' = \sqrt{m_1}\,x_1 + \sqrt{m_2}\,x_2$$

$$X'' = \sqrt{m_1}\,x_1 - \sqrt{m_2}\,x_2$$

We shall accept the fact that the normal coordinates of the system are known in the same vein in which we have in previous articles assumed solutions of differential equations, and checked them by substitution in the equations. The solution of the problem with these assumed values of normal coordinates will have the effect of showing that the normal coordinates do have the values given.

Because of the assumption of the relative values of the stiffnesses, the following equations will hold approximately:

$$m_1 \frac{d^2x_1}{dt^2} = -s_1x_1 + s_3x_2$$

$$m_2 \frac{d^2x_2}{dt^2} = s_3x_1 - s_2x_2$$

These can be written

$$\sqrt{m_1}\frac{d^2x_1}{dt^2} = -\frac{s_1}{m_1}\sqrt{m_1}\,x_1 + \frac{s_3}{\sqrt{m_1m_2}}\sqrt{m_2}\,x_2 = -\omega^2\sqrt{m_1}\,x_1 + \frac{s_3}{\sqrt{m_1m_2}}\sqrt{m_2}\,x_2$$

$$\sqrt{m_2}\frac{d^2x_2}{dt^2} = \frac{s_3}{\sqrt{m_1m_2}}\sqrt{m_1}\,x_1 - \frac{s_2}{m_2}\sqrt{m_2}\,x_2 = \frac{s_3}{\sqrt{m_1m_2}}\sqrt{m_1}\,x_1 - \omega^2\sqrt{m_2}\,x_2$$

We therefore have for the equation of the normal coordinates,

$$\frac{d^2}{dt^2}X' = \sqrt{m_1}\frac{d^2x_1}{dt^2} + \sqrt{m_2}\frac{d^2x_2}{dt^2} = -\left(\omega^2 - \frac{s_3}{\sqrt{m_1m_2}}\right)X'$$

$$\frac{d^2}{dt^2}X'' = \sqrt{m_1}\frac{d^2x_1}{dt^2} - \sqrt{m_2}\frac{d^2x_2}{dt^2} = -\left(\omega^2 + \frac{s_3}{\sqrt{m_1m_2}}\right)X''$$

The solutions of these equations are

$$X' = Ae^{j\omega_1 t}, \qquad \omega_1 = \sqrt{\omega^2 - s_3/\sqrt{m_1m_2}}$$

$$X'' = Be^{j\omega_2 t}, \qquad \omega_2 = \sqrt{\omega^2 + s_3/\sqrt{m_1m_2}}$$

From the equations of the normal coordinates, we can solve for x_1 and x_2:

$$x_1 = \frac{X' + X''}{2\sqrt{m_1}} = \frac{1}{2\sqrt{m_1}}(Ae^{j\omega_1 t} + Be^{j\omega_2 t})$$

$$x_2 = \frac{X' - X''}{2\sqrt{m_2}} = \frac{1}{2\sqrt{m_2}}(Ae^{j\omega_1 t} - Be^{j\omega_2 t})$$

The interpretation of these equations is similar to that of the simpler system, except that the equations show the influence of the masses on the relative motions, and also the influence of the coupling constant on the normal frequencies.

Since in these articles the theoretical point of view predominates, the subsequent articles of this chapter will consider only symmetric systems, with the object of connecting up vibration theory and wave theory.

1.13 Electrical and Acoustical Analogues of Coupled Oscillators

Given the circuit consisting of three capacitors and two inductors shown in Fig. 1.131, let us develop the equations of current and voltage in the circuit by the use of Kirchhoff's laws. It is necessary to establish positive directions of current and voltage in the circuit. Positive currents are defined as currents

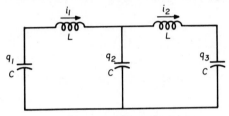

Fig. 1.131. Coupled electric circuits.

to the right in the inductors, and positive voltages exist when the upper plates of the capacitors are positive with respect to the lower plates.

Applying Kirchhoff's voltage law to the two meshes, we have

$$\frac{1}{C}q_1 = -L\frac{di_1}{dt} + \frac{1}{C}q_2 \qquad \frac{1}{C}\frac{dq_1}{dt} = -L\frac{d^2i_1}{dt^2} + \frac{1}{C}\frac{dq_2}{dt}$$

$$\frac{1}{C}q_2 = -L\frac{di_2}{dt} + \frac{1}{C}q_3 \qquad \frac{1}{C}\frac{dq_2}{dt} = -L\frac{d^2i_2}{dt^2} + \frac{1}{C}\frac{dq_3}{dt} \tag{1.131}$$

Also, we find the following relations between current and charge by Kirchhoff's current law, and the assumed positive sense of the currents and voltages:

$$-\frac{dq_1}{dt} = i_1, \quad \frac{dq_3}{dt} = i_2, \quad \frac{dq_2}{dt} = i_1 - i_2 \tag{1.132}$$

Substitution of Eq. (1.132) into Eq. (1.131) gives

$$-\frac{1}{C}i_1 = L\frac{d^2i_1}{dt^2} + \frac{1}{C}(i_1 - i_2)$$

$$\frac{1}{C}(i_1 - i_2) = L\frac{d^2i_2}{dt^2} + \frac{1}{C}i_2 \tag{1.133}$$

$$L\frac{d^2i_1}{dt^2} + \frac{1}{C}(2i_1 - i_2) = 0$$

$$L\frac{d^2i_2}{dt^2} + \frac{1}{C}(2i_2 - i_1) = 0$$

(1.134)

These relations are similar in every way to the differential Eqs. (1.121) of the coupled masses; consequently the electric circuit of Fig. 1.131 is the analogue of the coupled masses of Fig. 1.121.

The acoustical analogue consists of three cavities (acoustic compliances) joined by two constrictions (inertances), as in Fig. 1.132. Although the figure has the same symmetry as the electric circuit of Fig. 1.131, appearances are sometimes deceptive in analogous reasoning, so we shall carry through the

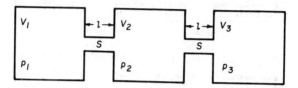

Fig. 1.132. Coupled acoustic circuits.

analysis of the acoustical circuit to obtain equations in which analogous quantities occupy corresponding positions when compared to Eq. (1.134). We have

$$\rho l\frac{d^2x_1}{dt^2} = p_1 - p_2 = \frac{BS}{V}x_1 - \frac{BS}{V}(x_1 - x_2)$$

$$\rho l\frac{d^2x_2}{dt^2} = p_2 - p_3 = \frac{BS}{V}(x_1 - x_2) - \frac{BS}{V}x_2$$

(1.135)

Simplifying, we have

$$\frac{d^2x_1}{dt^2} = \frac{BS}{V\rho l}(-2x_1 + x_2)$$

$$\frac{d^2x_2}{dt^2} = \frac{BS}{V\rho l}(x_1 - 2x_2)$$

(1.136)

Comparing these with the differential equations of the coupled electric and mechanical oscillators, the similarity is obvious. We could solve these equations as we solved those of the mechanical oscillators, but our main purpose is to clarify the analogy. The reason for this will become apparent when we begin to build up systems composed of mechanical, electric, and acoustical elements.

1.14 Beats

In the treatment of coupled oscillators we were led to the addition of two sinusoidal waves of different frequencies. When the frequency difference is comparable with the component frequencies, as in Art. 1.12, the motion of each particle loses all sinusoidal characteristics, and its periodicity has no simple relation to the component frequencies. Let us now consider the addition of two harmonic vibrations in which the frequency difference is a small fraction of the vibration frequencies. For simplicity the amplitudes may be considered equal; that is, let us solve the equation

$$x = A(\cos \omega_1 t - \cos \omega_2 t)$$

By the trigonometric identity,

$$\cos \theta + \cos \varphi = 2 \cos \frac{\theta + \varphi}{2} \cos \frac{\theta - \varphi}{2}$$

we obtain

$$x = 2A \cos \frac{\omega_1 - \omega_2}{2} \cos \frac{\omega_1 + \omega_2}{2}$$

This can be interpreted as a vibration occurring at the *average* of the component frequencies but having a variable *amplitude* $2A \cos (\omega_1 - \omega_2)/2$ (Fig. 1.141). As a result, the strength of the vibration waxes and wanes. The phenomenon is called *beating*, and the *beats* occur at the difference frequency. It appears from the equation that the amplitude varies at one-half the difference frequency, but actually the *sign* of the amplitude term $2A \cos (\omega_1 - \omega_2)/2$ is unimportant. The nulls occur at the difference frequency, and the structure of the variation is essentially similar between any two nulls.

It is important to note that the curve $\cos (\omega_1 - \omega_2)/2$ does not represent the continuous variation of any physical quantity even though it dominates the characteristic beat figure. It is sometimes said that a new tone is generated at the beat frequency when two tones are mixed. It is true that this often happens, but it is not a necessary result of mixing. In Art. 8.6 it will be shown that the mixing device must possess *nonlinearity* if a new tone in the correct sense is to be produced. It is true that the nonlinear device is often present when the beat phenomenon appears. The beat effect is frequently used to tune two tones to the same frequency. The tones are adjusted in frequency until 'zero beat' is obtained. This is a very sensitive method of frequency adjustment. If the two component tones are of high frequency, a beat of audible frequency (say 100 cycles) may be produced. Because of the nonlinearity of the ear, this may appear as an actual tone.

1.15 Vibrating Systems

The coupled oscillators of Art. 1.12 represent the simplest extension from the linear oscillator to the vibrating system. A further extension must be made before one can come to grips with the more complex vibrators that occur in nature and in acoustical apparatus. As an example, one might consider a multiplicity of mass particles coupled together by a multiplicity of

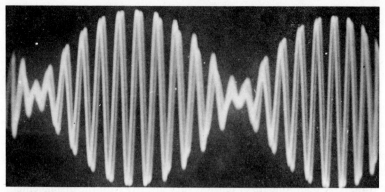

Fig. 1.141(a). Oscillogram showing beats between two frequencies of almost equal strength.

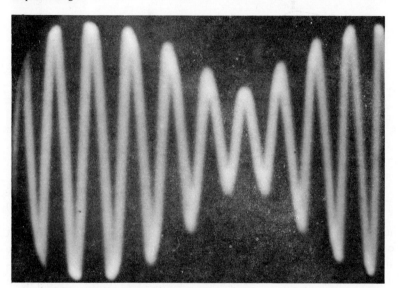

Fig. 1.141(b). Photo of beats due to two components of unequal amplitude. The components are shown in (c).

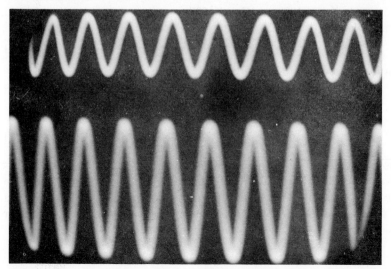

Fig. 1.141(c). Component vibrations which produced beats of Fig. 1.141(b).

linear elastic elements. As the number of mass particles increases, the complexity of the general system becomes very great, especially if no restriction is placed on the geometry of the system. For this reason, Lagrange, in initiating the study of vibrating systems, supposed a number of equal mass particles to be arranged in line, and connected with *strings* of negligible mass and equal length and tension. If very small transverse displacements are given to the mass particles (i.e. displacements much smaller than the horizontal distances between the particles) the tension in the strings remains effectively constant, but the transverse components of tension vary linearly with the displacements

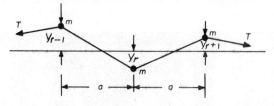

Fig. 1.151. The loaded string.

of the particles. The equation of motion of any particle can be written in terms of its displacement, the displacement of the two neighboring particles, the common tension T, and the common distance a, between particles (Fig. 1.151 and Eq. 1.151):

$$m \frac{d^2 y_r}{dt^2} = \frac{T}{a}(y_{r-1} - 2y_r + y_{r+1}) \tag{1.151}$$

The solution can best be obtained by complex methods. In Art. 1.12 it was found that the equation for the displacement of either particle can be written as a sum of exponentials, where these exponentials are found by solving for the normal modes of the system. If we apply the method here, we make the single assumption that there is a common frequency (in a normal mode) and a common phase for all particles (strictly, the phase angles will be either zero or exactly 180°, see Fig. 1.152).

That is, let

$$y_r = A_r e^{j\omega t}, \quad y_{r-1} = A_{r-1} e^{j\omega t}, \quad y_{r+1} = A_{r+1} e^{j\omega t} \tag{1.152}$$

Substitution of Eqs. (1.152) into Eq. (1.151) gives

$$\frac{ma\omega^2}{T} A_r = A_{r-1} - 2A_r + A_{r+1}$$

or

$$-A_{r-1} + \frac{2 - m\omega^2 a}{T} A_r - A_{r+1} = 0 \tag{1.153}$$

This is the necessary relation connecting the amplitudes of any three consecutive particles in a normal mode. Equation (1.153) may be used to solve for the normal modes of a system consisting of any number of particles on a string fixed at both ends. We shall, for simplicity, illustrate the method for three masses (Fig. 1.152). For a greater number, the mathematics becomes involved, but the physics of the problem is essentially the same. To simplify the appearance of the equations, let $(2 - ma\omega^2)/T = C$.

Taking r in Eq. (1.153) to be, successively, 1, 2, and 3, and noting that $A_0 = A_4 = 0$, we have

$$CA_1 - A_2 \quad\quad = 0$$
$$-A_1 + CA_2 - A_3 = 0 \quad (1.154)$$
$$- A_2 + CA_3 = 0$$

We can look upon these as simultaneous equations to be solved for A_1, A_2, and A_3 in terms of the parameters, m, a, ω, and T. However, because the right side of each equation is zero, we would find that the only solution which gives definite values for all three quantities is: $A_1 = A_2 = A_3 = 0$, which is a

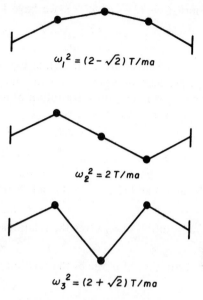

$$\omega_1^2 = (2 - \sqrt{2})\, T/ma$$

$$\omega_2^2 = 2\, T/ma$$

$$\omega_3^2 = (2 + \sqrt{2})\, T/ma$$

Fig. 1.152. Normal modes for three mass particles on string of negligible mass.

trivial solution. We may see this readily if we write the solution for A_1 as a determinant:

$$A_1 = \frac{\begin{vmatrix} 0 & -1 & 0 \\ 0 & C & -1 \\ 0 & -1 & C \end{vmatrix}}{\begin{vmatrix} C & -1 & 0 \\ -1 & C & -1 \\ 0 & -1 & C \end{vmatrix}} = \frac{0}{\Delta} = 0 \quad \text{if } \Delta \neq 0$$

Similarly
$$A_2 = A_3 = \frac{0}{\Delta} = 0 \quad \text{if } \Delta \neq 0$$

The A's need not all be zero, however, if the determinant of the coefficients Δ is zero. The vanishing of this determinant, then, is the necessary and sufficient condition that the normal mode equations have a nontrivial solution. The importance of this fact is that it gives only certain *allowable* values of C, and consequently of ω, these latter being the frequencies of the normal modes.

Equating Δ to zero, and solving for C,

$$C(C^2 - 1) - C = 0$$
$$C(C^2 - 2) = 0$$

$$\left.\begin{array}{l} C_1 = \sqrt{2} \\ C_2 = 0 \\ C_3 = -\sqrt{2} \end{array}\right\} \text{Solutions}$$

Since $C = (2 - ma\omega^2/T)$, we have for the normal frequencies

$$\omega_1^2 = \frac{(2 - \sqrt{2})T}{ma}, \quad \omega_2^2 = \frac{2T}{ma}, \quad \omega_3^2 = \frac{(2 + \sqrt{2})T}{ma} \tag{1.155}$$

If we substitute ω_1 in each of Eqs. (1.154) we can find the relative values of the particle amplitudes in the first normal mode, and similarly for the second and third modes on substitution of ω_2 and ω_3.

Substitution of ω_1 gives

$$\sqrt{2}A_1 - A_2 = 0 \quad (1)$$
$$-A_1 + \sqrt{2}A_2 - A_3 = 0 \quad (2)$$
$$- A_2 + \sqrt{2}A_3 = 0 \quad (3)$$

From (1) and (3), $A_1 = A_3$ and therefore from (2),

$$A_2 = \sqrt{2}A_1 = \sqrt{2}A_3 \tag{1.156a}$$

Substitution of ω_2 gives the relations

$$A_1 = - A_3, \quad A_2 = 0 \tag{1.156b}$$

Substitution of ω_3 gives the relation

$$A_2 = - \sqrt{2}A_1 = - \sqrt{2}A_3 \tag{1.156c}$$

As in the case of the coupled particles, none of the masses has in general a simple periodic motion. The normal coordinates can be shown to be

$$\frac{1}{\sqrt{2}}y_1 + y_2 + \frac{1}{\sqrt{2}}y_3$$

$$y_1 - y_3 \tag{1.157}$$

$$\frac{1}{\sqrt{2}}y_1 - y_2 + \frac{1}{\sqrt{2}}y_3$$

These may be equated respectively to $A_1e^{j\omega_1 t}$, $A_2e^{j\omega_2 t}$ and $A_3e^{j\omega_3 t}$, where the ω's are defined in Eqs. (1.155), and these equations can be solved for the equation of motion of each of the particles. The rotating vector concept may be used to get a picture of the motion. The motion is quite complicated unless the system is vibrating in a normal mode.

Example: Show that the relative amplitudes of mode I in Fig. 1.152 are obtained when the second and third normal coordinates, $y_1 - y_3$ and $(1/\sqrt{2})y_1 - y_2 + (1/\sqrt{2})y_3$ are equated to zero.

Solution:

If $\qquad y_1 - y_3 = 0 \quad$ and $\quad \frac{1}{2}\sqrt{2}y_1 - y_2 + \frac{1}{2}\sqrt{2}y_3 = 0$

then $\qquad y_1 = y_3 \quad$ and $\quad y_2 = \frac{2}{\sqrt{2}}y_1 = \sqrt{2}y_1$

But these are just the relative amplitudes when the loaded string is vibrating in its first normal mode.

This solution means that at every instant, the displacement of the second mass is $\sqrt{2}$ times that of the first and third. Previously, we had found the same relative values for the amplitudes, plus the fact that the particles vibrated in phase. The meanings are equivalent.

This article is an introduction to the theory of *loaded strings*. The next extension of the theory would be to increase the number of masses indefinitely. Although we could not in this case obtain definite values for the normal frequencies, we could obtain the general form of the dynamic equation. By allowing both a and m to approach zero in such a manner that the mass per unit length remained constant, we would have progressed from the vibration of mass particles to the vibration of a *uniform string*. From the viewpoint of integrating physical concepts, this procedure is worth while, but the treatment is fairly lengthy; and for the purpose of acoustical theory, largely unnecessary. It is better to start with a new approach in which the assumption of distributed mass is made from the beginning. This is the subject of the second chapter.

Before investigating the continuous string, however, we shall examine one final system composed of mass particles. We have seen that if an elastic system with a single particle is "disturbed", the result is SHM. For a system with several particles, the result is not in general SHM, but it was shown to consist of a superposition of SHM's having frequencies which are called the normal frequencies of the system. We now consider the result of increasing the number of mass particles without limit. It will be found that the effect of a general disturbance on such a system is not primarily vibration, but the production of a *wave*.

1.16 The Compressional Wave

Consider a system composed of an infinite number of particles of equal mass joined together by springs of equal length and stiffness and of negligible mass, and resting in a frictionless groove (Fig. 1.161). Assume the system to be initially in equilibrium, and suppose the first spring suddenly compressed a distance Δ. Since a finite mass cannot acquire a finite displacement instantaneously, the unbalanced force on the first particle becomes instantaneously $s\Delta$, and the acceleration becomes $s\Delta/m$. During the succeeding short time interval δt, its velocity will attain the value $(s\Delta\delta t)/m$, and its displacement, the value $[s\Delta(\delta t)^2]/2m$. The curves of acceleration, velocity, and displacement values are shown in Fig. 1.161 for a *short* period after the initial time, and it will be noticed that they are quantities of successively smaller orders of magnitude.

The unbalanced force on the second mass particle at the end of a short time is proportional to the *displacement* of the first particle, which, it is apparent, is increasing very slowly. Consequently, the force impressed on the second particle *lags that impressed on the first*. This process of analysis may be continued from one particle to another; that is to say, the acceleration of the second particle after time δt will be approximately $(\Delta/2)(s/m)^2(\delta t)^2$, and its displacement will be proportional to the fourth power of δt. Since the first particle starts into motion faster than the second, the second faster than the third, and so forth, it comes about that *each spring suffers a compression in the*

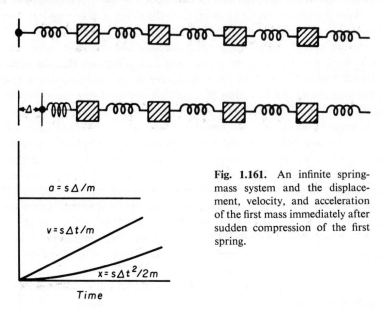

Fig. 1.161. An infinite spring-mass system and the displacement, velocity, and acceleration of the first mass immediately after sudden compression of the first spring.

$a = s\Delta/m$

$v = s\Delta t/m$

$x = s\Delta t^2/2m$

Time

early part of the motion, the magnitude of the compression diminishing from spring to spring.

Consider further what must follow from this initial motion. Since the first particle has an initial velocity and acceleration greater than the second, it will begin to overtake the second. Since the forward motion of the first particle decreases the compression in the first spring, while its relative motion with respect to the second particle increases the compression in the second spring, the compression begins to pass from the first to the second spring; and since the compressive *force* in the first spring is decreasing and that in the second spring is increasing, these forces eventually become equal, and the first particle begins to decelerate. During all this time the first spring has been expanding and the second has been contracting. Eventually, because of the deceleration of the first particle, the velocity of the second particle begins to exceed that of the first. This, of course, means that the second spring begins to expand. A little thought will show that the region of maximum compression has passed to the third spring. The region of maximum compression thus progresses through the system, and we say that a *wave* of *compression* has been produced.

We may also make an interesting qualitative observation. The heavier the masses and the more compressible the springs, the less quickly the compression in the first spring will be relieved, and the more slowly will the wave of compression travel down the system. Thus the *wave velocity* is a function of s/m.

If the displacement Δ had been negative or to the left, the first spring would initially have been extended; and from analysis similar to the foregoing, it follows that a wave of extension (or negative compression) would be sent down the system. Alternate positive and negative displacements of the end point would mean that alternate positive and negative compressions passed down the system.

In developing the picture of a compressional wave we have used three simplifying assumptions: a sudden displacement, concentrated masses, and weightless springs. These turn out to be sources of complexity rather than simplification if we try to carry the discussion further quantitatively, and in addition, have little application to ordinary cases of sound transmission. It would be better to consider the case of a homogeneous spring with mass and elasticity distributed evenly throughout, and to assume a somewhat smoother initial disturbance. We would then find a smooth *gradient* of the compression along the spring, where the gradient is defined as the change in the compression per unit distance. This will be the point of view in Chapter 3, in which we develop the equation of a compressional wave from the assumption of an initial gradient of the strain in an elastic medium.

References

Shortley and Williams, *Elements of Physics*, 2nd ed., Prentice-Hall, Englewood Cliffs, N.J., 1955.

A. E. Fitzgerald, *Fundamentals of Electrical Engineering*, McGraw-Hill, New York, 1945.

Morse, *Vibration and Sound*, 2nd ed., McGraw-Hill, New York, 1948.

Problems

1. In Fig. 1.21(b), what must be the stiffness constants of the individual springs if the stiffness constant of the system is to be k? What must be the compliances of the individual springs if the system compliance is to be C?

2. Derive Eq. (1.28) from Eq. (1.23) and show that the transformation Eqs. (1.29) hold.

3. In Eq. (1.211), set R_A and p equal to zero and solve for X as a function of t. Similarly, in Eq. (1.213), set R_E and e equal to zero and solve for q as a function of t. Differentiate the result to find i as a function of t.

4. In a mechanical oscillator, $m = 10$ g, $R_m = 100$ dynes sec cm^{-1} (mechanical ohms), and $s = 10^6$ dynes cm^{-1}. Find the time constant, logarithmic decrement, decay rate, and Q.

5. Show that $x = e^{(j\omega - R_m/2m)t}$, where $\omega = \sqrt{s/m - (Rm/2m)^2}$ is a solution of Eq. (1.41), and that therefore Eq. (1.43) is a solution.

6. A mass of 10 g oscillates at the end of a spring of stiffness 10^6 dynes cm.$^{-1}$ Initially the amplitude is 2.71828, and at the end of 10 sec the amplitude is 1 cm. Find the natural frequency, the logarithmic decrement, and Q of the oscillator.

7. Find the energy of a simple harmonic oscillator in free vibration if the mass is 111 g, the stiffness is 10^6 dynes cm, and the amplitude is 1 cm. If a driven oscillator of the same stiffness and mass has the same amplitude under a driving force of 10 dynes rms at the resonant frequency, find the power input to the driven oscillator.

8. Find the time averages of the kinetic and potential energies of a simple harmonic oscillator.

9. Show that the rate of dissipation of energy against the damping force of a freely vibrating oscillator is equal to the rate of loss of energy of the oscillator.

10. Find the frequency at which the displacement amplitude of a driven oscillator is a maximum. Find also the frequency at which the velocity amplitude is a maximum. Are these frequencies the same?

11. A force is applied to a spring-mass system as shown in Fig. P1.11. Show that the analogous electric circuit is an inductor and capacitor in parallel across a generator. Compare with the analogy of Figs. 1.71 and 1.72.

Fig. P1.11.

12. Plot mechanical impedance and admittance curves for a vibratory system of mass 1 g, stiffness 10^6 dynes/cm, and mechanical resistance 100 ohms mechanical. From these curves find the resistive and reactive components of velocity and also the velocity magnitude for a constant force of 10 dynes/rms. Find the resistive and reactive components and the magnitude of the force necessary to maintain a constant velocity of 5 cm/sec rms. In each case draw a curve of power input vs frequency.

13. Derive Eq. (1.151) for the loaded string.

14. By a treatment similar to that of the 3×3 determinant of Art. 1.15, find the allowable frequencies if *four* particles are connected together by weightless strings with equal separation. Also sketch the four normal modes of the system. Show that in both cases it is possible to draw a sine wave through the vibrating particles, and assuming this to be possible for any number of particles, find the relative amplitudes for the cases of five and six particles vibrating in normal modes.

15. A cabinet for a phase inverter loudspeaker consists of a box $100 \times 100 \times 40$ cm. The box has a collar 10 cm long and 10 sq cm cross section by which it communicates with the open air. Find the resonant frequency of the cabinet considered as a Helmholtz resonator. For this problem take $B/\rho = c^2$, where c, the velocity of sound in air, equals approximately 34,500 cm/sec. *Ans.* 9 cycles.

Chapter 2

VIBRATING STRINGS

Sound is transmitted from source to receiver by means of waves which have their origin in the vibration of a material body of finite size. The string is uniquely important in the science of acoustics because it is at one and the same time the simplest example of an *extended* vibrator and the simplest example of a medium of wave transmission.

The vibration and the wave are the most fundamental of acoustic concepts. Since we have discussed the important characteristics of vibration in the preceding chapter, we choose first in the study of the string to emphasize its function as a carrier of waves, and to consider vibration in the string as a particular case of wave motion where special conditions are imposed.

In the first article of the text, sound was defined as an alteration of pressure, stress, particle velocity, or particle displacement which is propagated in an elastic medium. The general notion of an alteration or disturbance which is propagated is the essence of the wave concept. Though it is true that most sounds have periodicity of some sort, and that acoustic theory is chiefly concerned with periodic waves, we wish to demonstrate the important wave concept in its greatest generality. Therefore we choose first to illustrate the propagation of a nonperiodic transverse deformation on a string.

2.1 The Progressive Wave on a String

Consider a string of very great (effectively, infinite) length under a steady tension T and having mass per unit length μ. Consider it to be deformed from a straight line between points A and D by a hollow tube, perfectly smooth inside. For definiteness, take $\widehat{AB}$, $\widehat{BC}$, and $\widehat{CD}$ to be arcs of circles with radius of curvature much greater than the arc length (Fig. 2.11).

Initially, suppose the string to be at rest relative to the tube. Then along

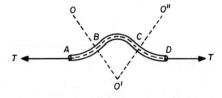

Fig. 2.11. Progressive wave on a string.

51

arcs $\overset{\frown}{AB}$ and $\overset{\frown}{CD}$ the string will exert a pressure against the inner wall of the tube which is away from the line of the undeformed string (toward O'' and O, respectively), whereas along arc $\overset{\frown}{BC}$ the pressure will be toward the line of the string (toward O').

Supposing relative motion to take place between the tube and the string, let us solve the mechanical problem of the forces between the string and the wall of the tube. As far as the ultimate solution of the problem is concerned, it makes no difference whether the string or the tube is moving, but it is easier to picture the tube at rest in a certain coordinate system, while the string is moving *in this system*.

It is our object to show that there is a definite relative velocity at which all forces between tube and string vanish. As long as the deformation of the string is small, the tension in the string has the constant value T at all points of the string, and is tangent to the string. If the string were at rest, the force against the inner wall would be $T\theta$, as we find by resolving the tensions at A and B into components perpendicular to, and tangential to, the tube wall.

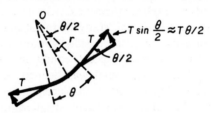

Fig. 2.12. Resolution of pressure on tube wall into tangential and normal components.

The details of this resolution are shown in Fig. 2.12. However, the motion of the string causes this force to be reduced by the amount $\mu\theta c^2$, where c is the tangential velocity and θ is the angle subtended by the arc $\overset{\frown}{AB}$. We obtain this quantity from the expression for centrifugal force:

$$\text{C.F.} = \frac{mc^2}{r} = \frac{\mu r\theta c^2}{r} = \mu\theta c^2 \tag{2.11}$$

Therefore the net force of the string against the tube wall is

$$P = T\theta - \mu\theta c^2 \tag{2.12}$$

Similar expressions will be found for arcs $\overset{\frown}{BC}$ and $\overset{\frown}{CD}$.

We now note that it is possible for the net force to be zero if

$$T\theta = \mu\theta c^2$$

or

$$c^2 = \frac{T}{\mu} \tag{2.13}$$

If a similar computation is carried out on arcs $\overset{\frown}{BC}$ and $\overset{\frown}{CD}$ it is found that this relation between velocity, tension, and density will give a net zero force on all *three* arcs. We can conclude only that the deformation introduced by the tube, once set up, will continue to exist *without the presence of the tube,* as long as the relative velocity c persists.

Though the deformation was built up of three circular arcs, the solution is independent of the curvature of the arcs, and the analysis would be similar, regardless of the shape of the deformation, as long as the tube can be assumed to be made up of infinitesimal circular arcs. This can be done for any but the most exceptional cases.

We have shown that a particular velocity results in the existence of zero force at all points of the deforming tube. But since the velocity in question is the relative velocity between string and tube, it follows that a deformation once set up on a string at rest in space must travel along the string with the velocity $c = \sqrt{T/\mu}$, without further change of shape.

This article and the last article of the previous chapter (Art. 1.16) have been included to demonstrate that the idea of a wave velocity follows from elementary mechanical principles, and that the value $c = \sqrt{T/\mu}$ is readily obtained. The conventional method of attacking the problem is to derive a differential equation for the forces on an element of a deformed string by a direct application of Newton's law. This is the subject of the next article.

2.2 Development of the Wave Equation in the String

Suppose a long, horizontal elastic string to be held under tension between two supports. When static equilibrium exists, the tension will be constant along the string, and each elementary length will be subjected to two equal and opposite tensions. If, for any reason, a very small transverse deformation is set up in some region of the string, the elements of that region, in the

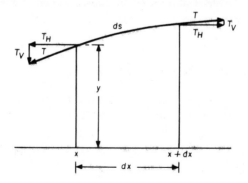

Fig. 2.21. A segment of a string under tension, showing variation of transverse component of tension because of curvature of string.

absence of constraint, will no longer be in static equilibrium. We may neglect the very small change in the horizontal component of the tension, since, on a relative basis, the horizontal component is still practically equal to the static tension T. The vertical (or transverse) component of tension, however, must be reckoned with. The transverse tension on either end of an element will be proportional to the slope at that end; and if there is a change in slope over the element, there will be a net transverse force on the element. Further, the net force will be proportional to the rate of change of slope over the element.

By Newton's law, an unbalanced force on a mass results in a proportional acceleration, which we have seen to be equal to the second time derivative of the displacement. Since the unbalanced force is proportional at one and the same time to a space derivative and to a time derivative of the displacement, it will be necessary to employ the symbolism of partial derivatives to show this relation analytically.

From Fig. 2.21, the net force on the element is evidently

$$T\frac{\partial^2 y}{\partial x^2}\,dx$$

The mass of the element is the product of the linear density μ and the length of the element dx. Thus, by Newton's law,

$$T\frac{\partial^2 y}{\partial x^2}\,dx = \mu dx\frac{\partial^2 y}{\partial t^2}$$

$$\frac{\partial^2 y}{\partial t^2} = \frac{T}{\mu}\frac{\partial^2 y}{dx^2} \tag{2.21}$$

Equation 2.21 is a *linear* partial differential equation since it involves only the first powers of the derivatives. It states that the acceleration at a point of a string is directly proportional to the rate of change of slope at the point. Linear equations are of great importance in physics, not only because they simplify analysis, as has already been remarked, but also because they are connected with the physical principle of *superposition*, by which the total displacement of two or more component waves is additive. The same can be said of the mathematical solutions of a linear differential equation.

2.3 General Solution of the Wave Equation

The solution of the wave equation in terms of two independent, arbitrary functions is formally quite simple. Let us consider as a trial solution,

$$y = f_1(x - ct) + f_2(x + ct) \tag{2.31}$$

where $c \equiv \sqrt{T/\mu} \equiv$ const. We can show by differentiation that this form satisfies Eq. (2.21) since

$$\frac{\partial y}{\partial t} = -cf'_1(x - ct) + cf'_2(x + ct), \qquad \frac{\partial y}{dx} = f'_1(x - ct) + f'_2(x + ct)$$

$$\frac{\partial^2 y}{\partial t^2} = c^2 f''_1(x - ct) + c^2 f''_2(x + ct), \qquad \frac{\partial^2 y}{\partial x^2} = f''_1(x - ct) + f''_2(x + ct)$$

and obviously

$$\frac{\partial^2 y}{\partial t^2} = c^2\frac{\partial^2 y}{\partial x^2}$$

There is only one interpretation to be made from this solution; i.e. that there is a propagation of arbitrary wave forms in opposite directions with velocity $c = \sqrt{T/\mu}$. It is to be noted that this result agrees with the conclusion of Art. 2.1, both giving $c = \sqrt{T/\mu}$ for the velocity, and both holding for

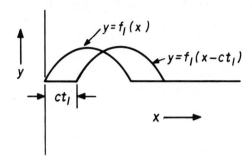

Fig. 2.31. Progression of the arbitrary wave form $f_1(x - ct)$ to the right, with velocity c.

arbitrary wave forms. In both cases the value $\sqrt{T/\mu}$ came about as a necessary condition for an equality of forces. Let us show that the first form (Eq. 2.31) represents a wave moving in the direction of increasing x with this velocity (Fig. 2.31). At $t = 0$, $y = f_1(x)$; and at $t = t_1$, $y = f_1(x - ct_1) = f_1(x - x_1)$.

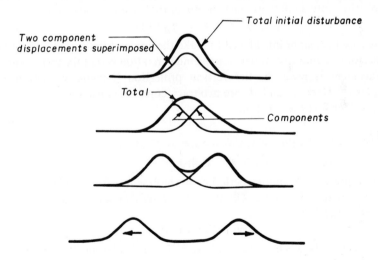

Fig. 2.32. Development of two transverse traveling waves from initial transverse deformation of string.

We know from analytic geometry that the effect of replacing x by $(x - x_1)$ throughout a function is to displace every point on the function a distance x_1 to the right. (For example, compare the parabolas $y = x^2$ and $y = (x - x_1)^2$.) Thus whatever form the function has at $t = 0$, it will have at $t = t_1$, except that it will be displaced a distance $ct_1 = x_1$, to the right. Since this takes place in time t_1, the velocity is c. The result agrees with the conclusion of the analysis in Art. 2.1, and in addition, it answers the question of the direction of travel. An initial transverse disturbance will actually produce two waves of equal amplitude traveling in opposite directions. This is quite plausible, since there is no reason why either direction should be favored if the initial displacements are transverse. The amplitude of each of the traveling waves is half the amplitude of the initial disturbance. Successive positions of the wave are shown in Fig. 2.32. We note that, though the form of the initial disturbance changes, the form of the components remains unchanged. The discussion in Art. 2.1 was based on an investigation of one of the two traveling deformations.

It is quite possible to proceed with the general solution, consisting of arbitrary functions, by imposing boundary conditions. Actually, in some cases, interpretation may be more direct with arbitrary functions than with special functions. However, in wave theory, as in vibration theory, most of the important concepts are based on the assumption of harmonic vibration, and the notation traditionally found in acoustic theory shows that this assumption is, practically speaking, essential if the mathematical difficulties are to be kept within reasonable bounds. This amounts to imposing an initial condition in which the string has a sinusoidal shape over its entire length.

We therefore shall consider henceforth the harmonic solution,

$$y = A_1 e^{jk(ct-x)} + A_2 e^{jk(ct+x)} \tag{2.32}$$

where k is a constant introduced to make the angle of the complex number a dimensionless quantity, and where the interpretation is that the instantaneous displacement is given by the vertical projection (imaginary part) of the complex y. Here A_1 and A_2 are arbitrary complex constants.

Consider first the function

$$y = A_1 e^{jk(ct-x)} \tag{2.33}$$

For any fixed value of x, this reduces to the form

$$y = \text{Const } e^{jkct} \tag{2.34}$$

which represents a simple periodic displacement with angular frequency $\omega = kc$, so that $k = \omega/c$. On the other hand, at any instant Eq. (2.33) reduces to the form

$$y = \text{Const } e^{-jkx} \tag{2.35}$$

which represents a sinusoidal variation of the displacement with distance, the angle of lag increasing in the positive-x direction. Where ωt is the "phase" of the vector displacement in simple harmonic vibration, the phase of the harmonic wave is given by ωt-kx.* We note that y goes through a cycle of displacement in time for any fixed value of x if t increases by the amount $2\pi/\omega = 1/f$, which is the period, and that it completes a cycle of displacement

---

* In both cases we are ignoring the initial phase angle.

in space when x increases by the amount $2\pi/k = \lambda$ for any fixed value of time. Therefore λ is called the *wavelength*, and k is called the *wavelength constant*. As in the previous chapter, there is little loss of generality in making the amplitude constant a real number, since it simply gives an initial displacement of zero at the origin. An extension of the vector diagram of the previous chapter is admirably suited to portray the functional dependence of y on x and t. If we consider one cycle of a sine wave, and represent vectorially the *instantaneous* displacements of points separated by $\frac{1}{8}$ wavelength, we obtain Fig. 2.33(a). Now if each of these points is in simple harmonic vibration, the

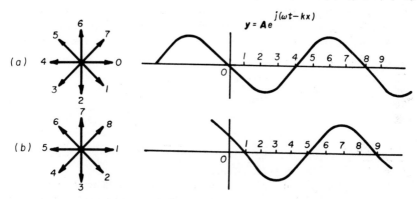

Fig. 2.33. Wave progressing in positive-x direction.

motion of the group is shown by rotation of their vectors; that is, by *rotation of the vector diagram as a whole*. Vector diagrams and corresponding positions of the wave are shown for two instants separated by $\frac{1}{8}$ period in the figure, and it will be observed that rotation of the diagram through 45° corresponds to motion of the entire wave segment through $\frac{1}{8}$ wavelength, or 45° in space (Fig. 2.33(b).

The vector diagram may also be used to show that the function $Ae^{j(\omega t + kx)}$, in which the phase increases in the positive-x direction, represents a wave progressing in the negative-x direction. This is shown in Fig. 2.34.

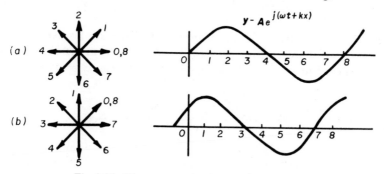

Fig. 2.34. Wave progressing in negative-x direction.

2.4 Characteristic Impedance of the String

There are several equivalent definitions of the *characteristic impedance* of the string, all of them in some way analogous to the mechanical impedance of an oscillator. We remember that Z_m was defined as the ratio between the driving force and the velocity of the mass particle. The characteristic impedance of a string is defined as the ratio of the transverse tension to the (transverse) velocity at any point on an infinite string which is carrying a progressive wave. Since equal and opposite tensions exist at each point, to avoid ambiguity in sign we take the tension to be that tension exerted on the portion of the string in the direction of travel of the wave. For a wave proceeding in the positive-x direction, the tension will be $-T\partial y/\partial x$. The velocity is given by the time derivative of the displacement. This gives for the characteristic impedance:

$$Z_s = \frac{-T(\partial y/\partial x)}{\partial y/\partial t}$$

$$= \frac{jkTy}{j\omega y} = \frac{k}{\omega}T = \frac{T}{c} = \sqrt{T\mu} \qquad [y = Ae^{j(\omega t - kx)}] \quad (2.41)$$

When we investigate the driven string, we shall see the reason for the choice of sign of the transverse tension.

The development of Eq. (2.41) was based on the expression for a progressive wave proceeding in the positive-x direction. If the expression for the wave proceeding in the negative-x direction had been used, the value obtained for the characteristic impedance would have been $-\sqrt{T\mu}$. There is, of course, a certain arbitrariness in the sign, but it is necessary to take this fact into account in certain analyses involving characteristic impedance.

2.5 Effect of a Boundary on Waves in the String

Any one of the three harmonic functions

$$y = A_1 e^{j(\omega t - kx)}$$
$$y = A_2 e^{j(\omega t + kx)}$$
$$y = A_1 e^{j(\omega t - kx)} + A_2 e^{j(\omega t + kx)}$$

satisfies the differential equation of the string. We find, however, that the form containing both functions is needed when boundary conditions are also to be satisfied, and also that the functions are no longer independent. As an

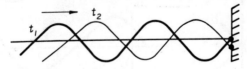

Fig. 2.51. A single traveling wave on a string which violates boundary conditions at a rigid wall.

example, we consider a harmonic wave advancing in the positive-x direction on a half-infinite string extending from $x = -\infty$ to $x = 0$, and attached to a rigid support at $x = 0$ (Fig. 2.51).

The function $A_1 e^{j(\omega t + kx)}$ predicts that the point of support is in SHM with amplitude A, which violates the boundary condition. But if a second wave exists on the string which reduces to $y_{x=0} = -A_1 e^{j\omega t}$, the superposition of these two waves will make the displacement zero at all times at the point of support. We need not interpret the meaning of these functions to the right of the boundary, since our functions are *defined* only from $x = -\infty$ to $x = 0$. The end point, however, is considered part of the region. The mathematical statement of the solution is the following:

$$y = A[e^{j(\omega t - kx)} - e^{j(\omega t + kx)}] \quad (x \le 0)$$
$$y = 0 \quad (x > 0)$$
$$(2.51)$$

From Eq. (1.57) (derived from Euler's equation), Eq. (2.51) can be written

$$y = 2A(\sin kx)e^{j\omega t} \tag{2.52}$$

This form no longer represents a progressive wave. The representation is rather a set of points in simple harmonic motion with amplitudes dependent upon the value of sin kx. It is called a "standing wave". Where the amplitudes of all points are equal for the progressive wave $Ae^{j(\omega t - kx)}$ and there is a gradual phase lag at any instant in the direction of increasing x, the standing wave has an amplitude dependent upon x, but constant phase over any half wavelength. (At the nodes there is an abrupt phase shift of 180°) (see Fig. 2.52).

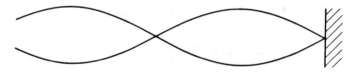

Fig. 2.52. A standing wave on a string.

Following the convention of rotating vector diagrams, we can show the development of a standing wave from two waves of equal amplitude and wavelength proceeding in opposite directions (Fig. 2.53).

In Fig. 2.53 the two component waves are shown proceeding in opposite directions. The vector diagram to the left of the wave pattern is associated with the wave advancing in the negative-x direction. Conditions are shown for four instants separated in time by one-eighth of a period. In (d) of the figure, the two waves are summed vectorially. The vertical projection of the vectors in (d) gives the instantaneous displacement of the standing wave at any instant.

One should note that in the standing wave case all the vectors are in line, whereas in the case of the progressive wave, the vectors are evenly distributed about the center.

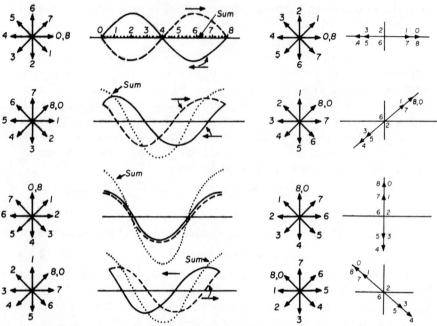

Fig. 2.53. Development of a standing wave from two progressive waves proceeding in opposite directions.

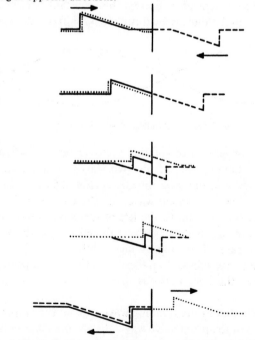

Fig. 2.54. Reflection of an arbitrary wave form by a rigid wall.

The standing-wave condition arises only when there is a continuous train of waves arriving at the boundary. If we consider a single pulse of arbitrary shape arriving at the boundary we find that a return pulse, or reflected pulse, is apparently called into being by the necessity of satisfying the boundary conditions. Figure 2.54 shows several instants in the creation of a reflected pulse from an incident pulse.

2.6 The String of Finite Length

The string of finite length between two rigid supports presents a problem in which there is a merging of the wave and vibration concepts. We have already mentioned, in Art. 1.15, that the homogeneous string of finite length could be considered a limiting case of the loaded string, which was solved as a vibration problem. On the other hand, in the article just completed, we saw how a traveling wave on a half-infinite string must ultimately produce standing waves (vibrations) by reflection at the rigid boundary. We shall follow this second line of reasoning in the problem of the finite string.

Let the string be of length L, tension T, and linear density μ, and let the boundaries be at the points $x = 0$ and $x = L$. In Eq. (2.52) we have found the relation which must be true on account of the rigid boundary at $x = 0$. It is rewritten for convenience:

$$y = 2A(\sin kx)e^{j\omega t}$$

In order that this solution shall also satisfy the boundary condition at $x = L$, it is necessary that

$$\sin kL = 0 \quad \text{or} \quad kL = n\pi \qquad (n \text{ any integer})$$

from which $k = n\pi/L$; and since $k = 2\pi/\lambda$,

$$L = \frac{n\lambda}{2} \quad \text{and} \quad \lambda = \frac{2L}{n} \tag{2.61}$$

This means that the only harmonic motions possible are those in which the half wavelength is contained an integral number of times in the length of the string. There are therefore only discrete frequencies of vibration possible on a string of finite length; namely, those frequencies which satisfy the equation

$$\omega_n = 2\pi f_n = \frac{2\pi c}{\lambda_n} = \frac{n\pi}{L}\sqrt{\frac{T}{\mu}}, \quad f_n = \frac{n}{2L}\sqrt{\frac{T}{\mu}} \tag{2.62}$$

These frequencies are called the normal frequencies of vibration of the finite string. The modes of vibration corresponding to the three lowest frequencies are shown in Fig. 2.61.

Thus any harmonic solution for the string of length L, tension T, and linear density μ is of the form

$$y_n = A_n\left(\sin\frac{n\pi x}{L}\right)e^{j\omega_n t} \tag{2.63}$$

The general form for the *instantaneous* value of the displacement in any mode is

$$y_n = (A_n \cos \omega_n t + B_n \sin \omega_n t) \sin \frac{n\pi x}{L} \tag{2.64}$$

This is true for any integral value of n. But differential equation theory tells us (and we may check by substitution) that the sum of any number of

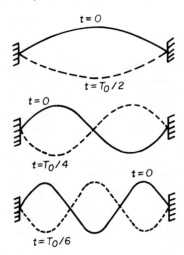

t = 0

t = T_0/2

t = 0

t = T_0/4

t = 0

t = T_0/6

Fig. 2.61. First, second, and third normal modes of a vibrating string fixed at both ends. T_0 = period of fundamental mode.

particular solutions, each with arbitrary multipliers, is also a solution of the differential wave equation for the finite string:

$$y = \sum_{n=1}^{n=\infty} (A_n \cos \omega_n t + B_n \sin \omega_n t) \sin \frac{n\pi x}{L} \tag{2.65}$$

Our method of deriving this solution corresponds to that employed to get the total displacements of coupled oscillators by adding the displacements of the several normal modes. We cannot write the total displacement in *vector* form because it has been obtained by adding harmonic motions of *different* frequencies, whereas the vector method is based on the supposition of a single frequency.

One can make the observation that the string of finite length behaves as a *vibrator* when the frequency coincides with a normal frequency, whereas the infinite string appears as a medium for wave transmission. This is a helpful comparison, but it should not be misunderstood. Though the finite string in a normal mode of vibration does not have progressive wave crests, it must be remembered that the standing wave has been interpreted as two waves proceeding in opposite directions.

2.7 Energy of the String

The vibrating string is merely a collection of elementary oscillators. If we take dx to be the elementary length, the mass of each elementary oscillator will be $\mu\, dx$, and its amplitude will be $A \sin n\pi x/L$, where A is the peak amplitude of any segment, and the factor $\sin n\pi x/L$ indicates that the element may be at some point not having peak amplitude. If the string is in vibration in its nth normal mode, it consists of n similar vibrating segments.

In Art. 1.8, we obtained as the energy of an oscillator

$$\tfrac{1}{2}mA^2\omega^2$$

We therefore have for the energy in any element of the string,

$$dE = \frac{1}{2}\omega^2 A^2 \left(\sin^2 \frac{n\pi x}{L} \right) \mu\, dx \tag{2.71}$$

and for the total energy,

$$E = \frac{n\mu}{2}\, \omega^2 A^2 \int_0^{L/n} \sin^2 \frac{n\pi x}{L}\, dx$$

$$= \frac{\mu\omega^2 A^2 L}{2\pi} \left(\frac{n\pi x}{2L} - \frac{L}{4n\pi} \sin \frac{2n\pi x}{L} \right)_0^{L/n}$$

$$= \frac{\mu\omega^2 A^2 L}{4} = \frac{m\omega^2 A^2}{4} \tag{2.72}$$

where m is the total mass of the string.

We can also introduce at this point the concept of average energy in the vibrating string as a *space* average, in a manner analogous to the treatment of the root mean square value in Chapter 1, except that the rms value was obtained by averaging over time. Since the configuration repeats itself every half wavelength, we have for the space average energy density,

$$\mathcal{E} = \frac{1}{\lambda/2} \int_0^{\lambda/2} \frac{1}{2} A^2 \omega^2 \sin^2 \frac{\pi x}{L} \mu dx = \frac{\mu A^2 \omega^2}{4}$$

The same result is obtained more directly by division of Eq. (2.72) by L. However, the integral indicates the method of space average.

For the string propagating a progressive wave, the displacement maxima all have equal value A, the gradually changing phase from segment to segment having no effect on the value of the energy in any segment. Therefore the energy per unit length of the string is

$$\mathcal{E} = \frac{\mu\omega^2 A^2}{2} \tag{2.73}$$

Now since the wave crests which give rise to the above expression for energy density (energy per unit length) are traveling down the string with velocity c, we can consider the energy to be carried along at a rate

$$I = \frac{\mu\omega^2 A^2}{2}\, c = \frac{1}{2} c\mu V_0^2 = \frac{1}{2} \sqrt{T\mu}\, V_0^2 \tag{2.74}$$

where V_0 is the velocity amplitude of any particle on the string. This rate of energy transfer is the rate of *power flow* in the string. We note that Eq. (2.74) is analogous to the power expression $\frac{1}{2}R_m V_0^2$ in the oscillator. This confirms the choice of the term "characteristic impedance" for the factor $\sqrt{T\mu}$, and also checks the fact that it is purely resistive.

Figure 2.53 shows that the amplitude of a standing wave is twice that of either component. On the energy viewpoint, each of the components possesses energy $\frac{1}{4}\mu\omega^2 A^2$ per unit length, so that, when the two are superposed, the energy per unit length is $\frac{1}{2}\mu\omega^2 A^2$. Since the standing wave amplitude is $2A$, we have by Eq. (2.72) for the energy density,

$$\mathcal{E} = \frac{\mu\omega^2(2A)^2}{4} = \mu\omega^2 A^2$$

This is an example of the equivalence of the wave and vibration viewpoints where reflection is present.

2.8 The Driven String

In the development of the wave equation of the string, we considered the acceleration of an infinitesimal mass element of the string to be proportional to the infinitesimal difference in transverse tension between the two ends of the element, and found this net transverse tension to be determined by the *rate of change of slope* over the element (see Fig. 2.21).

If the string terminates at a point which is maintained in transverse oscillation by some external agent, the transverse force which the string exerts on this *driving point* is proportional to the *slope* of the string at this point, and by Newton's third law the external agent must exert an equal force on the string. This force is called the *driving force* (Fig. 2.81). The ratio of the

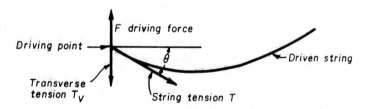

Fig. 2.81. The driven string:
$$T_V = T \tan \theta = T \, \partial y/\partial x_{(x=0)} \quad \text{and} \quad F = -T \, \partial y/\partial x_{(x=0)}.$$

driving force to the velocity of the end point is called the *driving-point imped-ance** of the string. If the string extends to infinity, we find the driving-point impedance to be equal to the characteristic impedance. Indeed, this is one of several definitions of characteristic impedance.

---

* The term *input impedance* is often used for this ratio. The term *driving-point impedance* is used here as having more meaning in the present discussion.

Figure 2.81 will help to make it clear that the driving-point impedance is given by the ratio $-T\dfrac{\partial y/\partial x}{\partial y/\partial t}$, the same ratio used in the definition of the characteristic impedance of the string. The value $\sqrt{T\mu}$ has already been obtained for this ratio in Art. 2.4. We note $\sqrt{T\mu}$ is a real number, and that therefore the infinite string acts as a pure *resistance* to the driving force. If A is the amplitude of the end point, its velocity amplitude is $A\omega$ and hence the power input to the string from the driver will be

$$P_{Av} = \tfrac{1}{2}\sqrt{T\mu}\,A^2\omega^2$$

This confirms the value derived in Art. 2.7 for power flow in the string.

If the string is of finite length and terminated by a rigid support, the driving-point impedance is no longer equal to the characteristic impedance, though it is still defined as the ratio of the driving force to the velocity of the end point. We solve below for the driving-point impedance of a string terminated by a rigid support.

$$y = A[e^{j(\omega t - kx)} - e^{j(\omega t + kx)}]$$

$$\frac{\partial y}{dx} = -jkAe^{j\omega t}(e^{-jkx} + e^{jkx})$$

$$\frac{\partial y}{\partial t} = j\omega Ae^{j\omega t}(e^{-jkx} - e^{+jkx})$$

$$Z_i = \frac{-T\,\partial y/\partial x}{\partial y/\partial t} = \frac{kT}{\omega}\frac{e^{-jkx} + e^{jkx}}{e^{-jkx} - e^{tkx}}$$

$$= -j\frac{k}{\omega}T\cot kx$$

$$= -j\sqrt{T\mu}\cot kx = -jZ_0\cot kx \qquad (2.81)$$

We see that the string of finite length terminated by a rigid support acts as a pure reactance, because Z_i is purely imaginary, and therefore the power input must be zero. Curves of driving tension, velocity of the driving point, and driving-point impedance are shown in Fig. 2.82 as a function of length of the string. For the more general problem of the driving-point impedance of a string of finite length terminated by a yielding boundary we need the concept of reflection coefficient, to be developed in the next article.

To make the problem of the driven string more concrete we shall consider an actual driving mechanism, shown in Fig. 2.83. The driving force is ultimately electric in origin, of magnitude DI, where D is an *electromagnetic coupling constant*, and I is the rms current in the drive coil. We assume that all the mass of the driving system is concentrated in the drive coil, and that springs of negligible mass supply the stiffness. The drive coil is constrained to move in the vertical direction by guides (not shown) which provide friction. We are interested in the force exerted on the string by the driver and in the amount of power supplied by the driver to the string in terms of the electric

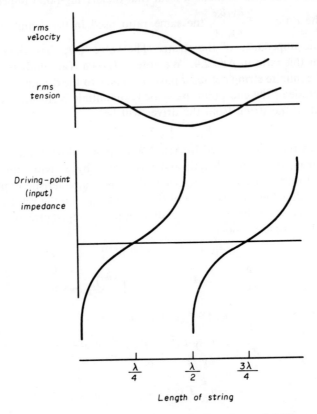

Fig. 2.82. Velocity, tension, and driving-point impedance of rigidly supported string, as a function of length of string.

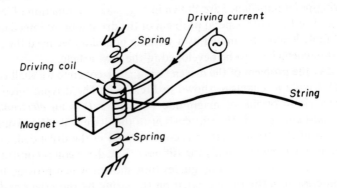

Fig. 2.83. Driving mechanism for string.

force DI, the mechanical impedance of the driver, Z_m, and the mechanical impedance of the string Z_i.

We shall take the string to be of infinite length, so that it has a driving-point impedance $\sqrt{T\mu}$. Since this impedance must be overcome in addition to the mass impedance, elastic impedance, and frictional impedance of the driving system, the total impedance of the vibrating system is $Z_m + Z_i$, where $Z_m = R_m + jX_m$, and $Z_i = \sqrt{T\mu} = R_0$.* We have for the velocity of the drive coil $V = DI/(Z_m + R_0)$. This enables us to compute both the force applied to the string, and the power input by the equations

$$F = VR_0 = \frac{DIR_0}{Z_m + R_0} \tag{2.82}$$

$$P_{Av} = V^2 R_0 = \frac{D^2 I^2}{|Z_m + R_0|^2} R_0 = \frac{D^2 I^2 R_0}{|R_m + R_0 + jX_m|^2} = \frac{D^2 I^2 R_0}{X_m^2 + R^2} \tag{2.83}$$

where $R = R_m + R_0$. We note that the applied force approaches its maximum as the characteristic impedance of the string increases, becoming DI as the string impedance approaches infinity.

We shall prove that the power input is maximum (for any constant force DI) when the impedance of the string matches the impedance of the driver. This is a case of a general condition in power transmission which is defined by the maximum power transfer theorem. We have

$$P_{Av} = \frac{D^2 I^2 R_0}{X_m^2 + R^2}$$

To maximize P_{Av} with respect to changes in R_0, we differentiate with respect to R_0 and equate to zero:

$$\frac{\partial P_{Av}}{\partial R_0} = D^2 I^2 \frac{X_m^2 + R^2 - 2RR_0}{(X_m^2 + R^2)^2} .$$

Equating to zero and using the relation $R = R_m + R_0$, we have

$$X_m^2 + R_m^2 + 2R_m R_0 - 2R_m R_0 - R_0^2 = 0$$

$$R_0^2 = X_m^2 + R_m^2 = |Z_m|^2$$

or

$$R_0 = |Z_m| \tag{2.84}$$

In this case we assumed that the phase angle of the vibrator was independent of the phase angle of the string (or in the language of communication theory, that the phase angle of the source was independent of the phase angle of the load), and found that maximum power transfer occurs when the magnitude of the string impedance matches the magnitude of the driver impedance. If it were possible to change the phase angle of either the source or the load, we would find that optimum power transfer occurs when one impedance is the

---

* The symbol Z_0 is generally used for characteristic impedance. However, R_0 is used where it is desired to stress the fact that R_0 is purely resistive. There are instances in communication theory in which the characteristic impedance is complex.

complex conjugate of the other. However, in many cases we do not have this control over impedances. As a matter of fact, in air acoustics the impedance of the driver or *source* is usually many times greater than that of the *load*, and indeed much design work consists of stratagems for raising the load impedance.

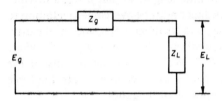

Fig. 2.84. Equivalent circuit for electric network.

In interpreting Eqs. (2.82) and (2.83), we have developed and utilized concepts which are stated precisely in the electrical theory of communications by Thevenin's theorem and the maximum power theorem. We show in Fig. 2.84 and Eq. (2.85) an electric circuit and an electrical equation that are analogous to Fig. 2.83 and Eq. (2.82).

$$E_L = \frac{E_g}{Z_g + Z_L} Z_g \quad \text{Where} \tag{2.85}$$

Z_g (internal impedance) replaces Z_m (mechanical impedance of driver)
Z_L (load impedance) replaces R_0 (impedance of string)
E_L (load voltage) replaces F_s (force on string)
E_g (source voltage) replaces DI (applied force)

It is obvious that Eq. (2.85) is a correct description of Fig. 2.84. Now Thevenin's theorem states that *any* two-terminal network consisting of generators and impedances can be replaced by the simple network of Fig. 2.84, where E_g is the open-circuit voltage measured between the terminals with the load impedance removed, and Z_g is the impedance measured between the output terminals with the load impedance removed and the source voltages eliminated (short-circuited). The analogous impedance diagram for the driven string is shown in Fig. 2.85.

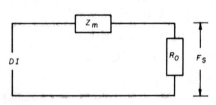

Fig. 2.85. Equivalent mechanical circuit for driven string.

The maximum power theorem also makes use of the circuit of Fig. 2.84. It states that maximum power will be delivered if Z_L is the conjugate of Z_g and that, in cases where the phase angles of the impedances are fixed, maximum power will be delivered where the load impedance is the equal of the source impedance in absolute magnitude.

Thevenin's theorem and the maximum power theorem are used wherever the system is composed of a generator and a load. The term "driver" and "source" are synonyms for the generator (of force or voltage) and its internal impedance. "Load" is rather generally used for the receiver of power, although "termination" is occasionally employed synonymously. It must be kept in mind that in electricity the *lower* the value of the load impedance, the *greater* is the load on the source. Thus if an electric generator has zero internal impedance, the current will be inversely proportional to the load impedance, and if this impedance is resistive, the power output is also inversely proportional to the load impedance $P = E^2/R$; that is, the generator is more heavily loaded for a low-impedance load. Occasionally, this terminology is rather awkward in the mechanical and acoustic circuits. For example, if a heavy string with a large value of tension is attached to the mechanical vibrator of Fig. 2.83, it would be analogous to a high-impedance electric load, whereas if a very light string with little tension were used, it would correspond to the low-impedance electric load. It would perhaps be more natural to denote the former as the heavily loaded case. The difficulty, fortunately, does not appear if we restrict the terminology to a simple statement of the value of load impedance.

2.9 The General Termination and the Reflection Coefficient

In the previous sections we have studied wave transmission in the infinite string and in the string terminated in the rigid wall. We are now prepared to consider the general case in which the string is terminated by a general mechanical impedance—as an example, an oscillatory system similar to the source impedance of the previous article but containing no force generator, i.e. a passive system. For any case other than that of the infinite string it is necessary to take the complete solution of the wave equation

$$y = A_i e^{j(\omega t - kx)} + A_r e^{j(\omega t + kx)} \tag{2.91}$$

where we have written A_i as the amplitude of an incident wave, and A_r as that of a reflected wave, assuming from previous discussions that a reflected wave will be present at any discontinuity. Further, at the termination, the expression $-T(\partial y/\partial x)$ will give the force which the string impresses on the terminating impedance and $(\partial y/\partial t)$ will give the velocity of motion of the terminating impedance. The ratio of these two terms must be equal to the vector Z_T, the terminating impedance. Differentiating both sides of Eq. (2.91), we find

$$-T\frac{\partial y}{\partial x} = jTke^{j\omega t}(A_i e^{-jkx} - A_r e^{jkx})$$

and

$$\frac{\partial y}{\partial t} = j\omega e^{j\omega t}(A_i e^{-jkx} + A_r e^{jkx})$$

and therefore,

$$\frac{-T(\partial y/\partial x)}{\partial y/\partial t} = \frac{Tk}{\omega} \frac{A_i e^{-jkx} - A_r e^{jkx}}{A_i e^{-jkx} + A_r e^{jkx}} \tag{2.92}$$

Since Tk/ω equals Z_0, we have

$$\frac{-T(\partial y/\partial x)}{\partial y/\partial t} = \frac{A_i e^{-jkx} - A_r e^{jkx}}{A_i e^{-jkx} + A_r e^{jkx}} \cdot Z_0.$$

It is convenient to take the discontinuity at the origin, where $x = 0$. Thus

$$Z_T = \frac{A_i - A_r}{A_i + A_r} \cdot Z_0 \tag{2.93}$$

If we let $K = (A_r/A_i)$ we can obtain

$$K = \frac{A_r}{A_i} = \frac{Z_0 - Z_T}{Z_0 + Z_T} \tag{2.94}$$

and also

$$\frac{Z_T}{Z_0} = \frac{1 - K}{1 + K} \tag{2.94a}$$

We call K, the ratio of the reflected to the incident amplitude vector, the complex reflection coefficient for amplitude.

Since power is proportional to amplitude squared, we define $\alpha_R = |K|^2$ as the power reflection coefficient, and $\alpha_T = 1 - \alpha_R = 1 - |K|^2$ as the power transmission coefficient.

For $Z_T = Z_0$, K is zero, and we have a case similar to termination by a string of infinite length and characteristic impedance Z_0. For $Z_T = \infty$, K is -1, and we have the case of termination by a rigid wall. For $Z_T = 0$, $K = 1$, a condition that would be approached if a heavy string were terminated in a very light string, or in a *dissipationless vibratory system at its resonant frequency*. If the termination is purely resistive, as in a resonant vibratory system with $R_m \neq 0$, the reflection coefficient is a real number of magnitude less than unity, and positive or negative, depending on whether R_m is less than or greater than Z_0. If the termination is purely reactive, the reflection coefficient has a magnitude of unity, since the denominator is the complex conjugate of the numerator, but K is complex. The general terminating impedance, with both resistive and reactive components, gives a complex reflection coefficient, the only limitation being that its magnitude cannot exceed unity.

Since $A_r = KA_i$, we have as the general expression for the amplitude

$$y = A_i e^{j\omega t}(e^{-jkx} + K e^{jkx}) \tag{2.95}$$

and by differentiation, or from Eq. (2.92), we can find the general expression for the input impedance at the point x:

$$Z_i = Z_0 \frac{e^{-jkx} - K e^{jkx}}{e^{-jkx} + K e^{jkx}} \tag{2.96}$$

We see that in general Z_i is a complex function of both x and K. A similar equation is of great importance in the theory of electric transmission lines. Because it does not yield readily to formal analytical solutions, communication engineers have developed charts by which solutions may be obtained for any given values of the variables in a manner similar to slide-rule computations.

The standing wave condition was discussed in Art. 2.5 for a rigid boundary. In this case we find *nodes*, or points of zero amplitude, at $kx = n\pi$, and *antinodes*, or points of maximum amplitude, where $kx = (n + 1/2)\pi$, where x is the distance to the boundary. For arbitrary termination, the standing-wave condition is characterized by maxima and minima rather than by nodes and antinodes; and the ratio of maximum to minimum amplitude, the *standing-wave ratio* (SWR) is an important constant of the string and its termination. In addition, the positions of maxima and minima are functions of the terminating impedance. We can find the reflection coefficient by measuring the SWR and observing the position of the nodes. If we know the characteristic impedance we can then find the terminating impedance from Eq. (2.94a).

By taking the terminating impedance to be a positive real value, we can readily show how to calculate the terminating impedance from the SWR. Equation (2.94) shows that K will be a real number. Referring to Eq. (2.95), we find that y has its maximum magnitude $(1 + |K|)$ for $kx = (2n + 1)\pi/2$, and its minimum $(1 - |K|)$ for $kx = n\pi$. We thus have

$$\text{SWR} = \frac{y_{Max}}{y_{Min}} = \frac{1 + |K|}{1 - |K|}$$

$$K = \frac{\text{SWR} - 1}{\text{SWR} + 1} \tag{2.97}$$

For Eq. (2.84) we have

$$K = \frac{Z_T/Z_0 - 1}{Z_T/Z_0 + 1} \tag{2.98}$$

and therefore $\text{SWR} = Z_T/Z_0$ for a resistive load.

Equations (2.94) and (2.95) are employed to find the general (complex) terminating impedance, but the solution is more difficult because of the complex K and Z_T.*

2.10 The String in Damped Resonant Vibration

The solution for the normal modes of the string in Art. 2.6 was obtained on the explicit assumption of rigid supports, and the implicit assumption of zero damping. This solution corresponds to the solution of the problem of the undamped free simple harmonic oscillator. Indeed, the string was actually interpreted as a collection of simple harmonic oscillators in the subsequent discussion of its energy (Art. 2.7). An actual string, if set into vibration, will ultimately cease to vibrate because of three causes: (1) loss of energy to the surrounding medium by radiation; (2) losses caused by the internal friction of the string; (3) loss of energy to the supports. In this article, we shall neglect

---

* As in the case of the input impedance, the terminating independence can also be found by chart. The Smith chart is one of the most useful.

losses from the first two causes, and study the decay of a freely vibrating string because of transmission of energy to the supports. For convenience, the supports will be assumed to have a finite mechanical impedance which is purely resistive. It will simplify the problem to assume that the terminating impedances, though finite, are high compared with the characteristic impedance of the string, so that the normal mode solutions obtained in Art. 2.6 hold closely—that is, that the displacement at the supports, though not zero, is very small, and that the natural frequencies of vibration are practically the same as in the undamped string. This corresponds to the relation existing between the undamped simple harmonic oscillator and the oscillator with small damping.

A considerable gain in clarity can be achieved by broadening the scope of the term "instantaneous" for this discussion of damping. If we assume, as is usually done, that many cycles of oscillation will occur with only small change in amplitude, the average power flow to the supports will decrease slowly with time. By the instantaneous value of power flow we shall mean the average flow during a certain short period of the total decay time, which period, however, shall include several cycles, so that average power flow at the end of the period is slightly less than at the beginning of the period. This is a different usage of the term from its definition in Art. 1.9, but a usage which is justified in this discussion. With this usage, it can be stated that the instantaneous rate of loss of the energy of the string equals the instantaneous power loss to the supports, and an equation can be derived for the rate of loss of energy in terms of the characteristic impedance of the string and the impedance of the supports, i.e. in terms of the transmission coefficient of the supports.

Let us for definiteness suppose that the string is in its fundamental mode. Let V_0 be the velocity amplitude at the center of the string. The energy of the string will then be

$$E = \tfrac{1}{4}\mu L V_0^2 = \tfrac{1}{4}m V_0^2 \tag{2.101}$$

where E is now slowly variable with time.

The standing wave is composed of two progressive waves, each of velocity amplitude $V_0/2$. The power flow toward each support will then be

$$\frac{1}{2}Z_0\left(\frac{V_0}{2}\right)^2 = \frac{1}{8}Z_0 V_0^2 = \frac{1}{8}\mu c V_0^2$$

The rate at which energy is lost to each support, by the definition to the transmission coefficient, will be

$$\frac{-dE}{dt} = \frac{1}{8}\mu c \alpha_T V_0^2 \tag{2.102}$$

Since the rate of loss of energy in the string equals the rate of loss of energy to the supports, the differential equation of the energy of the string will be

$$\frac{-dE}{dt} = -2\left(\frac{\alpha_T}{8}\mu c V_0^2\right) = -\frac{\alpha_T c}{L}E$$

and therefore we have for the decay rate of energy

$$a_E = \frac{\alpha_T c}{L}$$

(which has dimensions $\sec^{-1}$ as it should). Decay rate was originally defined as the quantity appearing in the exponential, as in Art. 1.4. An equivalent definition is to define the decay rate as $\dfrac{-(dE/dt)}{E}$. This definition will be employed in subsequent articles.

No great significance is to be attached to the decay rate in the string, and no attempt will be made to seek applications for this expression. The investigation has been carried through to set the stage for the computation of the decay rate of standing waves in rooms, which is a fundamental quantity in architectural acoustics. As we shall see, when the source of sound in a room is interrupted, the sound energy in the room exists in the form of a complex of normal modes, and the decay rate of these modes depends primarily on the impedance of the walls. If the walls were perfectly rigid, and there were no other source of loss, the standing waves would persist forever. The decay of these standing waves gives the room a reverberant quality which can be characterized by a decay rate, just as the decay rate was found for the standing wave in the string. The parameters of the decay rate in a room are analogous to those in the string, but other quantities must be defined before the analogy can be made clear.

2.11 Initial Conditions—Fourier Series and Complex Vibration

We have found the solution of the finite string with rigid supports to be the infinite series

$$y = \sum_{n=1}^{n=\infty} (A_n \cos \omega_n t + B_n \sin \omega_n t) \sin \frac{n\pi x}{L} \qquad \left[\omega_n = \left(\frac{n\pi}{L}\right) \sqrt{\frac{T}{\mu}} \right] \quad (2.111)$$

where the constants A_n and B_n are completely independent of each other. The interpretation is that the general vibration of the string consists of a superposition of normal modes, where both the amplitudes and phases of these modes are completely independent.

If we assume definite initial conditions, we find that the constants must satisfy definite relations. As an instance, let us suppose that the initial shape of the string is defined by $y = y_0(x)$, where

$$y_0 = y_{(t=0)} = \sum_{n=1}^{n=\infty} A_n \sin \frac{n\pi x}{L} = y_0(x) \qquad (2.112)$$

(i.e. a function of x alone),

The problem is to find the values of the coefficients such that the series represents the function which gives the initial form for all values of x on the string (i.e. between $x = 0$ and $x = L$). We have seen already in Art. 1.5 that any reasonable function can be represented by a power series. We are now faced with the not unlike problem of representing functions by trigonometric series.

In the development of this series we must make use of the value of a definite integral that can be evaluated by methods of ordinary calculus:

$$I = \frac{2}{\pi} \int_0^\pi \sin mu \sin nu \, du = \begin{cases} 0, & m \neq n \\ 1, & m = n \end{cases} \qquad (2.113)$$

This is called a *condition of orthogonality*. We say that the sines of multiple angles are orthogonal to one another over the interval $x = 0$ to $x = \pi$ because the integral of their product over this interval is zero, the only exception being the product of sines of like multiplicity. The fact that the exceptional case has a value of unity is a *condition of normalization*, and has general importance throughout physics. At present, however, the condition of orthogonality is the more important, it being sufficient for our purpose that we obtain a *nonzero* value for one value of m, and zero for all other values.

If we make the substitution $u = \pi x/L$, we have $du = \pi dx/L$, and the limits are 0 and L. The integral becomes

$$I = \frac{2}{L} \int_0^L \sin \frac{m\pi x}{L} \sin \frac{n\pi x}{L} dx = \begin{cases} 0, & m \neq n \\ 1, & m = n \end{cases} \qquad (2.114)$$

If we multiply the series of Eq. (2.112) term by term by $\sin (m\pi x/L) \, dx$, where m is any integer, and then integrate the products term by term between 0 and L, we have the expression

$$\int_0^L y_0(x) \sin \frac{m\pi x}{L} dx = \sum_{n=1}^{n=\infty} \int_0^L A_n \sin \frac{n\pi x}{L} \sin \frac{m\pi x}{L} dx \qquad (2.115)$$

Now by the condition of orthogonality, all but one of the terms in the series on the right vanishes, the one remaining being that for which n has the value m. We therefore have

$$A_m = \frac{2}{L} \int_0^L y_0(x) \sin \frac{m\pi x}{L} dx \qquad (2.116)$$

To find the constants B_n, we must know the velocity of each point on the string at the initial instant. That is, we must know the velocity function

$$V_0(x) = V(x)_{t=0} = \left(\frac{\partial y}{\partial t}\right)_{t=0} = \left(\frac{\partial y}{\partial t}\right)_0$$

On differentiating Eq. (2.111) partially with t and allowing t to vanish, we have

$$V_0(x) = \left(\frac{\partial y}{\partial t}\right)_0 = \sum_{n=1}^{n=\infty} \omega_n B_n \sin \frac{n\pi x}{L}$$

and by a procedure strictly analogous to that used for the A_n's we have

$$B_n = \frac{2}{\omega_n L} \int_0^L V_0(x) \sin \frac{n\pi x}{L} dx \qquad (2.117)$$

We shall illustrate the use of Fourier series by solving the problem of the "plucked string," that is, a string which is pulled outward at one point (the center for simplicity) and suddenly released (Fig. 2.111). It corresponds in

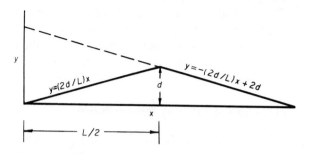

Fig. 2.111. Initial configuration of a string plucked at the center.

initial condition to the simple harmonic oscillator that originally has maximum displacement and zero velocity. Initially, the shape of the string is defined by the function

$$y_0(x) = \left\{ \begin{array}{ll} 2\left(\dfrac{d}{L}\right)x & 0 < x < \dfrac{L}{2} \\ -2\left(\dfrac{d}{L}\right)x + 2d & \dfrac{L}{2} < x < L \end{array} \right\}$$

and from Eq. (2.116) the general expression for the constants A_m becomes

$$A_m = \frac{4d}{L^2}\left[\int_0^{L/2} x \sin\frac{m\pi x}{L}dx + \int_{1/2}^L \left(L - x \sin\frac{m\pi x}{L}\right)dx\right] \qquad (2.118)$$

The evaluation of this integral is tedious but straightforward. We find for the general term,

$$A_m = \frac{8d}{m^2\pi^2}\sin\frac{m\pi}{2} \qquad (2.119)$$

The first three components (first, third, and fifth harmonics) are plotted in Fig. 2.112. The sum of the three appears as a fair approximation of the shape of the plucked string.

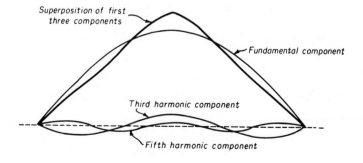

Fig. 2.112. Sum of first three normal modes of a string whose Fourier series gives a triangular wave form.

We can see from Eq. (2.117) that the constants B_n are identically zero.

Nonsinusoidal forces can be resolved into sinusoidal components by Fourier series, just as displacements can. When such a force acts on a vibrating system, this system will, in general, offer a different impedance to each component of the driving force. The resultant motion of the system is a superposition of component motions, but the proportion of the strengths of these components may be quite different from the components of the force. This important case is illustrated in the article which follows.

2.12 Response of Systems to Arbitrary Driving Forces

We have illustrated Fourier series by an example in which an arbitrary function of x is represented by a series of sinusoidal functions of x. The Fourier series method can also be applied to representation of an arbitrary function of time as a series of sinusoidal time functions. As an example, we may have a force imposed on an oscillatory system which has the time variation shown in Fig. 2.121. Such a variation is called a "square wave." The problem may be to find the response of the oscillatory system to this force.

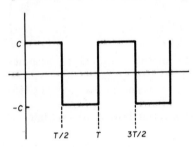

Fig. 2.121. A square wave.

Since our treatment of forced vibration is based on the application of a sinusoidal force, it is advantageous to be able to represent the square wave of force as a superposition of sinusoidal forces. Then the impedance of the system may be computed for each of the harmonic frequencies, and the corresponding velocities found. The velocity response is found by superposing the component velocities.

By analogy with Eq. (2.92), we shall assume that the force function can be represented by a series of the form*

$$\mathscr{F}(t) = \sum A_n \sin \frac{n\pi}{T} t \tag{2.121}$$

with the function defined by the boundary conditions

$$\mathscr{F}(t) = \begin{cases} + C & 0 < t < T/2 \\ - C & T/2 < t < T \end{cases} \tag{2.122}$$

By analogy with Eq. (2.96), we have for the general coefficient of the series,

$$A_m = \frac{2}{T} \int_0^T \mathscr{F}(t) \sin \frac{m\pi t}{T} dt \tag{2.123}$$

---

* Fourier series in general necessitate the use of both sine and cosine functions. The force function chosen, however, can be evaluated by sines alone.

By our boundary conditions, we have

$$A_m = \frac{2}{T}\left[\int_0^{T/2} C \sin\frac{m\pi t}{T}dt + \int_{T/2}^{T}(-C)\sin\frac{m\pi t}{T}dt\right]$$

The integration is less complicated than that of Eq. (2.118), so we shall carry it out in some detail. We have

$$A_m = \frac{2C}{T}\left[\frac{T}{m\pi}\left(-\cos\frac{m\pi t}{T}\right)_0^{T/2} + \frac{T}{m\pi}\left(\cos\frac{m\pi t}{T}\right)_{T/2}^{T}\right]$$

$$= \frac{2C}{m\pi}\left(1 - 2\cos\frac{m\pi}{2} + \cos m\pi\right) \tag{2.124}$$

It will be found by trying various values of m that the bracket is given by the general function

$$\left(1 - 2\cos\frac{m\pi}{2} + \cos m\pi\right) = \begin{cases} 4 & m = 4n + 2 \\ 0 & m \neq 4n + 2 \end{cases}$$

As a result, we have for the force function

$$\mathscr{F}(t) = \frac{8C}{\pi}\left[\frac{\sin(2\pi t/T)}{2} + \frac{\sin(6\pi t/T)}{6} + \frac{\sin(10\pi t/T)}{10} + \cdots\right]$$

$$= \frac{4C}{\pi}\left(\sin\omega t + \frac{1}{3}\sin 3\omega t + \frac{1}{5}\sin 5\omega t + \cdots\right) \tag{2.125}$$

If a force defined by Eq. (2.125) is imposed upon a *resistance-controlled* oscillatory system, each of the velocity components will be proportional to the corresponding force component, and in addition, the phase relations will be the same, since each velocity component is in phase with the corresponding force component, i.e. the velocity function will be

$$V(t) = \frac{4C}{R_m\pi}\left(\sin\omega t + \frac{1}{3}\sin 3\omega t + \frac{1}{5}\sin 5\omega t\right) \tag{2.126}$$

On the other hand, if the force defined by Eq. (2.125) is imposed on a *mass-controlled* system, the mechanical impedance will be proportional to the frequency, and the velocity components will be inversely proportional to the *square* of the frequency, and the velocity function will have the form

$$V(t) = +\frac{4C}{jm\pi}\left(\sin\omega t + \frac{1}{9}\sin 3\omega t + \frac{1}{25}\sin 5\omega t + \cdots\right) \tag{2.127}$$

where, in this equation, m represents the mass of the oscillator, and the j indicates that each term lags the corresponding term in the force function by 90°.

The velocity function for the mass-controlled oscillator is shown in (b) of Fig. 2.122 for the first three terms. The result of summing the first four terms of the force function is shown in (a) of the figure and similar plot is obtained for the velocity response of a resistance-controlled oscillator. If enough terms are taken, the plot of Eq. (2.127) will approach a triangular wave, a wave having the shape of the plucked string. This may be concluded

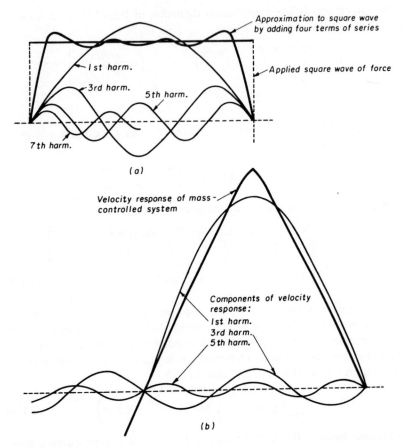

Fig. 2.122. Response of mass-controlled system to square-wave applied force. Each velocity component lags the corresponding force component by 90 degrees.

from the fact that the components of Eq. (2.127) follow the law of variation given by Eq. (2.119).

References

Slater and Frank, *Mechanics*, McGraw-Hill, New York, 1947.
John D. Ryder, *Networks, Lines and Fields*, 2nd ed., Prentice-Hall, Englewood Cliffs, N.J., 1955.

Problems

1. Show that for a progressive sinusoidal wave on a string the particle velocity at any point is equal to the negative of the product of the slope of the string and the wave velocity. Illustrate for waves progressing in both the positive-x and negative-x directions.

2. Explain the numbering of the vectors in Fig. 2.33 for the wave proceeding in the negative-x directions. Is it logical that the rotation of the vector diagram should be counterclockwise regardless of the direction of propagation of the wave?

3. Does the function of Eq. (2.51) predict that each point to the right of the support shall be at rest at every instant?

4. Find the tension necessary to tune a string of linear density 0.1 g and length 40 cm to a frequency of 100 cycles.

5. It is stated in the text that the sum of any number of particular solutions of a linear differential equation is also a solution of the equation. Show that this depends ultimately on the theorem of elementary calculus that the derivative of a sum is the sum of the derivatives of the terms of the sum.

6. A string is terminated by a rigid wall. In terms of the parameters of the string, find the frequency ranges over which it will act as a pure stiffness, and those over which it will act as a pure mass.

7. (a) Show that the energy of a vibrating string is independent of the number of segments in which it vibrates if the frequency and amplitude are maintained constant. (b) Two strings have equal length and density. They are vibrating at the same frequency, but one string vibrates in one segment and the other in three segments. Find the relative values of the tensions.

8. Show that the complex reflection coefficient has an angle of 90° when the terminating impedance is purely reactive and equal in magnitude to the characteristic impedance of the string.

9. With the incident amplitude vector as reference vector, find the incident and reflected components of displacement, velocity, and transverse tension for the following amplitude reflection coefficients: -1, $+1$, j, $-j$, $\frac{1}{2}/45°$, $\frac{1}{2}/135°$. Taking the value of the characteristic impedance to be unity, find the value of the load impedance in each case.

Hint. Sum the velocity components and the components of transverse tension to find the total tension and total velocity. The ratio of tension to velocity will be the load impedance.

10. Following the rotating vector method of Art. 2.3, show that the following standing-wave configurations are obtained for the reflection coefficients of the previous problem:

(a) SWR $= \infty$	Displacement	node	at support
	Velocity	node	at support
	Force	antinode	at support

(b) SWR $= \infty$	Displacement	antinode	at support
	Velocity	antinode	at support
	Force	node	at support
(c) SWR $= \infty$	Displacement	antinode	$L/8$ from support
	Velocity	antinode	$L/8$ from support
	Force	node	$L/8$ from support
(d) SWR $= \infty$	Displacement	node	$L/8$ from support
	Velocity	node	$L/8$ from support
	Force	antinode	$L/8$ from support
(e) SWR $= 3$	Displacement	maximum	$L/16$ from support
	Velocity	maximum	$L/16$ from support
	Force	minimum	$L/16$ from support
(f) SWR $= 3$	Displacement	maximum	$3L/16$ from support
	Velocity	maximum	$3L/16$ from support
	Force	minimum	$3L/16$ from support

Find the reflection coefficient if the SWR is 6 and a force maximum occurs at a distance $L/16$ from the support.

11. State analytically the boundary conditions and initial conditions for the case in which a string of length L is attached to two rigid supports and initially pulled out a distance h at a point $L/3$ from the support on the right and released.

12. A string of tension T and density μ is terminated in a resistive impedance of magnitude $\sqrt{T\mu}$. At the driving end, it is attached to a vibrator, as in Fig. 2.83. (a) Draw a curve of the velocity of the driving point as a function of frequency with the following values of the parameters: $T = 10^6$; $\mu = 0.01$; $m = 1$ g; $s = 10^6$ dynes cm^{-1}; $R_m = 100$; $D = 10^5$; $I = 1$ amp. (b) Find the frequency of maximum power input and the value of this power. (c) Find the half-power frequencies.

13. Write the solution of the plucked string in the form of Eq. (2.31).

14. Prove the orthogonality and the normalization conditions expressed by Eq. (2.113).

15. Assuming the energies to be independent, compare the energies in the first and the third harmonic of a string plucked at the center.

16. The initial configuration of a plucked string can be considered as a superposition of two equal triangular wave forms, each of equal amplitude. When the string is released, these wave forms proceed in opposite directions, being reflected at the walls (Figs. 2.23 and 2.54). Show that the successive configurations of the string will be as shown in the Fig. P2.16. Show that this result can also be obtained from the Fourier series development of Art. 2.11 by considering each of the components a standing wave, and summing the components at equal time intervals, remembering that the frequency of each component (and hence the phase shift per unit time) is proportional to the order of the harmonic. A good approximation can be obtained by considering only the first, third, and fifth harmonics.

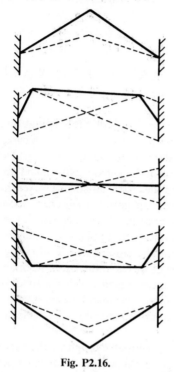

Fig. P2.16.

Chapter 3

PLANE SOUND WAVES

In the first two chapters of this text the oscillation and the wave have been defined and described in their essentials. In each case, an idealized model was chosen, so that the fundamentals might stand apart from accidental complications. Waves that occur in extended elastic media are the ordinary means of transmitting sound, and the characteristics of waves that have been introduced, such as their velocity of propagation, their energy content, power flow, reflection at discontinuities, and the impedance which the medium offers to their propagation, must therefore be applied to extended media. Though wave fundamentals are essentially similar in the vibrating string and in extended media, the propagation of waves in the latter becomes more complex for both geometrical and mechanical reasons. When a small source is in oscillation in an extended elastic medium, the sound waves spread in widening spheres and therefore the propagation of spherical waves in elastic media must ultimately be discussed.

However, it is often permissible to ignore the curvature of wave surfaces if one is far from the source of the waves. As an example from optics, light from a source only moderately distant can be used to find the focal length of a lens, even though the definition of focal length requires that the light wave front be absolutely plane where it strikes the lens. Results obtained by assuming a plane surface, where a spherical surface actually exists, may contain some small percentage of error, but the advantage gained from the simplicity of the geometry justifies the slight loss of accuracy. Therefore, for the first approach to waves in extended media, one investigates the propagation of plane waves. Even with this simplification, the waves are much more difficult to visualize than are the transverse waves of the string.

Besides the fact that the wave is harder to visualize in matter in bulk, the mechanics of the problem changes. When it is considered that waves consist of disturbances, or deformations, one calls to mind the properties of matter that resist deformation. These properties are three: (1) elasticity, by which resistance is offered to changes of density in all classes of matter, and also to changes of shape (shear) in solids; (2) viscosity, by which resistive forces are developed proportional to the time rate of deformation; (3) inertia, by which resistance is offered to acceleration by particles of the disturbed medium which move because of the deformation. If the investigation is restricted to

82

fluids, the *bulk modulus* is the only elastic modulus that need be considered. If it is further restricted to *perfect fluids*, the viscosity is zero. Since the inertia of a particle of matter is proportional to its density, it turns out that the two most important properties of matter having to do with wave propagation in perfect fluids are the bulk modulus and the density.

The optical analogy referred to suggests a tendency to emphasize the *transmission* of sound in plane wave theory, and for the most part to ignore the source. The analysis follows closely methods that originated in electrical communication theory for the analysis of transmission lines, filters, and wave guides. The wave equations are similar; the action at discontinuities can be treated in a manner essentially similar; the characteristic impedance and reflection coefficient are expressed by similar forms. The propagation of plane waves in pipes resembles in many respects the propagation of electromagnetic waves in wave guides. Filter theory for sound waves has developed directly from filter theory for electric waves, and in both branches, the principles first established in filter theory have found widespread application in the general field.

The concept of impedance is further developed in this chapter, because of its immense usefulness in applied acoustics. It is the modern tendency in both acoustics and communication engineering to treat all problems similarly in the sense that an effect is to be brought about from a cause, with some type of impedance as the relation between the effect and the cause. For example, in pipe problems, a certain particle velocity is desired in the pipe, which may be either high, if the particular sound is to be transmitted, or low, if the sound is to be suppressed. If a certain driving pressure exists, the particle velocity can be computed if the effect of the transmitting pipe can be expressed as an impedance. In radiation, a certain strength of radiated field is desired. If the relation between the radiated field and the strength of the source can be expressed as an impedance, the source strength necessary for any desired radiation field can be provided. Of course, the use of the impedance concept necessitates a characterization of both "cause" and "effect" in the particular case. For a particular field of application, this characterization rests on fundamental physical entities proper to that field. The transmission of plane waves of sound is based on concepts found in fluid dynamics. Once these concepts have been defined, the treatment follows closely the methods of the previous chapter.

Whereas the source of plane waves is remote, the source of spherical waves is near at hand. Therefore, spherical wave theory tends to emphasize *radiation* —that is, the transfer of energy from the source to the medium. The transmission of spherical waves is of course not precisely the same as that of plane waves, but only minor modifications are necessary.

Although atomic and molecular theory have shown that matter is far from homogeneous, it is often useful to ignore its microscopic structure, and picture it as a continuum. This is done in the static and dynamic theory of fluids, and to a lesser degree, in thermodynamics and electromagnetism. In general, physicists are not overly concerned with the reality of the model they employ, so long as it permits them to obtain results in accord with observation. Since the basic concepts of fluid dynamics are so vital in the analysis of the propagation of waves of sound, we shall review the more important of these concepts in the next article.

3.1 Elementary Fluid Mechanics

If a fixed mass of a fluid undergoes a change of volume, the ratio between the increment of volume and the original (static) volume is called the *dilatation*, Δ; i.e.,

$$\Delta = \frac{V' - V}{V}, \qquad V' = V(1 + \Delta)$$

where $V' \equiv$ instantaneous volume and $V \equiv$ static volume.

If a fixed volume of fluid undergoes a change of density, the ratio between the increment of density and the original (static) density is called the *condensation*, s; i.e.,

$$s = \frac{\rho' - \rho}{\rho}, \qquad \rho' = \rho(1 + s)$$

where $\rho' \equiv$ instantaneous density and $\rho \equiv$ static density.

In most sound applications, changes of density and volume in a fluid are the result of pressure changes. The increment of pressure, or excess pressure, is called the acoustic pressure p. Thus $p = p' - p_0$ where $p' \equiv$ instantaneous pressure and $p_0 \equiv$ static pressure.

The *bulk modulus B*, which is nearly constant in most cases of interest, is defined for a fixed mass of fluid as the ratio between the excess pressure and the (negative) dilatation, i.e.,

$$p = - B\Delta$$

Also, since

$$V'\rho' = V\rho = V\rho(1 + \Delta)(1 + s),$$

we find (neglecting the second-order differential, $s\,\Delta$) that $s = - \Delta$, so that

$$p = Bs$$

Since only infinitesimal departures from static conditions occur, Δ, s, and p are of the order of differential quantities. The inconsistency in the notation (note p_0 and ρ) is purely a matter of convenience. Many of the terms introduced are necessary for the development of the fundamental equations of acoustics, but they do not appear in the final equations. For simplicity, symbols without subscripts should be chosen for terms that appear in the ultimate equations. Of all the terms introduced above, the acoustic pressure and static density are found most frequently in the final equations, and therefore these have been written without subscripts.

The term *particle* in the mechanics of continuous media signifies a volume small enough that all mechanical quantities, such as density, velocity, etc., may be considered constant over the extent of the volume. Thus we speak of the *particle velocity* and *particle displacement*. A curious feature of the analysis of continuous media is the use of regions of different orders of "smallness." At times it will be helpful to consider a "small" volume element,

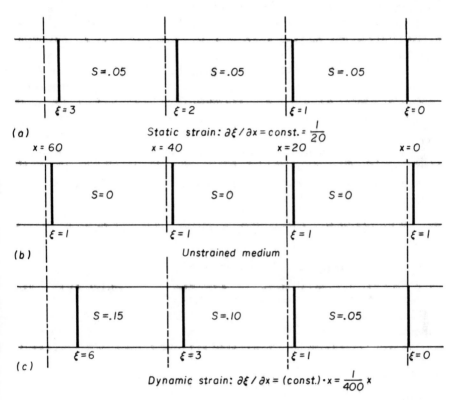

Fig. 3.11. Static and dynamic strain. Note: values given for dynamic strain are approximate.

in which there is a significant, though small, pressure differential between two faces. The element is thus larger than a particle, since we consider pressure variation, but it is still small enough that we may treat it as a "differential" volume in the calculus sense. The symbols, x, y, z, are used for the coordinates of the equilibrium positions of fluid particles and ξ, η, and ζ for the components of instantaneous displacement of these particles from their equilibrium positions. Since x, y, z are finite, while ξ, η, ζ are infinitesimal, the coordinates of a particle remain the same regardless of the values of its displacements.

In plane waves with longitudinal displacements in the positive-x direction, the *gradient* of a component of displacement or particle velocity is the partial derivative of that component with respect to x. (Actually, only x-components of displacement and particle velocity will exist.) If the gradient of the displacement is zero throughout the medium, the medium is said to be *unstrained*; if the gradient is constant, the medium is in a state of *static strain*—that is, it is in static equilibrium under the strain; if the gradient itself is variable with position—that is, if $\partial \xi / \partial x \neq 0$, the medium is in a state of *dynamic strain*. It is this third condition that gives rise to compressional waves in fluids. The three cases of zero strain, static strain, and dynamic strain are shown in Fig. 3.11.

The unstrained medium is shown in (b) of the figure for comparison with the two strained states. It will be seen that although displacement occurs in (b), the *strain* is zero. Some rough quantitative observations can be made. Thus in (a), the condensation is alike in each of the volume elements, and from the ξ and x values of the figure, its value is approximately 0.05. Since the condensation is equal in all elements, equal pressures also exist, of value $0.05B$, and therefore static equilibrium exists after the strain as before. In (c), there is a gradual increase in the condensation, from 0.05 in the first element

TABLE 3.11

Table of Symbols Used in Discussion of Sound Waves in Fluids

	Static or Quiescent	Varying Component		Total Instantaneous	Vector
		Instantaneous	Peak		
Displacement	0	ξ	ξ_0	ξ	$\boldsymbol{\xi}$
Particle velocity ..	0	u	u_0	u	$\boldsymbol{u}$
Density	ρ	ρs	ρs_0	ρ'	ρs
Pressure....	p_0	p	P_0	p'	p

to 0.10 in the second, and 0.15 in the third. Therefore since the pressure is lower on the right side of the second element than on the left, there will be an acceleration of this element in the direction of positive x. In most sounds encountered in practice, the condensations are very much smaller than those of the figure (of the order of magnitude of 10^{-6}) and the relative pressure changes are, of course, of the same order of magnitude. Since atmospheric pressure is approximately 10^6 dynes/cm^2, acoustic pressures are of the order of magnitude of 1 dyne/cm^2. (The threshold of hearing is about 0.0002 dyne/cm^2.)

Mathematically, the *strain* is given by the quantity $\partial\xi/\partial x$, and therefore the *gradient* of the *strain* is given by the quantity $\partial^2\xi/\partial x^2$. It is clear that over a constant cross section, both the dilatation and the condensation are proportional to the strain. Treatment of the wave in Art. 1.16 demonstrated a relation between the wave and the gradient of the strain. We shall now see that by assuming a medium in a state of *dynamic strain* we can derive an equation similar to the wave equation of the string.

The presence of a rather large number of different quantities makes the notational problem somewhat difficult. Table 3.11 contains the more important quantities and their symbols.

3.2 The Equation of a Plane Longitudinal Wave

Let us consider a volume element $S\,dx$ in a region of a fluid which is in a condition of dynamic strain (Fig. 3.21). Let ξ represent the displacement at position x, which is one boundary of the volume element; we then have $\xi + (\partial\xi/\partial x)dx$ for the displacement at the other boundary, and $S(\partial\xi/\partial x)dx$ for the volume increment due to the strain. Since dilatation is a relative increment, we have $\Delta = [S(\partial\xi/\partial x)dx]/S\,dx = \partial\xi/\partial x$. We have shown in Art. 3.1 that there is a pressure differential across the element in the general case of dynamic strain. If we take p' to be the pressure at x, we have

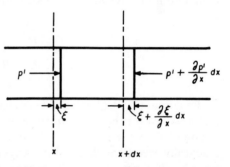

Fig. 3.21.   Element of strained medium.

$p' + (\partial p'/\partial x)dx$ as the pressure at the other face ($x + dx$), and therefore $(\partial p'/\partial x)dx = (\partial p/\partial x)dx$ as the pressure differential, and $-S(\partial p/\partial x)dx$ for the net force in the positive-x direction.

This net force brings about an average acceleration of the volume element. The mass of the element can be written $S\rho dx$ and the average particle acceleration $\partial^2\xi/\partial t^2$.

We thus have the dynamic equation,

$$-S\frac{\partial p}{\partial x}dx = S\rho\,dx\frac{\partial^2\xi}{\partial t^2}, \qquad -\frac{\partial p}{\partial x} = \rho\frac{\partial^2\xi}{\partial t^2} \qquad (3.21)$$

Taking into account the relation between pressure and volume strain, we have

$$\frac{\partial p}{\partial x} = B\frac{\partial s}{\partial x} = -B\frac{\partial\Delta}{\partial x} = -B\frac{\partial^2\xi}{\partial^2 x} \qquad (3.22)$$

If we combine Eqs. (3.21) and (3.22), we obtain the wave equation for the displacement:

$$\frac{\partial^2 \xi}{\partial t^2} = \left(\frac{B}{\rho}\right)\frac{\partial^2 \xi}{\rho x^2} \tag{3.23}$$

If we treat Eqs. (3.21) and (3.22) in a slightly different manner, we obtain a similar equation (Eq. 3.24) for the condensation. Thus, differentiating Eq. (3.22) with respect to x, we obtain

$$-\frac{\partial^2 p}{\partial x^2} = \rho\frac{\partial}{\partial x}\left(\frac{\partial^2 \xi}{\partial t^2}\right) = \rho\frac{\partial^2}{\partial t^2}\left(\frac{\partial \xi}{\partial x}\right)$$

and, since $(\partial \xi/\partial x) = -s$,

$$\frac{\partial^2 p}{\partial x^2} = \rho\frac{\partial^2 s}{\partial t^2} \tag{3.24}$$

By using the fundamental relation $p = Bs$ with the above equation we can obtain both the pressure and condensation equations:

$$\frac{\partial^2 p}{\partial t^2} = \frac{B}{\rho}\frac{\partial^2 p}{\partial x^2} \tag{3.25}$$

$$\frac{\partial^2 s}{\partial t^2} = \frac{B}{\rho}\frac{\partial^2 s}{\partial x^2} \tag{3.26}$$

Equations (3.23), (3.25), and (3.26) have a form which is exactly similar to that obtained for the wave equation of the string, if we interpret B/ρ as the square of the wave velocity c. Because of the similarity of these equations, practically everything deduced for waves in the string can be taken over for plane longitudinal waves, with appropriate changes of constants. Thus, if the treatment is again limited to harmonic waves, the displacement, condensation, and pressure all have solutions of the form

$$A_1 e^{j(\omega t - kx)} + A_2 e^{j(\omega t + kx)}$$

The particle velocity u is of the same form, since $u = \partial \xi/\partial t = j\omega \xi$.

3.3 Plane Progressive Waves—Characteristic Impedance

As we saw in the study of the string, certain fundamental concepts and relations are based on the progressive-wave solution of the wave equation. In plane compressional waves the important relations are those involving the pressure, particle velocity, condensation, and particle displacement. If we assume the displacement to be the reference vector, and suppose a progressive wave in the direction of positive-x, we have

$$\xi = A e^{j(\omega t - kx)} \tag{3.31}$$

By differentiation, and the use of the fundamental relations developed in the previous articles, we have for the particle velocity, condensation, and pressure,

$$u = \frac{\partial \xi}{\partial t} = j\omega\xi \qquad \text{(a)}$$

$$s = -\frac{\partial \xi}{\partial x} = jk\xi \qquad \text{(b)} \qquad (3.32)$$

$$p = Bs = jkB\xi \qquad \text{(c)}$$

Thus, the pressure, condensation and particle velocity are in phase at any point in a progressive wave, and each leads the displacement at the point by 90°, as shown in Fig. 3.31. We have also

$$u = \frac{\omega}{k} s = cs \qquad (3.33)$$

$$p = \frac{kB}{\omega} u = \frac{B}{c} u = \rho c u \qquad (3.34)$$

The last equation is of great importance throughout acoustics. When a plane progressive wave is propagated in a medium, the ratio between the pressure and particle velocity at a point in the medium is found to be a real number ρc, which is a function only of the physical properties of the material, and is therefore called the *characteristic impedance*. The characteristic impedance is a special case of the specific acoustic impedance z, which is defined as the ratio between pressure and particle velocity at a point *in general.** We shall find that in general this ratio is complex, indicating that a phase difference between pressure and particle velocity can occur.

Fig. 3.31. Phase relations between variables in a plane progressive wave.

If the pressure and particle velocity are computed by Eq. (3.32) for a plane progressive wave propagating in the negative-x direction, the value $-\rho c$ is obtained for the characteristic impedance. It may seem somewhat arbitrary that a physical property of a medium should be determined by the direction of the waves passing through it, but since the characteristic impedance is a *vector* ratio, a mere change of sign should not cause concern. As a matter of fact, an interesting deduction can be drawn from this change of sign: if the pressure is above normal at a point ($+p$), and the particle velocity is to the *right* ($+u$), the wave crests in a progressive wave are moving toward the right. In general, similarity of signs of the pressure and particle velocity indicate progress in the positive-x direction, while oppositeness of sign indicates progress in the negative-x direction. We shall find use for this relation when we discuss the subject of reflection.

---

* The characteristic impedance is thus the specific acoustic impedance for a *plane progressive* wave.

Having begun the investigation with a discussion of *progressive* waves, as for the string, we shall subsequently introduce boundary conditions in the x direction. However, it may be helpful at this point to remark on the boundary conditions in the y and z directions. While it is true that they are tacitly implied in almost any discussion of plane waves, we shall, in the interests of clarity, make these conditions explicit.

The key fact is that Eqs. (3.24) to (3.26) hold at every point of space, even though they contain only a single space coordinate, x. Thus *all* points having the same x-value must have equal displacements, pressures, etc. The collection of all points having the same x-value is a plane parallel to the y–z coordinate plane. Thus the wave fronts determined by the above equations are infinite planes perpendicular to the x axis (Fig. 3.32).

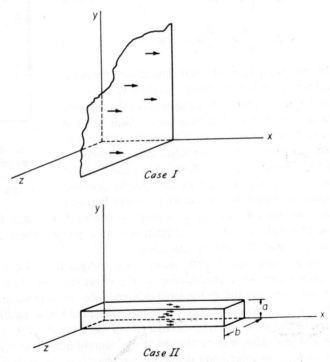

Fig. 3.32. Case I, the infinite plane wave front:

$$\xi = A_1 e^{j(\omega t - kx)} + A_2 e^{j(\omega t + kx)}$$
$$-\infty < x < \infty, \quad -\infty < y < \infty, \quad -\infty < z < \infty$$

Case II, the restricted plane wave front:

$$\xi = A_1 e^{j(\omega t - kx)} + A_2 e^{j(\omega t + kx)}$$
$$-\infty < x < \infty, \quad 0 < y < a, \quad 0 < z < b$$

While the preceding paragraph is rigorously true, Eqs. (3.24) and (3.26) are often employed without regarding the wave fronts as planes of infinite extent. In such instances, we tacitly assume a region in which the equation is to hold, and neglect all other regions. Thus if sound is confined to a rectangular duct of constant cross section extending in the direction of the x axis, the equations hold for certain values of y and z, say $0 < y < a, 0 < z < b$, while the dependent variable ξ is identically zero at all points and at all times outside these values. This should not be taken to mean that sound waves which are transmitted in ducts, pipes, or tubes which extend in the x direction must necessarily consist of plane waves with the plane wave front perpendicular to the x direction. Other modes of transmission may occur. The mode indicated in Fig. 3.32, however, is the only mode which is governed by Eqs. (3.24) to (3.26), and it shall be understood in later discussions of waves in tubes that this mode is the only one which exists. In the theory of guided waves, it is called the principal mode.

3.4 Energy Density in a Medium Propagating a Harmonic Wave

From elementary thermodynamics, the work done in a compression process is

$$W_P = -\int p' \, dV' \tag{3.41}$$

where p' is total instantaneous pressure, V' is instantaneous volume. From the definition of the bulk modulus,

$$dV' = -\frac{V}{B} dp'$$

If the pressure changes from its static value p_0 to the instantaneous value p', we have

$$W_P = \frac{V}{B} \int_{p_0}^{p'} p' \, dp' = \frac{V}{2B}\left[(p')^2 - p_0^2 \right] = \frac{V}{2B}(2p_0 p + p^2) \tag{3.42}$$

This is the potential energy of a volume which has undergone condensation due to a rise in acoustic pressure from 0 to p, or a rise in total pressure from p_0 to p'.

The kinetic energy of this volume will be $\frac{1}{2}\rho V u^2$, where u is the average instantaneous particle velocity over the volume. The total energy therefore will be

$$W = W_K + W_P = \frac{1}{2}V\left(\rho u^2 + \frac{\rho^2 c^2 u^2}{B} + \frac{2p_0 \rho c u}{B} \right)$$

$$= V\left(\rho u^2 + \frac{p_0}{c}u \right) \tag{3.43}$$

This gives for the instantaneous energy density,

$$E_{\text{Inst.}} = \frac{W}{V} = \rho u^2 + \frac{p_0}{c}u \tag{3.44}$$

The instantaneous energy density is variable with time at any point, and from point to point at any time. However, as in the case of the string, it is possible to find a time average of the energy density at any point, and a space average of the energy density at any time. The two are equal. The computation will be carried through for the time average. Integrating over a cycle, we have

$$E_{Av} = \frac{1}{T} \int_0^T \left(\rho u^2 + \frac{p_0}{c} u \right) dt \tag{3.45}$$

For a harmonic wave,

$$u = \omega A \cos(\omega t - kx)$$

and therefore

$$E_{Av} = \frac{\rho \omega^2 A^2}{T} \int_0^T \cos^2(\omega t - kx) dt + \frac{\omega A p_0}{cT} \int_0^T \cos(\omega t - kx) dt \tag{3.46}$$

The first integral has the value $\frac{1}{2}T$, and the second integral has the value zero. Therefore we have for the average energy density,

$$E_{Av} = \frac{\rho \omega^2 A^2}{2} = \frac{1}{2} \rho u_0^2 \tag{3.47}$$

The concept of space average of energy density is of fundamental importance in architectural acoustics, where a basic problem is the energy content of a room in terms of the strength of the normal modes of vibration that exist in the room. We shall employ this concept in Chapter 9 in computing the decay time of a standing wave in a room as determined by the energy lost by transmission into the walls of the room.

It is sometimes more useful to have the energy density in terms of the pressure. Since $u_0 = P_0/\rho c$, Eq. (3.47) gives

$$E_{Av} = \frac{1}{2} \rho \frac{P_0^2}{\rho^2 c^2} = \frac{1}{2} \cdot \frac{P_0^2}{\rho c^2} \tag{3.48}$$

The above expression is for a progressive wave. If a standing wave exists, expressions are obtained similar to those for the string. The standing wave can be considered to be composed of two progressive waves, so that average energy density is

$$E_{SW} = \frac{P_0^2}{\rho c^2} \tag{3.49}$$

If terms of the maximum pressure amplitude in the standing wave this will be:

$$E_{SW} = \frac{P_{Max}^2}{4\rho c^2} \tag{3.410}$$

This expression will find use in the discussion of the decay of standing waves in pipes in Art. 3.19, which is included primarily as a preparation for Chapter 9.

3.5 Acoustic Intensity

Acoustic intensity is defined as the average rate of flow of acoustic energy through unit area, or the acoustic power flow through unit area. Since, in our treatment of power in the oscillator, we have defined the instantaneous power as the product of the instantaneous force and the instantaneous velocity, the instantaneous power flow through unit area is the product of the instantaneous *pressure* and the instantaneous particle velocity.

$$i = p'u \tag{3.51}$$

If we average the product $p'u$ over a cycle on any cross section perpendicular to the direction of travel of the wave, we shall find the average rate at which acoustic energy is flowing across unit area of the section. We may shorten the computations, however, by writing $p'u = p_0 u + pu$, and noting from the previous article that the static pressure contributes nothing to average energy. Thus,

$$I = \frac{1}{T}\int_0^T pu\, dt = \frac{1}{T}\int_0^T P_0 u_0 \sin^2(\omega t - kx)\,dt = \frac{P_0 u_0}{2} = \frac{P_0^2}{2\rho c} \tag{3.52}$$

We may develop the expression for acoustic intensity alternatively from the energy density and the wave velocity, if we consider a unit cross section of a plane progressive wave, and take into account the fact that the *wave front* is traveling forward with velocity c.

The energy in a volume of unit cross section and length c is cE. The wave front of the plane wave would have traveled from one end to the other of this volume in one second. If we assume the energy to be carried forward by the wave front, this energy cE is the amount which crosses unit area per second, i.e., $I = cE$, and since $E = \tfrac{1}{2}\rho u_0^2$,

$$I = \frac{1}{2}\rho c u_0^2 = \frac{1}{2}\cdot\frac{P_0^2}{\rho c}$$

which agrees with Eq. (3.52), and also with Eq. (3.48).

If the rms pressure P is used, the intensity has the value

$$I = \frac{P^2}{\rho c}$$

When a plane wave is confined within a pipe, and the direction of propagation is along the length of the pipe, the power flow is given simply as $P_{Av} = SI$, where S is the cross section of the pipe. If the relation $P_{Av} = SP_0^2/2\rho c$ is written in the form $P_{Av} = (P_0^2/2)/(\rho c/S)$ and compared to the expression relating power and force in the oscillator, the quantity $\rho c/S$ resembles an impedance. It is useful to consider this ratio as the *acoustic impedance* Z_A. We have already defined the volume velocity U as the product of particle velocity u and cross section S. The acoustic impedance is actually defined as the ratio of pressure to volume velocity: $Z_A = p/U$. It is left to the student to show that this definition agrees with the power aspect by which the quantity Z_A was introduced above.

3.6 The Bulk Modulus—Velocity of Sound in Gases

The equations which have so far been deduced are correct for perfect fluids. Fluids include both gases and liquids, and several important acoustic relations can be derived from elementary gas laws. These laws define the ideal gas, and are only approximately true for real gases. However, air at normal temperature and pressure (273°K and 1.013×10^6 dynes cm^{-2}) approaches closely an ideal gas, and the ideal gas laws will be used without further qualification.

The laws important to this analysis are:

(1) *Boyle's law*, which states that with temperature held constant, the density is proportional to the absolute (total) pressure; (2) *Charles' law*, which states that with pressure constant, the density of any gas is inversely proportional to its absolute temperature; and (3) *Avogadro's law*, which states that at the same temperature and pressure the density is proportional to the molecular weight.

Putting all these proportionalities together we have

$$\rho' \propto p'\frac{M}{T}$$

This proportionality may be converted into an equation by means of a proportionality constant,

$$\rho' = \frac{p'M}{RT} \tag{3.61}$$

This equation is called the *general gas law*. It holds for all gases, if they are in an attentuated state, with the same value of R; therefore R is called the universal gas constant.

If V' and m are the volume and mass of a gas sample, we can rewrite Eq. (3.61) in the form,

$$p'V' = \frac{mRT}{M} \tag{3.62}$$

Since a molecular weight of any gas occupies 22,400 cm^3, at normal temperature and pressure, R has the value,

$$R = \frac{22,400 \times 1.013 \times 10^6}{273} = 8.31 \times 10^7 \text{ erg deg}^{-1}$$

The simplest expansions involving pressure and volume change (both of which must occur to enable us to compute B) are isothermal and adiabatic expansions.* In the former we have

$$p'V' = \text{Const} \tag{3.63}$$

and in the latter it may be shown that

$$p'(V')^\gamma = \text{Const} \tag{3.64}$$

---

* Isothermal expansions take place at constant temperature. Adiabatic expansions take place with zero heat transfer.

where γ is the *ratio* of *specific heats* of the gas. We shall find the value of the bulk modulus in these two cases.

(a) *Isothermal Bulk Modulus*

$$p'V' = \text{Const}$$
$$p'\,dV' + V'\,dp' = 0$$
$$dp' = -p'\frac{dV'}{V'} \approx -p_0\frac{dV'}{V'}$$

In our notation this can be written

$$p = p_0 s \tag{3.65}$$

which gives the *static pressure* as the *isothermal bulk modulus* B_I.

(b) *Adiabatic Bulk Modulus*

$$p'(V')^\gamma = \text{Const}$$
$$\gamma p'(V')^{\gamma-1}\,dV' + (V')^\gamma\,dp' = 0$$
$$dp' = -\gamma p'\frac{dV'}{V'} \approx -\gamma p_0\left(\frac{dV'}{V'}\right)$$

which is, in our notation,

$$p = \gamma p_0 s \tag{3.66}$$

which gives γp_0 as the *adiabatic bulk modulus* B_A.

If each of these is substituted in the equation $c = \sqrt{B/\rho}$ for the velocity of sound, the adiabatic bulk modulus gives a result in accord with observation, whereas the isothermal bulk modulus does not. It is concluded that the expansions and compressions that occur in the transmission of sound in gases are adiabatic in the frequency regions for which observations have been made.

The equation for the velocity of sound in gas can therefore be written

$$c = \sqrt{\gamma p_0/\rho} = \sqrt{\gamma RT/M} \tag{3.67}$$

The mean molecular weight of air is 29; γ is 7/5. If T is 300°K, (23°C),

$$c = \sqrt{\tfrac{7}{5} \times 8.31 \times 10^7 \times \tfrac{300}{29}} = 34{,}600 \text{ cm/sec} \tag{3.68}$$

which is in good agreement with the measured sound velocity in air.

Furthermore, the increase in velocity per degree Kelvin will be

$$\frac{dc}{dT} = \tfrac{1}{2}\sqrt{\gamma R/MT} = \tfrac{1}{2}\sqrt{(\tfrac{7}{5} \times 8.31 \times 10^7)/29T}$$

At 300°K we have

$$\frac{dc}{dT} = \tfrac{1}{2}\sqrt{(\tfrac{7}{5} \times 8.31 \times 10^7)/(29 \times 300)}$$

or about 60 cm/sec K°, which also is in good agreement with the observed value in air.

Since the molecular weight of hydrogen is about 2, the velocity of sound in hydrogen exceeds that of air by a factor of $\sqrt{29/2}$, or about 3.8 times. The wavelength is proportionately longer at the same frequency. In measurements in which the dimensions of the apparatus should be small compared to the wavelength, hydrogen gas is sometimes used instead of air to extend the frequency range of the measurements. One example is the reciprocity calibration of microphones by the chamber method. (See Art. 10.4 for a description of reciprocity calibration of microphones.)

No such simple theory exists for bulk moduli in liquids. However, measurements of sound velocity and density can be used to compute an effective bulk modulus, which gives important clues to liquid structure. Henceforth B will be used without a subscript. For gases, we are to understand it to be the adiabatic bulk modulus, and for liquids, the acoustic bulk modulus. Actually, the static bulk modulus in liquids agrees fairly well with the acoustic bulk modulus.

Equation (3.67) states that the velocity of the sound wave is a function only of the properties of the medium. This is true regardless of the velocity of the source of the wave with respect to the medium of transmission. While this is in the nature of an assumption, it is more important at this point to consider the ramifications of this fact rather than to formulate a proof. The most significant effect is as follows: If an observer is moving relatively to the source of sound, the frequency observed differs from the frequency emitted. This is called the *Doppler effect.*

The problem is most general if the directions of motion of the source and the receiver are oblique to each other. However, it may be quickly established that only the components of relative motion are effective, so that it is sufficient to assume that the velocities are in the same straight line, which we may take to be the x axis. Aside from this simplification, we shall impose no limitations on the motions; the source may be moving in either the positive-x or negative-x direction, and the observer may be moving in either direction.

We shall consider first the motion of the source with respect to the medium. If the source is in motion in the direction of propagation, the wavelength will be reduced. If it is moving in the opposite direction the wavelength will be increased. If we consider the direction of propagation to be positive, the wavelength in the medium will be given by the expression,

$$\lambda = \frac{c - v}{f} \qquad (3.69)$$

where c = wave velocity, v = velocity of the source (positive or negative), f = frequency of the wave.

A fixed observer will observe a wave of wavelength $\lambda = (c - v)/f$ moving with velocity c. To this observer, the wave will have an apparent frequency,

$$f' = \frac{c}{\lambda} = \frac{c}{c - v} f \qquad (3.610)$$

However, an observer moving with velocity v' has a relative velocity with respect to the wave crests. To him, the velocity appears to be $c - v'$, and the frequency would have an apparent value,

$$f'' = \frac{c - v'}{\lambda} \qquad (3.611)$$

If we substitute λ from Eq. (3.69) into Eq. (3.611), we obtain the general expression for frequency:

$$f'' = \frac{c - v'}{c - v} f \qquad (3.612)$$

where $v' =$ observer's velocity relative to the medium; $v =$ source velocity relative to the medium, $f'' =$ observed frequency, $f =$ frequency of the source.

Problem: Find the apparent frequency in terms of the source frequency in the following cases:

1) $v = \frac{1}{2}c$, $v' = -\frac{1}{3}c$
2) $v = \frac{1}{3}c$, $v' = -\frac{1}{2}c$
3) $v = v'$
4) $v = c$
5) $v' = c$
6) $v = -2c$, $v' = \frac{1}{2}c$
7) $v = -\frac{1}{2}c$, $v' = \frac{1}{3}c$

The Doppler effect is an example of the kind of theorizing that takes place in consideration of a source emitting a wave in a medium, where several relative velocities exist. In the study of light waves, the situation is even more complicated, because the medium of propagation is not nearly so well defined as the medium of propagation of compressional waves. In some mysterious way, the velocity of light between any two objects will be the same regardless of their relative velocities. The proof of this fact need not concern us here, but it is mentioned to give some idea of the problems attached to relative motion considered along with wave propagation. In spite of the fact that the velocity of light is considered a constant, an increase in observed wavelength will take place if the source is receding from the observer. The observed "red shift" (shift in the direction of longer wavelength) in the spectra of distant stars has led to the "expanding universe" theory of Abbé Le Maitre.

3.7 Intensity Measurement—The Bel and the Decibel

Because of the tremendous variation of intensities occurring in normal sound phenomena (and also because of the characteristics of the human ear, the most important sound instrument), it is customary, instead of giving the intensity of a sound directly, to relate it logarithmically to some standard intensity. The base level of intensity used in this text will be 10^{-9} erg/sec cm^2

or 10^{-16} watt/cm², which is approximately the lower limit of intensity for audibility in air for frequencies of the order of 1,000 cycles. The corresponding acoustic pressure is 0.000204 dyne/cm² in air at 20°C.

If we wish to characterize a sound which has 100 times the intensity of the sound which is used as the base intensity, we have as its *intensity level*

$$\text{I.L.} = \log_{10} \frac{100 I_0}{I_0} = 2 \text{ bels} \tag{3.71}$$

The more intense sound would be said to have an intensity level of 2 *bels* with respect to the weaker. If the base is thoroughly agreed upon, it is enough to say that the sound has an intensity level of 2 bels. The base levels given above will be understood to hold throughout the remainder of the text. To rate an intensity in *decibels*, we have the relation

$$\text{I.L. (in decibels)} = 10 \log_{10} I/I_0$$

where I and I_0 are in the same units of intensity; e.g. watts/cm².

We have seen in a previous article that the intensity is proportional to the square of the pressure for the same characteristic impedance. Thus, for the same ρc, the intensity level in decibels may be expressed by the relation,

$$\text{I.L.} = 10 \log_{10} \frac{p^2}{p_0^2} = 20 \log \frac{p}{p_0}$$

where p_0 is used here for a base acoustic pressure, not the static pressure.

The foregoing relations are equivalent to the electrical cases in which the power gain of an amplifier is

$$10 \log_{10} \frac{W_{\text{Out}}}{W_{\text{In}}} \quad (\text{decibels})$$

while the voltage gain is

$$20 \log_{10} \frac{E_{\text{Out}}}{E_{\text{In}}} \quad (\text{decibels})$$

As an example of the use of decibel notation, we compute the intensity and acoustic pressure of a sound that has an intensity level of 70 decibels compared to threshold level (written 70db re 0.0002 dyne/cm² or 70db re 10^{-9} erg/sec cm²). This is approximately the sound level of ordinary conversation.

$$20 \log_{10} \frac{p}{0.0002} = 70 \qquad\qquad 10 \log_{10} \frac{I}{10^{-9}} = 70$$

$$\log_{10} \frac{p}{0.0002} = 3.5 \qquad\qquad \log_{10} \frac{I}{10^{-9}} = 7$$

$$\frac{p}{0.0002} = 3160 \qquad\qquad \frac{I}{10^{-9}} = 10^7$$

$$p = 0.632 \text{ dyne/cm}^2 \, (Ans.) \qquad I = 10^{-2} \text{ erg/sec cm}^2$$

$$= 10^{-9} \text{ watt/cm}^2 \, (Ans.)$$

The decibel is also used in the important field of vibration study, where the base used is a source vibration of 1 cm/sec rms. Here, a rating of 40 decibels would be equivalent to an rms velocity of 100 cm/sec. In underwater acoustics the value 1 dyne/cm² is often used for the base acoustic pressure. Conversion from a base of 1 dyne/cm² to one of 0.0002 dyne/cm² requires an addition of 74 decibels. This is a frequently used conversion factor in naval acoustics. We thus have n db re 1 dyne/cm² $= (n + 74)$ db re 0.0002 dyne/cm².

Since normal atmospheric pressure is approximately 10^6 dynes/cm², the base pressure 1 dyne/cm² is approximately one one-millionth of the normal barometer reading. As such, it is called the *microbar* (μbar). Although the term dyne/cm² will be employed in this text almost exclusively, the term μbar may be encountered in some of the references.

3.8 Change of Medium—Reflection Coefficient

When a compressional wave passes from one medium to another across an abrupt boundary in the plane of the wave front, the phenomenon is similar to that of a wave on a string approaching a support. In general, reflection will occur, and the condition will no longer be one of purely progressive waves. The ratio of pressure to particle velocity in a progressive wave has been found to be the quantity ρc, which has been called the characteristic impedance of the medium. But the ratio of pressure to particle velocity *in general* has been defined as the *specific acoustic impedance z*. The specific acoustic impedance depends in part on the properties of the medium, but it depends on other factors as well.

In an infinite medium, the specific acoustic impedance will be equal to the characteristic impedance at every point; but in a medium of finite extent, the specific acoustic impedance may change from point to point, much as the input impedance of a string varies with the length of the string. In elementary acoustics it is found (e.g. in the Kundt's tube experiment) that both velocity nodes and pressure nodes occur in a resonant tube. But where a velocity antinode exists, there is a node of pressure, and vice versa. Thus the specific acoustic impedance is high at velocity nodes and low at pressure nodes.

An important acoustic principle in connection with boundary conditions is that discontinuities of pressure and velocity are not allowed. Consider the volume element of Fig. 3.21. As the length dx decreases without limit, the pressure differential also decreases without limit (if the pressure is continuous with x) and the acceleration of the element is finite, or at the worst, indeterminate. But if the pressure differential were to remain finite while dx (and hence the mass) decreased without limit, the acceleration would become infinite. Since infinite accelerations are contrary to experience, it is concluded that discontinuities of pressure do not exist. The same conclusion can be reached with regard to density by the equation $p = Bs$. Now consider the same volume element with regard to velocity. Because of the continuity of density, the flow into and out of the element will be closely proportional to the velocity at the two bounding faces. A little thought will show that the rate of increase of density is proportional to the velocity gradient across the element. But if this velocity gradient is infinite, as it would be if there were a discontinuity in the velocity, the density would approach infinity, which is again contrary to experience. Therefore neither do discontinuities of velocity exist.

The conclusions of the preceding paragraph are true in all cases. But practically, the occasions in which one might inadvertently imply such discontinuities are at boundaries between two media—for here the abrupt change in physical properties might seem to permit equally abrupt changes in other physical entities. Therefore it is specifically stated that *pressure and velocity are continuous across a boundary.* The same holds true for displacement and condensation.*

Since it has already been concluded that reflection will exist at the boundary, the expression for the displacement in the first medium may be written

$$\xi = A_i e^{j(\omega t - k_1 x)} + A_r e^{j(\omega t + k_1 x)} \tag{3.81}$$

It is advantageous to take the origin at the boundary (Fig. 3.81), with x measured positive to the right. Then x is negative in the original medium,

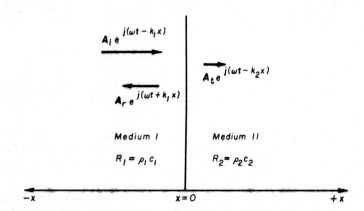

Fig. 3.81. Incident, reflected, and transmitted waves at boundary between two media.

and positive in the second medium. The first term of Eq. (3.81), however, still represents a wave advancing to the right, and the second represents a wave advancing to the left.

---

* And for other physical quantities in other branches of physics.

Differentiation of the displacement equation gives the pressure and the particle velocity:

$$p = -B\frac{\partial \xi}{\partial x} = jk_1 Be^{j\omega t}(A_i e^{-jk_1 x} - A_r e^{jk_1 x})$$

$$u = \frac{\partial \xi}{\partial t} = j\omega e^{j\omega t}(A_i e^{-jk_1 x} + A_r e^{jk_1 x}) \tag{3.82}$$

Since $x = 0$ at the boundary, the expressions for pressure and particle velocity at the boundary are

$$p_{(x=0)} = jk_1 Be^{j\omega t}(A_i - A_r)$$

$$u_{(x=0)} = j\omega e^{j\omega t}(A_i + A_r) \tag{3.83}$$

By the condition of continuity of pressure and velocity, these equations apply at points infinitesimally to the left of the boundary (in the first medium) and infinitesimally to the right (in the second medium). Let us assume at the outset that the second medium extends to infinity. The ratio of the pressure to the velocity at any point in the second medium is then $\rho_2 c_2$. We therefore have

$$\frac{p_{(x=0)}}{u_{(x=0)}} = \frac{k_1 B}{\omega} \cdot \frac{A_i - A_r}{A_i + A_r} = \rho_2 c_2 \tag{3.84}$$

But

$$\frac{k_1 B}{\omega} = \rho_1 c_1 \tag{3.85}$$

and therefore

$$\rho_2 c_2 = \frac{A_i - A_r}{A_i + A_r} \rho_1 c_1 \tag{3.86}$$

This equation can be modified to give the ratio A_r/A_i in terms of the characteristic impedances of the two media:

$$\frac{A_r}{A_i} = \frac{\rho_1 c_1 - \rho_2 c_2}{\rho_1 c_1 + \rho_2 c_2} = \frac{R_1 - R_2}{R_1 + R_2} \tag{3.87}$$

The right-hand side of this equation is often given as the amplitude reflection coefficient for sound passing from medium I to medium II. By the use of this equation, one can readily settle a question that is often a source of disagreement in elementary physics courses, namely, whether a phase change takes place in a particular instance of reflection. The equation shows that the reflected *amplitude* will be in phase with the incident amplitude if the first medium is of greater characteristic impedance than the second ($R_1 - R_2$ is positive) and vice versa. As we shall see, the converse is true of the incident and reflected pressures. So many important applications of reflection are handled by this equation that it may seem pedantic to insist that it covers only the special case in which the terminating impedance is purely resistive; i.e. a medium extending to infinity. At this point we can state only that in general, the specific acoustic impedance at the boundary must be used rather than the characteristic impedance of the second medium. (How the specific acoustic impedance is determined will be the subject of the next article.) The general expression for the amplitude reflection coefficient at a boundary is therefore

$$\frac{A_r}{A_i} = \frac{R_1 - z_2}{R_1 + z_2} \tag{3.88}$$

This ratio of the reflected amplitude vector to the incident amplitude vector A_r/A_i is called the *complex reflection coefficient for amplitude* K_A. We can also compare the reflected and incident pressure and velocity vectors. In Eq. (3.32), the pressure and particle velocity in a plane progressive wave are given in terms of the displacement. Therefore we can make the following substitutions in Eq. (3.82):

$$\begin{aligned} p_i = jkBA_i, \qquad p_r = -jkBA_r \\ u_i = j\omega A_i, \qquad u_r = j\omega A_r \end{aligned} \tag{3.89}$$

The Eqs. (3.82) then give the total pressure and total velocity at a point in terms of incident and reflected pressures and velocities:

$$\begin{aligned} p = (p_i e^{-jkx} + p_r e^{jkx})e^{j\omega t} \\ u = (u_i e^{-jkx} + u_r e^{jkx})e^{j\omega t} \end{aligned} \tag{3.810}$$

We have also from Eq. (3.89),

$$\frac{p_i}{u_i} = \frac{kB}{\omega} = \rho c, \qquad \frac{p_r}{u_r} = -\frac{kB}{\omega} = -\rho c \tag{3.811}$$

Thus, though the ratio of the total pressure to the total velocity is not in general equal to the characteristic impedance, the ratio of incident pressure to incident velocity does give the characteristic impedance, since each of these is a progressive wave form. The same is true for the reflected components.

We can now define the complex reflection coefficients for pressure and velocity:

$$K_P = \frac{p_r}{p_i}; \qquad K_u = \frac{u_r}{u_i} \tag{3.812}$$

From Eq. (3.89),

$$\frac{p_r}{p_i} = -\frac{A_r}{A_i}, \quad \text{and} \quad \frac{u_r}{u_i} = \frac{A_r}{A_i}$$

and from the definition of the amplitude coefficient,

$$K_P = -K_A = \frac{z_2 - R_1}{z_2 + R_1}, \qquad K_u = K_A = \frac{R_1 - z_2}{R_1 + z_2} \tag{3.813}$$

Only one of the three reflection coefficients is needed. Henceforth the pressure reflection coefficient will be employed exclusively, with subscript omitted. From its definition, this coefficient, as a ratio of two complex numbers, is in general a complex coefficient.

The incident intensity is proportional to the square of the *magnitude* of

p_i, while the reflected intensity is proportional to the square of the magnitude of p_r. We define the *sound reflection coefficient* α_R as the ratio of these two intensities:

$$\alpha_R = \frac{|p_r|^2}{|p_i|^2} = |K|^2 = \frac{|z_2 - R_1|^2}{|z_2 + R_1|^2} \tag{3.814}$$

The ratio between the *transmitted* energy and the incident energy is defined as the *sound transmission coefficient* α_T. By this definition,

$$\alpha_T = 1 - \alpha_R = 1 - |K|^2 \tag{3.815}$$

In the special case where the second medium is of infinite extent,

$$K = \frac{R_2 - R_1}{R_2 + R_1} = \frac{\rho_2 c_2 - \rho_1 c_1}{\rho_2 c_2 + \rho_1 c_1} \tag{3.816}$$

It is interesting to note the relation of *reciprocity* that exists for the sound reflection coefficient. For example, α_R has the same value whether the sound passes from water ($\rho c = 1.5 \times 10^5$) to aluminium ($\rho c = 1\cdot4 \times 10^6$) or from aluminium to water. The (pressure) reflection coefficient K will have the same *numerical* value in both cases, but will be *positive* when the sound passes from the rarer to the denser medium and negative in the opposite case.

To illustrate the meaning of positive and negative K, assume a pulse of compression traveling through the first medium toward the boundary. As this pulse travels through the medium, the excess pressure in any region takes on a positive value and returns to its static value p_0, without ever having a negative value. If, at the boundary, the pulse encounters a medium in which $R_2 > R_1$, a returning pulse of positive excess pressure is generated. Throughout the passage of the incident and reflected pulses, no point in the medium will ever have experienced a negative excess pressure. On the other hand, if the compressive pulse encounters a medium of lesser characteristic impedance, a negative acoustic pressure will be generated at the boundary, and a wave of extension or rarefaction will be reflected. Each region in the medium thus experiences both positive and negative excess pressures during the passage of the incident and reflected pulses.

Where the second medium is not infinite in extent, the coefficient K may have any complex value. We shall study this complex reflection coefficient when we consider transmission through three media. However, we shall continue for the present to make the assumption of an infinite terminating medium, and derive expressions for the variation of the specific acoustic impedance of a terminated fluid column with distance from the boundary. We shall also show that the specific acoustic impedance at any fixed point is a function of the reflection coefficient; i.e. of the terminating impedance.

Equations (3.810) can also be written in terms of the incident pressure (or velocity) and the pressure reflection coefficient. We obtain

$$p = p_i \left(e^{-jkx} + Ke^{jkx}\right)e^{j\omega t}$$
$$u = u_i \left(e^{-jkx} - Ke^{jkx}\right)e^{j\omega t} \tag{3.817}$$

From Eqs. (3.817), we can readily find the general expression for the specific acoustic impedance in a medium where reflection is present. Dividing the pressure by the velocity, we have

$$z = \rho c \frac{e^{-jkx} + Ke^{jkx}}{e^{-jkx} - Ke^{jkx}} \tag{3.818}$$

It will be noted that the specific acoustic impedance reduces to the characteristic impedance ρc if the reflection coefficient is zero.

3.9. Specific Acoustic Impedance of Fluid Columns of Finite Length

At the end of the previous article an expression was derived for the specific acoustic impedance of a plane wave in the case where the boundary is normal to the direction of travel of the wave. This ratio is most useful in the study of the propagation of plane waves in fluid columns, in which it gives the specific acoustic impedance at every point of the column as a function of the characteristic impedance of the medium, the reflection coefficient at the boundary, and the distance from the point to the boundary. The specific acoustic impedance is most often found in practical cases at the input end of the column, and is then referred to as the specific acoustic impedance "of the column," thus identifying the distance to the boundary with the length of the column. A knowledge of the specific acoustic impedance as a function of length and termination is important where the reaction of the column on a driver is sought. As a matter of fact, the expression which we shall derive is entirely similar in form to that of the driving impedance of a string. Extreme values of specific acoustic impedance are associated with resonance conditions, and because of the universal importance of resonance, it is useful to be able to express the condition in terms of impedance.

The expression for specific acoustic impedance of a column simplifies in two important cases: (1) as a function of length, when the reflection coefficient has a magnitude of unity; (2) as a function of reflection coefficient, for certain critical values of length.

At a distance L from the boundary in the first medium, $x = -L$, and if $|K|$ is unity,

(a) If $K = 1$,

$$z = \rho_1 c_1 \frac{e^{jkL} + e^{-jkL}}{e^{jkL} - e^{-jkL}} = -j\rho_1 c_1 \cot kL \tag{3.91}$$

(b) If $K = -1$,

$$z = \rho_1 c_1 \frac{e^{jkL} - e^{-jkL}}{e^{jkL} + e^{-jkL}} = j\rho_1 c_1 \tan kL \tag{3.92}$$

It should be noted that these equations correspond to those for the driving impedance of a string.

When the length of the column is a half wavelength, $kx = 2\pi x/\lambda = -\pi$, and

$$z = \rho_1 c_1 \frac{e^{j\pi} + Ke^{-j\pi}}{e^{j\pi} - Ke^{-j\pi}} = \rho_1 c_1 \frac{1 + K}{1 - K}$$

If the second medium is infinite in extent, $K = (R_2 - R_1)/(R_2 + R_1)$ and we have

$$z = \rho_1 c_1 \frac{R_2}{R_1} = R_2$$

In words, this states that the input impedance of a half wavelength column equals its terminating impedance. As a simple example, a half wavelength of *any* characteristic impedance which is terminated by a rigid boundary presents an infinite impedance to a wave approaching it from the left. Thus if a resilient material is applied to a rigid wall for damping purposes, the front face of this material will act as a rigid boundary to a sound wave whose half wavelength is equal to the thickness of the resilient material.

The terminating impedance is, in a sense, *transferred* to the front face; one might say that the half-wavelength column acts as a 1:1 transformer. This is an almost trivial example of impedance transformation. As another example, a half-wavelength thickness of any material can serve as a separation between two media of equal characteristic impedance without interfering with transmission between the two.

For the quarter-wavelength column, $kx = 2\pi x/\lambda = \pi/2$.

$$z = \rho_1 c_1 \frac{e^{j\pi/2} + Ke^{-j\pi/2}}{e^{j\pi/2} - Ke^{-j\pi/2}} = \frac{1 - K}{1 + K} \rho_1 c_1$$

and if the second material is infinite in extent,

$$z = \rho_1 c_1 \frac{R_1}{R_2} = \frac{R_1^2}{R_2} \tag{3.93}$$

In words, this states that the input impedance is *inversely* proportional to the terminating impedance. However, in this case, the characteristic impedance of the material which makes up the quarter-wavelength section also enters into its input impedance. The transformer ratio in this case is actually $(R_1/R_2)^2$, since we have the equality,

$$z = \frac{R_1^2}{R_2} = \left(\frac{R_1}{R_2}\right)^2 R_2 \tag{3.94}$$

Example: A wave travels in a medium of characteristic impedance 42. It is to be terminated by a material of characteristic impedance 4,200. Find the characteristic impedance of a quarter-wave section which, if applied to the boundary of the material of higher characteristic impedance will present an input impedance of 42, so that perfect transmission will be effected. *Ans.* 420.

Lastly, we can show that a thin separation between two media has little effect on the transmission of sound.

$$z_\varepsilon = \rho c \frac{e^{j\varepsilon} + K e^{-j\varepsilon}}{e^{j\varepsilon} - K e^{-j\varepsilon}} \approx \rho c \frac{1 + K}{1 - K}$$

But this is the value of the input impedance for a passage directly from the first medium into the terminating medium.

For analysis of the specific acoustic impedance as a general function of x and K, a special type of vector diagram is very useful. The interpretation of Eq. (3.818) in the general case will be accomplished by these vector diagrams in the next article.

3.10 Vector Diagrams of Pressure and Velocity in Fluid Columns

The vector diagram employed to represent pressure and velocity variations in fluid columns is similar in many ways to the vector diagrams introduced in Art. 2.5 for the study of the string. This vector diagram enables one to compute the rms values of pressure and velocity at different distances from a reflecting boundary, and also gives the relative phases of the quantities at these points. Vector diagrams of both pressure and velocity are shown in Fig. 3.101 for the following combinations of characteristic impedances:

$$R_2 \gg R_1, \quad R_2 = 3R_1, \quad R_2 = R_1, \quad R_2 = \tfrac{1}{3}R_1, \quad R_2 \ll R_1.$$

Before we interpret these diagrams, certain conventions must be explained. Points distant $\lambda/8$, $\lambda/4$, $3\lambda/8$, and $\lambda/2$ from the wall are numbered 1, 2, 3, 4, and the point at the wall is 0. Incident vectors are shown with half full arrowheads, reflected vectors with half dashed arrowheads, and total vectors with full arrowheads. It will be noted that the incident vectors at other points lead the vector at the wall, with the angle of lead increasing with distance from the wall. On the other hand, for the reflected vectors, the angle of lag increases with distance from the wall. Since the terminating impedance is purely resistive, the reflected vector at the wall is either in phase or exactly out of phase with the incident vector (Eq. 3.813). The relative magnitudes and phases of the two vectors at the wall are found from the reflection coefficient. The sum vector at each point is determined by the vector addition of the two components at that point. In some cases, the vector diagram may require careful study, since one vector may coincide with another, as the total velocity vector at point 4 and the reflected velocity vector at point 0 in (b) of the figure. A number at the origin signifies a total vector value of zero [see the total velocity at points 0 and 4 in (a)].

As an example of the use of the diagram, let us interpret (a) of the figure. Since $R_2 \gg R_1$, then R_2 may be assumed infinite (rigid boundaries) and therefore $K_p = 1$ and $K_u = -1$ with small error. At the termination, $u_r = -u_i$, so that the total velocity is zero, and the total pressure is $2p_i$, since $p_r = p_i$. The incident vector at point 1 leads that at 0 by 45°, and the reflected vector

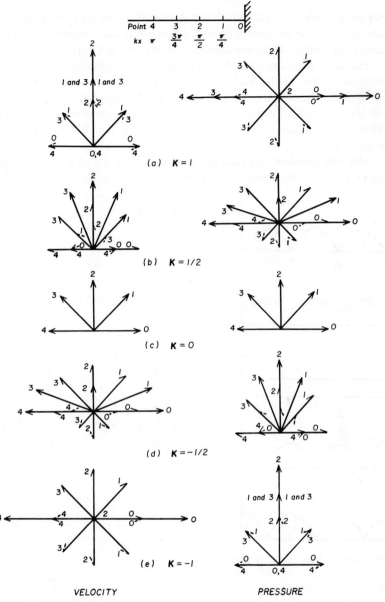

Fig. 3.101. Vector diagrams of particle velocity and pressure where incident and reflected waves are present.

at 1 lags that at 0 by 45°. The reflected velocity at the wall is equal and opposite to the incident velocity at the wall. Therefore the incident and reflected velocity vectors at point 1 are equal in magnitude and 90° out of phase, with the result that the total velocity is $\sqrt{2}$ times the incident velocity magnitude. We note also that the total velocity at point 1 falls on the vertical axis and the total pressure falls on the horizontal axis, confirming the purely reactive character of the impedance, as expressed in Eq. (3.91).

The other diagrams differ from (a) only in the magnitudes and signs of the reflected vectors at the wall. Thus the reflected vectors in (b) have phase relations similar to those in (a) and magnitudes one-half as great, while (d) and (e) are the converse of (a) and (b) with regard to pressure and velocity. Where the reflections coefficient is zero, in (c), the diagram is that of a progressive wave.

The rms pressure and velocity at points along the path of the wave are shown in Fig. 3.102, which is the plot of the magnitudes of the total vectors

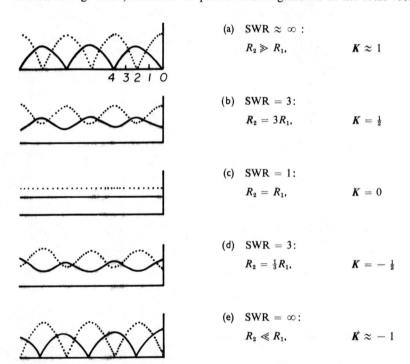

(a) SWR $\approx \infty$:
$R_2 \gg R_1,$ $K \approx 1$

(b) SWR $= 3$:
$R_2 = 3R_1,$ $K = \frac{1}{2}$

(c) SWR $= 1$:
$R_2 = R_1,$ $K = 0$

(d) SWR $= 3$:
$R_2 = \frac{1}{3}R_1,$ $K = -\frac{1}{2}$

(e) SWR $= \infty$:
$R_2 \ll R_1,$ $K \approx -1$

Fig. 3.102. Rms pressure and particle velocity for various values of terminating impedance.

of Fig. 3.101. In Fig. 3.102, it is clear that a pressure maximum occurs at the same points as a velocity minimum, and vice versa. This diagram also helps to illustrate the concept of standing wave ratio, defined in Art. 2.9, where it is shown that the SWR is related to K by the equation

$$\text{SWR} = \frac{1 + |K|}{1 - |K|}$$

A plot of pressure, or velocity, enables the SWR to be computed, and from the SWR one can find the reflection coefficient, and ultimately the terminating impedance. (A method similar to this is used to find the acoustic impedance of material used for the acoustical treatment of walls.) It is also possible to plot the specific acoustic impedance from the vector diagrams. One finds its magnitude at a point by dividing the pressure magnitude by the velocity magnitude at that point, and its phase by subtracting the phases. However, the specific acoustic impedance can be more readily computed by finding its real and imaginary parts, and plotting them separately, as shown below. The

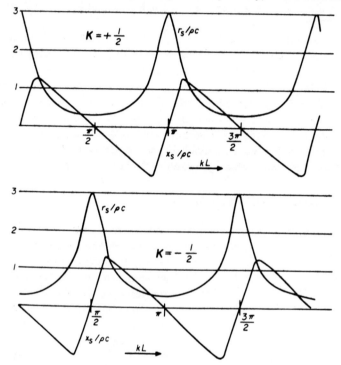

Fig. 3.103. Curves of specific acoustic impedance as a function of column length.

real part is called the specific acoustic resistance r_s, and the imaginary part is called the specific acoustic impedance x_s. We have

$$z = \rho c \frac{e^{jkL} + K e^{-jkL}}{e^{jkL} - K e^{-jkL}}$$

$$= \frac{1 + K e^{-2jkL}}{1 - K e^{-2jkL}} \tag{3.101}$$

Converting to Cartesian form and rationalizing, one obtains

$$z = \rho c \frac{1 - K^2 - 2jK \sin 2kL}{1 + K^2 - 2K \cos 2kL} \tag{3.102}$$

from which,

$$r_s = \rho c \frac{1 - K^2}{1 + K^2 - 2K \cos 2kL} \tag{3.103}$$

$$x_s = \rho c \frac{- 2jK \sin 2kL}{1 + K^2 - 2K \cos 2kL} \tag{3.104}$$

Curves of r_s and x_s as a function of x for $K = \frac{1}{2}$ and $K = -\frac{1}{2}$ are shown in Fig. 3.103.

Having developed the specific acoustic impedance of a medium in terms of the distance to the boundary, we are now in a position to discuss the transmission of sound through three media. The typical problem is one in which the sound, having originated in medium I, must pass through a finite thickness of medium II to arrive in medium III. We have already made reference to such transmission where the thickness of the intervening medium was a quarter- or half-wavelength, or where the thickness was very small compared with the wavelength. We now consider the more general case where the thickness may have any value compared with the wavelength.

3.11 Transmission through Three Media

In Art. 3.9, the specific acoustic impedance of various sections was expressed in terms of the terminating impedance and the distance to the terminating boundary (thickness of the section). In the discussion of the quarter-wave section it was shown that the characteristic impedance of the material composing the section also enters into the expression for its input specific acoustic impedance. The example employed to illustrate the impedance of the quarter-wave section makes it clear that this theory may often involve the transmission of sound through three media; first, the medium in which the sound originates; second, the terminating medium; third, a section of finite length which divides the medium of origin of the sound from the terminating medium. The problem is the following: given a certain incident intensity in the medium of origin—how does the intensity in the terminating medium (which is infinite in extent) depend on its

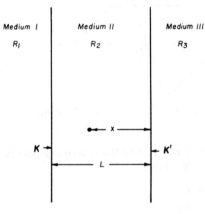

Fig. 3.111. Transmission through three media.

characteristic impedance and on the characteristic impedance and thickness of the intervening section? Referring to Fig. 3.111, medium III extends to infinity, and thus the terminating impedance is purely resistive. The specific acoustic impedance at the boundary of media I and II can thus be expressed in terms of L, R_3, and R_2. The transmission of sound from the first medium depends only on its characteristic impedance and the specific acoustic impedance at the I-II boundary, since the sound transmission coefficient at this boundary can be computed from these two factors alone (see Eqs. 3.814 and 3.815).

It is important that this transmission coefficient gives the sound intensity which is present *in the terminating medium*. It is not merely the transmission coefficient of the partial system consisting of medium I and medium II, since the total effect of both the second and the third media are taken into account in the computation of the specific acoustic impedance at the I-II boundary. The entire discussion is on a steady-state basis, so that intensities of transmission in all three media are constants, and therefore the net power flow across any cross section is the same, whether this cross section be taken in medium I, medium II, medium III, or at either of the two boundaries. It is sometimes felt that the solution to this problem gives the proportion of the sound energy which will pass the I-II boundary, but that some of this energy will subsequently be reflected at the II-III boundary. It will be stated again that the effect of reflection at the II-III boundary has already been taken into account in the computation of the specific acoustic impedance at the first boundary. Thus it is entirely proper to say that the transmission coefficient which we are calculating in this article is actually the transmission coefficient from medium I to medium III.

We can express the specific acoustic impedance at the I-II boundary in the form:

$$z_2 = R_2 \frac{e^{jk_2L} + K'e^{-jk_2L}}{e^{jk_2L} - K'e^{-jk_2L}} \tag{3.111}$$

Converting the complex numbers to real and imaginary components, we have

$$z_2 = \frac{(1 + K') \cos k_2L + j(1 - K') \sin k_2L}{(1 - K') \cos k_2L + j(1 + K') \sin k_2L}$$

but, since

$$1 + K' = \frac{2R_3}{R_3 + R_2}$$

$$1 - K' = \frac{2R_2}{R_3 + R_2}$$

we can rearrange the equation to obtain

$$z_2 = R_2 \frac{R_3 \cos k_2L + jR_2 \sin k_2L}{R_2 \cos k_2L + jR_3 \sin k_2L}$$

$$= \frac{R_3 \cos k_2L + jR_2 \sin k_2L}{\cos k_2L + j(R_3/R_2) \sin k_2L}$$

If K is the reflection coefficient at the I-II boundary, we have

$$K = \frac{z_2 - R_1}{z_2 + R_1}$$

$$= \frac{R_3 \cos k_2 L + R_2 j \sin k_2 L - R_1 \cos k_2 L - (R_1 R_3 / R_2) j \sin k_2 L}{R_3 \cos k_2 L + R_2 j \sin k_2 L + R_1 \cos k_2 L + (R_1 R_3 / R_2) j \sin k_2 L}$$

which simplifies to

$$K = \frac{(R_3 - R_1) \cos k_2 L - j(R_1 R_3 / R_2 - R_2) \sin k_2 L}{(R_3 + R_1) \cos k_2 L + j(R_1 R_3 / R_2 + R_2) \sin k_2 L} \qquad (3.112)$$

Dividing the numerator and denominator by R_3, and writing R_1/R_3 in the form R_{13}, etc.,

$$K = \frac{(1 - R_{13}) \cos k_2 L - j(R_{12} - R_{23}) \sin k_2 L}{(1 + R_{13}) \cos k_2 L + j(R_{12} + R_{23}) \sin k_2 L}$$

The sound reflection coefficient is the square of the magnitude of this complex reflection coefficient.

$$\alpha_R = \frac{(1 - R_{13})^2 \cos^2 k_2 L + (R_{12} - R_{23})^2 \sin^2 k_2 L}{(1 + R_{13})^2 \cos^2 k_2 L + (R_{12} + R_{23})^2 \sin^2 k_2 L} \qquad (3.113)$$

And since the transmission coefficient $\alpha_T = 1 - \alpha_R$, we have, finally

$$\alpha_T = \frac{4 R_{13}}{(1 + R_{13})^2 \cos^2 k_2 L + (R_{12} + R_{23})^2 \sin^2 k_2 L} \qquad (3.114)$$

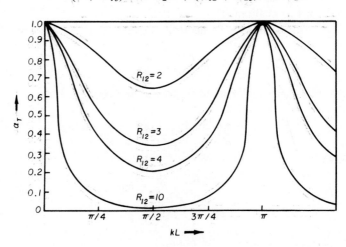

Fig. 3.112. Transmission coefficient for a medium of thickness L separating two media of equal characteristic impedances.

Since the transmission coefficient is in general a function of R_1, R_2, R_3, and L, it is not possible to plot a universal curve of the variation of this coefficient. However, in many important cases, $R_1 = R_2$, and the transmission coefficient simplifies to

$$\alpha_T = \frac{4}{4 \cos^2 k_2 L + (R_{12} + 1/R_{12})^2 \sin^2 kL} \tag{3.115}$$

For $R_{12} \gtrless 2$ (i.e. $R_1 \gtrless 2R_2$), we have

$$\alpha_T \approx \frac{1}{1 + \frac{1}{4}(R_{12}^2 - 2)\sin^2 kL} \tag{3.116}$$

We may readily plot α_T, as given by Eq. (3.116), as a function of L for chosen values of R_{12}. These curves are plotted in Fig. 3.112 for four values of R_{12}, namely, 2, 3, 4, and 10. When $R_2 \gtrless 2R_1$, we replace R_{12} in Eq. (3.116) by R_{21}. Figure 3.112 also applies for $R_{21} = 2$, 3, 4, and 10.

It should be noted that a 2:1 "mismatch" of characteristic impedances ($R_{12} = 2$) gives a transmission coefficient of about 0.7, or a transmission loss of about 2 db. In most cases this would be considered a small transmission loss. It is evident, then, that matching of impedances need not be perfect to effect good sound transmission.

3.12 Plane Waves in Pipes

In the discussion of the solution of the plane wave equation, in Art. 3.3, it was remarked that the propagation of plane waves in pipes could be handled by assuming that the wave fronts were normal to the direction of progress. In pipe systems in which changes of cross section occur, the wave front is not actually plane in the immediate vicinity of discontinuities, since either convergence or divergence must occur. However, it turns out that at moderate distances on either side of the discontinuity, the wave is approximately plane, and it is convenient to ignore the departure from the plane wave configuration, and assume that plane waves exist throughout the system. The discontinuity is then treated as an abrupt change in acoustic impedance, similar to the change in specific acoustic impedance that occurs at a boundary between two

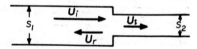

Fig. 3.121. Continuity of volume velocity at change of cross section in a pipe.

media. Thus the developments of the preceding articles can be carried over in their entirety, with the substitution of acoustic impedance for characteristic impedance. It is assumed that the same fluid is contained throughout the system.

In the case of a change of pipe area, the pressure and volume velocity must be continuous across the plane at the junction of the two pipes of different cross sections. If we take $x = 0$ at the junction (Fig. 3.121) we have

$$p_1 = p_i + p_r = p_t \tag{3.121}$$

$$U_1 = U_i + U_r = U_t \tag{3.122}$$

and

$$U_1 = S_1 (u_i + u_r) = \frac{S_1}{\rho c}(p_i - p_r) \tag{3.123}$$

where the subscript 1 refers to points just to the left of the junction, and the subscript t (for transmitted wave) refers to points just to the right.

Dividing, to find the acoustic impedance,

$$\frac{p_1}{U_1} = \frac{\rho c}{S_1} \cdot \frac{p_i + p_r}{p_i - p_r} = \frac{p_t}{U_t} \tag{3.124}$$

The ratio p_t/U_t is the acoustic impedance looking to the right at the junction. If the pipe to the right of the junction is of infinite length, its acoustic impedance will be $\rho c/S_2$. Therefore

$$\frac{\rho c}{S_1} \frac{p_i + p_r}{p_i - p_r} = \frac{\rho c}{S_2} \tag{3.125}$$

$$\frac{1 + K}{1 - K} = \frac{S_1}{S_2} \tag{3.126}$$

and we obtain for the reflection coefficient at the junction,

$$K = \frac{S_1 - S_2}{S_1 + S_2} \tag{3.127}$$

We then have for the transmission coefficient,

$$\alpha_T = \frac{4S_1 S_2}{(S_1 + S_2)^2} \tag{3.128}$$

With a single change of cross section, the transmission coefficient can be unity only if the change in cross section approaches zero, since the numerator will always be less than the denominator unless $S_1 = S_2$.

The derivation of the acoustic impedance at any point in a pipe follows in every detail the derivations for the specific acoustic impedance in Art. 3.9. We shall omit details and present only results.

For a pipe of cross section S_1 terminated by an infinite pipe of cross section S_2,

$$Z_A = \left(\frac{\rho c}{S_1}\right) \frac{e^{-jkx} + [(S_1 - S_2)/(S_1 + S_2)]e^{jkx}}{e^{-jkx} - [(S_1 - S_2)/(S_1 + S_2)]e^{jkx}}$$

Except for division by S_1, Eqs. (3.103) and (3.104) give the acoustic resistance R_A and acoustic reactance X_A, and Figs. 3.101, 3.102, and 3.103 apply with the same qualifications.

For the input acoustic impedance of a quarter-wavelength pipe of cross section S_1 terminated by an infinite pipe of cross section S_2,

$$Z_{A,1/4} = \left(\frac{S_2}{S_1}\right)^2 \frac{\rho c}{S_2} \tag{3.129}$$

The interpretation is similar to that of the quarter-wave section: the quarter-wavelength pipe has transformed the input impedance of the terminating pipe by the factor $(S_2/S_1)^2$. Pipes equal in length to odd multiples of a quarter wavelength act similarly to quarter-wavelength pipes.

For a half-wavelength pipe, or for any multiple of a half wavelength, the input impedance equals the acoustic impedance of the infinite terminating pipe.

3.13 Transmission through Three Pipes of Different Cross Sections

The problem of transmission of sound through three pipes of different cross sections is similar to that of transmission through three media, the only difference being the use of acoustic impedances rather than specific acoustic impedances. Thus the reflection coefficient from pipe II to pipe III will be (Fig. 3.131):

$$K' = \frac{S_2 - S_3}{S_2 + S_3} \tag{3.131}$$

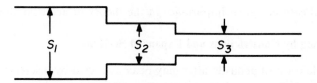

Fig. 3.131. Pipe with three different cross sections.

This gives for the acoustic impedance at the entry to pipe II,

$$Z_A = \frac{\rho c}{S_2} \cdot \frac{e^{jkL} + K' e^{-jkL}}{e^{jkL} - K' e^{jkL}} \tag{3.132}$$

Finally, we have for the complex reflection coefficient at the entry to pipe II,

$$K = \frac{Z_A - \rho c/S_1}{Z_A + \rho c/S_1} \tag{3.133}$$

The magnitude of this reflection coefficient is thus a function of S_1, S_2, S_3, and L, where L is the length of the intermediate pipe. Since the sound reflection coefficient is proportional to the square of K, and since the treatment is entirely similar to that for transmission through three media, the transmission coefficient is obtained from Eq. (3.114) by changing ratios of characteristic impedance to ratios of cross section.

$$\alpha_T = \frac{4S_{31}}{(1 + S_{31})^2 \cos^2 kL + (S_{21} + S_{32})^2 \sin^2 kL} \tag{3.134}$$

In particular, the curves of Fig. 3.112 hold for pipes with contracted or expanded sections as in Fig. 3.132. Here $S_1 = S_3$, and we obtain the transmission coefficient by a substitution of S_{12} for R_{12} in Eq. (3.116).

This gives
$$\alpha_T = \frac{1}{1 + \frac{1}{4}(S_{21}^2 - 2) \sin^2 kL} \qquad (3.135)$$

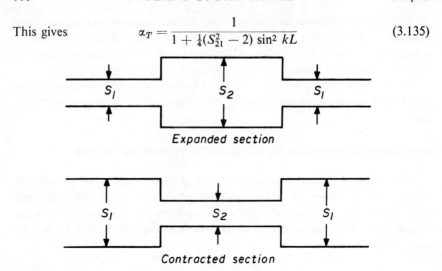

Expanded section

Contracted section

Fig. 3.132. Pipes with expanded and contracted sections.

This special case has great importance in the theory of acoustic filters.

3.14 Filtering by Constrictions and Expanded Sections

A simple form of acoustic filter may be constructed by inserting into the main transmitting pipe a short pipe of cross-sectional area larger or smaller than the cross section of the main transmitting pipe as in Fig. 3.132. The

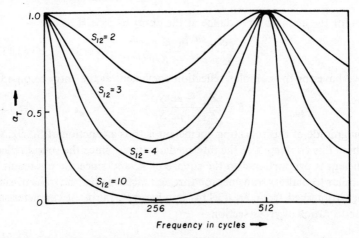

Frequency in cycles ➡

Fig. 3.141. Transmission coefficient as a function of frequency, for construction of 1-ft. length inserted in main transmitting pipe.

transmission curves of Fig. 3.112 can be modified slightly to give the variation of transmission coefficient with frequency for a fixed length, with the cross section of the intermediate pipe as the parameter. The wavelength in air is about 4 ft for a frequency of about 256 cycles. Taking the length of the intermediate pipe to be 1 ft, we show in Fig. 3.141 the transmission coefficient for $S_{12} = 2, 3, 4$, and 10, respectively.

Very often, for short lengths of the intermediate pipe, the important frequencies of a complex transmitted sound are below the frequency at which the first minimum of the transmission coefficient occurs. The element then functions as a *low-pass filter*, with an attenuation roughly proportional to frequency. The same variation of transmission with frequency can be attained in an electric transmission line by the insertion of a series inductor.

The similarity between the action of a short pipe and an inductance agrees with the analogy between the inductor and an inertance which was developed in Art. 1.2. This simplification is often employed in the analysis of acoustic filters. Conversely, a *cavity* in which all dimensions are small compared with the wavelength can be treated as an *acoustic compliance*. We shall treat pipes containing inertances and compliances at the conclusion of this study of acoustic filters. It is preferable at this point, however, to consider the effect of *branch pipes* on the transmission of sound through pipes.

3.15 Filtering by Branch Pipes

If open or closed pipes are attached as branches to the main transmitting pipe, they have a marked effect on the transmission of sound. If the branch is an open pipe, there may be a certain amount of sound energy radiated from the open end, but the more important effect on transmission is the change in acoustic impedance at the junction caused by the branch. We may, with little loss in generality, take the branch to be a closed pipe of diameter equal to that of the main transmitting pipe (Fig. 3.151). We shall show that the combination of branch and pipe extension presents to the input pipe an equivalent acoustic impedance which is

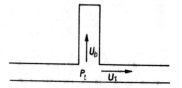

Fig. 3.151. Branch pipe.

similar in form to the electrical impedance of two elements in *parallel*.

By the continuity conditions, there is a common pressure p_t at the junction. Therefore the volume velocity into the branch U_b will have the value

$$U_b = \frac{p_t}{Z_b} \tag{3.151}$$

where Z_b is the acoustic impedance looking into the branch. The volume velocity U_t in the main transmitting pipe extending to the right will have the value

$$U_t = \frac{p_t}{Z_t} \tag{3.152}$$

where Z_t is the acoustic impedance looking into the infinite terminating pipe, and has the value $\rho c/S$.

The equivalent acoustic impedance $Z_{Eq.}$ is the common pressure divided by the vector sum of the velocities:

$$Z_{Eq.} = \frac{p_t}{U_b + U_t} \tag{3.153}$$

Combining Eqs. (3.151), (3.152), and (3.153),

$$Z_{Eq.} = \frac{p_t}{p_t/Z_b + p_t/Z_t} = \frac{1}{1/Z_b + 1/Z_t} = \frac{Z_b Z_t}{Z_b + Z_t} \tag{3.154}$$

which is similar to the equivalent impedance of two electrical impedances in parallel.

Since Z_b has the value $-j\rho c/S \cot kx$ (Eq. 3.94), we can express $Z_{Eq.}$ in the Cartesian form to get the equivalent resistance and reactance:

$$Z_{Eq.} = \frac{j(\rho c/S)^2 \cot kx}{j(\rho c/S) \cot kx + \rho c/S} = \frac{\rho c}{S} \cdot \frac{j \cot kx}{j \cot kx + 1}$$

Rationalizing,

$$Z_{Eq.} = \frac{\rho c}{S} \frac{\cot^2 kx + j \cot kx}{1 + \cot^2 kx}$$

$$= \frac{\rho c}{S}(\cos^2 kx + j \sin kx \cos kx) = R_{Eq.} + jX_{Eq.} \tag{3.155}$$

The curves for $R_{Eq.}$ and $X_{Eq.}$ can be easily plotted, but they are not needed for the immediate application, which is to find the expression for the transmission coefficient. The development is similar to that of previous articles. The more important steps are shown below.

$$K = \frac{Z_{Eq.} - \rho c/S}{Z_{Eq.} + \rho c/S} = \frac{(\rho c/S)(\cos^2 kx + j \sin kx \cos kx - 1)}{(\rho c/S)(\cos^2 kx + j \sin kx \cos kx + 1)}$$

$$|K|^2 = \frac{(1 - \cos^2 kx)^2 + \sin^2 kx \cos^2 kx}{(1 + \cos^2 kx)^2 + \sin^2 kx \cos^2 kx}$$

$$\alpha_T = 1 - |K|^2 = \frac{4\cos^2 kx}{(1 + \cos^2 kx)^2 + \sin^2 kx \cos^2 kx} \tag{3.156}$$

The denominator simplifies readily on expansion and the use of elementary trigonometric identities. We obtain, as a final expression for the transmission coefficient,

$$\alpha_T = \frac{4}{\sec^2 kx + 3} \tag{3.157}$$

The transmission coefficient is plotted as a function of kx in Fig. 3.152, and the filtering action of a 1-ft closed branch pipe is shown in Fig. 3.153.

Although the transmission coefficient of a transmitting pipe with a branch is not without importance in its own right, probably the most important feature of this article is that it introduces a method of treating elements which, so to speak, are in parallel with the main transmitting pipe. The constrictions and expanded sections discussed in previous articles may be said to be in series with the main pipe. In many cases, the series and parallel elements which will be utilized are quite small compared with the wavelengths of the transmitted sound, and are regarded as inertances and compliances, rather

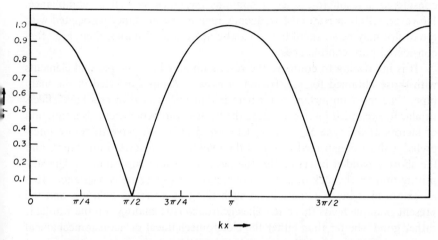

Fig. 3.152. Transmission coefficient of branch pipe as a function of length of the branch.

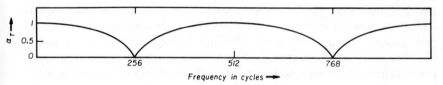

Fig. 3.153. Transmission coefficient of 1-ft. branch pipe as function of frequency.

than as pipes. The expressions $M = \rho L/S$ and $C = V/B$ were obtained in Art. 1.2. The acoustic impedances of these elements will evidently be

$$Z_M = \frac{j\rho L\omega}{S}, \qquad Z_C = -j\frac{B}{\omega V} = -j\frac{\rho c^2}{\omega V} \qquad (3.158)$$

More detailed consideration shows that the inertance of a short, narrow, open branch pipe does not approach zero as the length of the pipe approaches zero (that is, as the branch pipe approaches an orifice in the transmitting pipe). This is not unreasonable, since the air stream that passes through the orifice must move for some short distance with a cross section approximately equal to that of the orifice. Analysis shows that the acoustic impedance of an orifice is given to a close approximation by the expression

$$Z_{Or.} = j\frac{1.7\rho\omega}{\pi a} \qquad (3.159)$$

In this expression, a is the radius of the orifice, and the constant is determined by considering the loading effect of the external air on a piston equal in area to the orifice (see Art. 4.11).

Any cavity that is connected to a pipe by an orifice must ultimately be considered a resonator, since it contains inertance as well as compliance. However, within a restricted frequency region, the inertance associated with the orifice may be so small that it can be neglected. Cavities, then, are often considered pure compliances.

It is interesting to compare the results obtained for the parallel elements with those obtained for constricted or expanded pipes inserted in the main pipe. The most important point here is that constricted inserts have effects similar to expanded inserts, because the transmission coefficients is a function of factors of the type $S_{12} + 1/S_{12}$ (see Eq. 3.115). We have therefore interpreted a short constricted insert as the analogue of a series inductance, and the short expanded insert as the analogue of a shunt capacitance. The surprising thing is the lack of a structure analogous to a series capacitance. It is an axiom in logic that there is no such thing as a perfect analogy, and the present example bears this out. The electroacoustic analogy, on the whole, is rather good—better than either the electromechanical or acoustomechanical analogies—yet we have the anomalous result that shunt inertances, shunt compliances, and series inertances correspond to shunt inductances, shunt capacitances, and series inductances, as one would expect, while the series cavity is analogous, not to the series capacitance, but to the shunt capacitance. On closer examination, the result is not so mystifying as it appears at first glance. There is not much difference between a shunt cavity and a widening of the transmitting pipe. For instance, assuming a cylindrical cavity which surrounds the pipe, the lumped impedance theory is the same whether

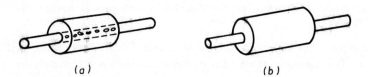

(a)　　　　　　　　　　(b)

Fig. 3.154. Simple form of a shunt cavity (*b*), as developed from a fundamental shunt cavity (*a*).

the cavity is connected to the main transmitting pipe by one or several orifices. As the number of orifices increases without limit, the section of pipe to which the cavity is appended gradually degenerates into an expanded section of diameter equal to the diameter of the cavity, and of length equal to the length of the cavity (Fig. 3.154). In the next article we shall treat lumped acoustic impedance filters, based on the electroacoustical analogue which we have discussed, together with the attenuation achieved electrically with well-known networks of lumped reactances.

Practically, the chief difference between filters which employ pipes of length comparable with the wavelength of the sound and those which use lumped impedances is that the former are *multiband filters*, while the latter have either a single transition frequency, as high-pass and low-pass filters, or have a single critical frequency, such as band-pass and band-suppression filters. The curves of Fig. 3.141 illustrate the operation of the multiband filter. In the next article we shall see how certain combinations of inertances and compliances act as acoustic filters, and the transmission curves obtained with such filters.

3.16 Acoustic Filters with Lumped Impedances

A well-integrated theory of the transmission characteristics of pure reactance networks has been built up, and occupies an important place in the field of electrical engineering. Such networks are constructed of *sections* which are

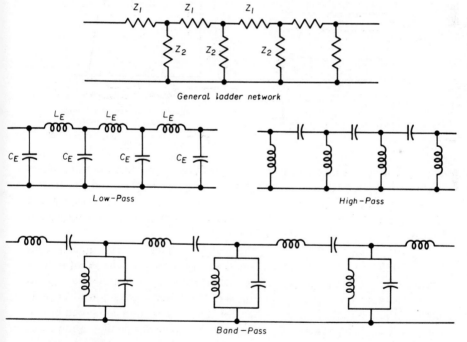

Fig. 3.161. A general ladder network with low-pass, high-pass, and band-pass filters comprised of such sections.

connected in *tandem* to form a *ladder network*. Each section consists of a series impedance Z_1, and a shunt impedance Z_2, and most of the important characteristics of such networks can be given in terms of these two impedances. A general ladder network is shown in Fig. 3.161, which also illustrates the meaning of tandem connection of the fundamental filter sections. Low-pass, high-pass, and band-pass filters built of such sections are also shown in the figure. We shall not develop the theory of such electric networks, although we may state that the *cutoff frequencies* for both low- and high-pass filters are given by

$$f_C = \frac{1}{\pi \sqrt{L_E C_E}}$$

The theory of acoustic filters has developed from the basis of such electric filters, on the two broad generalizations that an inertance in an acoustic system will have an effect similar to an inductance in an electric circuit, and a cavity will have an effect similar to a capacitance. As a simple example, an inductor inserted in series with the line forms a rudimentary low-pass filter,

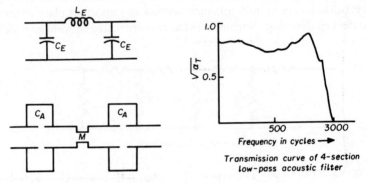

Fig. 3.162. Electric and acoustic low-pass pi filters.

and a short constriction in a pipe transmitting sound has the same effect within a restricted frequency region. If we go a step further, and construct a low-pass pi filter from a series inductor and two shunt capacitances, we find that the same effect can be produced acoustically by means of a constriction and two shunt cavities, as shown in Fig. 3.162.

Passing from the low-pass to the high-pass filter, we encounter a conceptual difficulty. Shunt inertances can be substituted for the shunt inductances of the electrical analogue, but since there is no acoustical analogue to the series capacitor, the analogous basis of the design breaks down. There is nothing to do but omit the series element, and try a section composed of two (or more) shunt inertances. Experimentation shows this configuration to be a highly successful high-pass filter, Fig. 3.163(a). Figure 3.163(b) is an experimental transmission curve for the filter shown in the figure. There is some theory to show that the length of transmitting pipe between the inertances, since it is of larger diameter than that of the inertances, approximates the action of a series capacitor, but the theory is by no means easy to follow, and somewhat less than satisfying. As so often happens, one performs the experiment, and explains it later, if at all.

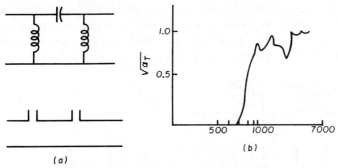

Fig. 3.163. Electric and acoustic high-pass filters.

Excepting for the omission of the series capacitor, the theory holds up well for the band-suppression and band-pass filters. The best band-suppression filter contains series resonant circuits across the line, and parallel resonant circuits in the line. However, a simple inductor in the line, in lieu

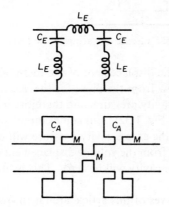

Fig. 3.164. Electric and acoustic band-suppression filters.

of a parallel resonant circuit, gives a serviceable band-suppression filter, and this form can be built acoustically by the use of a series inertance and Helmholtz resonators in parallel (Fig. 3.164).

A band-pass filter and its experimental transmission curve are shown in Fig. 3.165. It is similar to the band-suppression filter, except that it employs *reversed* Helmholtz resonators for the shunt elements. It is not obvious why this reversal of the resonator should transform its action from that of a series resonant circuit to that of a parallel resonant circuit. Reversal of the position of the inductor and capacitor in a series circuit will not accomplish the same result. However, it is not difficult to show this to be the case acoustically.

Although it can be proved analytically, we shall make use of a descriptive treatment. Since no inertance separates the cavity from the pipe (Fig. 3.165), the pipe pressure equals the cavity pressure. If this pressure is positive, there must be *net* volume displacement into the cavity, so that the equation $p = Bs$ can be obeyed. A certain portion of this volume displacement will come from displacement of the inertance which separates the cavity from the open air.

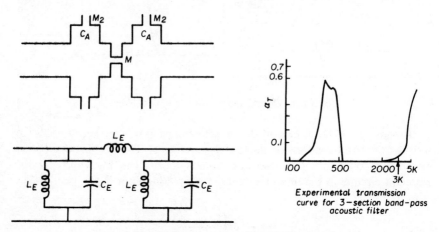

Fig. 3.165. Electric and acoustic band-pass filters.

It is easy to show that the displacement of the inertance is always of a phase to *reduce* the volume flow from the pipe; for the *acceleration* of the air mass M_2 is in phase with the cavity pressure, and therefore its *displacement* must be exactly out of phase (see Fig. 1.32). For some combination of inertance, compliance, and frequency, the excess cavity pressure will be exactly balanced by the condensation arising from the volume displacement of M_2, and the volume flow from the pipe to the cavity will be zero. This is the condition of parallel resonance.

The transmission curves of this article are taken from a pioneer paper on acoustic filters by G. W. Stewart.[*]

3.17 Radiation of Sound by a Piston in a Pipe

So far, the existence of a source of sound has been taken for granted. We shall now assume that the source of plane waves in a pipe is a close-fitting plane piston. The problem is to establish a relation between the rate of mechanical work done by the piston and the rate of sound power flow in the medium. We assume that the piston oscillates with rms velocity v, and that the fluid remains always in contact with the piston face, so that $v = u$, the particle velocity in the fluid at the piston face. The ratio between the force which the piston impresses on the pipe fluid and the piston velocity has the

[*] G. W. Stewart, *Phys. Rev.* **20**, 528 (1922).

dimensions of a mechanical impedance, which is called the *radiation impedance* Z_r. The radiation impedance varies with pipe length and termination in strict correspondence to the acoustic impedance and specific acoustic impedance. The radiation impedance will therefore, in general, have a real part, the *radiation resistance* R_r, and an imaginary part, the *radiation reactance* X_r. The relative values of R_r and X_r as a function of termination and length of pipe are given by Fig. 3.103, and since Z_r is a mechanical impedance, the theory of Art. 1.10 on mechanical impedance also applies.

By definition,

$$Z_r = \frac{F}{v} = \frac{pS}{u} = Sz \tag{3.171}$$

where $z =$ specific acoustic impedance of the pipe, $F =$ piston force, $v =$ piston velocity, $S =$ piston cross section, $u =$ particle velocity at the piston face.

Similarly,

$$Z_r = S^2 Z_A, \quad X_r = S^2 X_A, \quad R_r = S^2 R_A \tag{3.172}$$

We have also

$$R_r = Sr_s, \quad X_r = Sx_s$$

and for radiated power,

$$P_{Av} = v^2 R_r = \frac{|F|^2}{|Z_r|^2} R_r \tag{3.173}$$

The radiation impedance of a fluid column is essentially similar to the driving impedance of a string, and has the same dimensions. The driving piston would most probably be an element of a vibratory system driven

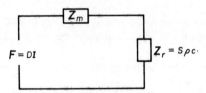

Fig. 3.171. The radiation impedance of a pipe represents a mechanical load on the mechanical vibratory system of the piston.

electromagnetically. The radiation impedance would then represent a purely mechanical load on the driver, and the radiated power would be obtained by the application of Thevenin's theorem as in the string. The mechanical circuit is shown in Fig. 3.171 for a pipe of infinite length.

3.18 Attenuation of Plane Longitudinal Waves

In Art. 3.2 the analysis of a strained element of a dissipationless fluid led to the equation

$$-\frac{\partial p}{\partial x} = \rho \frac{\partial^2 \xi}{\partial t^2} \tag{3.181}$$

which is a statement of Newton's law in the absence of friction. Now suppose that a frictional force exists in the medium, proportional to the velocity of motion. We then have for the equation of motion,

$$-\frac{\partial p}{\partial x} = \rho \frac{\partial^2 \xi}{\partial t^2} + a \frac{\partial \xi}{\partial t} \tag{3.182}$$

where a is the mechanical damping constant. Since $p = Bs = -Bd\xi/dx$,

$$B\frac{\partial^2 \xi}{\partial x^2} = \rho \frac{\partial^2 \xi}{\partial t^2} + a \frac{\partial \xi}{\partial t}$$

$$c^2\frac{\partial^2 \xi}{\partial x^2} = \frac{\partial^2 \xi}{\partial t^2} + \frac{a}{\rho} \frac{\partial \xi}{\partial t} \tag{3.183}$$

If a driver of frequency ω imparts a harmonic pressure to a dissipationless fluid column, it produces therein a wave of the same frequency, and amplitude constant with distance x, with an instantaneous phase lag proportional to x. We reason that a damping force in the medium will bring about an attenuation with x. In the study of the vibrator, we have seen that a real exponential characterizes damping. Therefore, purely as a trial, we assume as a solution of Eq. (3.183) a function of the form

$$\xi = Ae^{j\omega t}e^{-(\alpha + j\beta)x} \tag{3.184}$$

Differentiation with respect to x and t gives

$$\frac{\partial \xi}{\partial t} = j\omega\xi, \qquad \frac{\partial^2 \xi}{\partial^2 t} = -\omega^2\xi$$

$$\frac{\partial^2 \xi}{\partial x^2} = (\alpha + j\beta)^2\xi = (\alpha^2 + 2j\beta\alpha - \beta^2)\xi$$

If we take α as a small number and therefore neglect its square, substitution of the assumed solution and its derivatives in Eq. (3.163) gives

$$c^2(2j\beta\alpha - \beta^2) = -\omega^2 + j\frac{a}{\rho}\omega$$

$$c^2\beta^2 = \omega^2, \qquad \alpha = \frac{a}{2\rho c}\cdot\frac{\omega}{\beta c}$$

The relation $c\beta = \omega$ shows that, under the assumption of small α, $\beta = k$. Making this substitution in the equation for α, we have

$$\alpha = \frac{a}{2\rho c} \tag{3.185}$$

which gives α, the *attenuation coefficient*, in terms of a, the mechanical damping constant.

Equation (3.185) expresses the condition under which Eq. (3.184) is a solution of the dynamic Eq. (3.183). If the damping constant a is assumed to be determined by the viscosity of the fluid, it should, according to classical theory, have the value $a = \text{const } \eta/\lambda^2$, where η is the viscosity of the fluid, and λ is the wavelength of the sound. The origin of the attenuation of sound in fluids will be discussed in detail in Chapter 11. At this point we are not so much interested in the origin, as in the modification of the theory of this chapter because of the presence of attenuation. This can be illustrated by a comparison of the vector diagram of particle velocity in an absorbing fluid column with the vector diagram of Fig. 3.101 for a perfect fluid. A similar vector diagram could be obtained for the pressure.

This vector diagram appears in Fig. 3.181, and is formed similarly to those of Fig. 3.101, except that there is a steady decrease in the component velocity magnitudes with distance along the column. Vector addition of the velocity components gives alternate increases and decreases as the distance increases, but the figure differs from that of 3.102 for the dissipationless fluid because of the changing component magnitudes. In Fig. 3.181, the attenuation is greatly

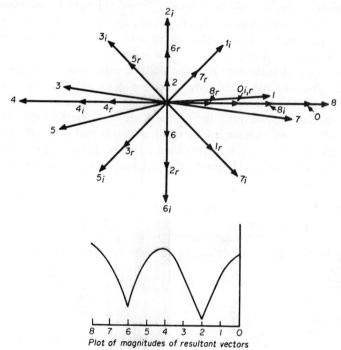

Fig. 3.181. Vector diagram of particle velocity in attenuating liquid column, with air above liquid surface.

exaggerated over that which would be found in practice. If a velocity- or pressure-measuring device is moved through the fluid column, the resulting velocity or pressure measurements may be used to calculate the attenuation coefficient. It is somewhat easier experimentally to use the driving piston itself as a pressure-measuring device, since the load which the fluid column presents to the driver is a function of its input impedance, which can be shown to be a function of column length, reflection coefficient, and attenuation coefficient. If this input impedance can be measured while the column length is changed, the attenuation coefficient can be computed.

In the greater portion of acoustic problems, the effects of absorption are minor at frequencies below about 10,000 cycles. As a matter of fact, more absorption measurements are made at ultra-audible than at audible frequencies, and the purpose of such measurements is often not so much the study of sound transmission as an end result, as it is an investigation of the modes of energy interchange in molecules (see Chapter 11).

3.19 Resonance in Pipes

Resonance in pipes is so closely analogous to resonance in strings that a detailed analysis can scarcely be justified. However, there is one aspect of resonance that is closer in pipes than in strings to several important applications, and this aspect will be briefly investigated. This is the aspect of the decay of the standing wave.

Let us assume that the pipe is closed on both ends, and that it is in axial resonance. The only modes that can exist are those in which the pressure maxima occur at the ends of the pipe. Let us first suppose that the side walls are rigid, but that the end walls, though hard, are not perfectly rigid—that is, their characteristic impedance is high compared with that of the fluid in the pipe, but not infinite. Let p_m be the maximum value of the pressure amplitude, and R_T be the value of the terminating impedance. Then the power flow into the end walls will be

$$\frac{p_m{}^2}{2R_T}S_1$$

where S_1 is the total area of the two end walls.

The space average energy density of the pipe is $p_m{}^2/4\rho c^2$, and therefore the total energy is

$$\frac{p_m{}^2}{4\rho c^2}V$$

The decay rate will therefore be

$$a_E = \frac{p_m{}^2 S_1}{2R_T}\frac{4\rho c^2}{p_m^2 V} = 2\frac{S_1}{V}\frac{\rho c^2}{R_T}$$

Let us now assume that the end walls are rigid, while the side walls are not. Because the pressure varies sinusoidally along the length of the pipe, the average square of the pressure is one-half the maximum pressure. Therefore the power flow into the side walls per unit area is only one-half that to the end walls. The total power flow to the side walls is therefore

$$\frac{p_m^2}{4R_T}S_2$$

where S_2 is the area of the side walls. Because the terminating impedances are high compared with the characteristic impedance of the fluid pipe, the transmission coefficient reduces to

$$\alpha_T = \frac{4\rho c}{R_T}$$

This may be seen by reference to Eqs. (3.814) and (3.815). Therefore we have for the decay rates in the two cases in terms of the transmission coefficients:

End walls:

$$a_E = \frac{\alpha_T S_1 c}{2V}$$

Side walls:

$$a_S = \frac{\alpha_T S_2 c}{4V}$$

We have now completed the study of the more important acoustic fundamentals that can be investigated with the plane-wave simplification. For further progress, it is necessary to develop the equation of the *spherical wave* and from it to derive expressions for intensity, acoustic pressure, and so forth, as we have done for the plane wave.

References

Shortley and Williams, *Elements of Physics*, 2nd ed., Prentice-Hall, Englewood Cliffs, N.J., 1955.

John D. Ryder, *Networks, Lines and Fields*, 2nd ed., Prentice-Hall, Englewood Cliffs, N.J., 1955.

Kinsler and Frey, *Fundamentals of Acoustics*, Wiley, New York, 1950.

Problems

1. Given a plane progressive wave of exponential form defined by its displacement equation $\xi = Ae^{j(\omega t - kx)}$, find the expressions for particle velocity and condensation by differentiation. (a) Now find the pressure and intensity under the assumption that the equation $p = Bs$ holds. (b) Find the pressure under the assumption that a somewhat more complicated relation obtains between the pressure and the density, namely, $p = Bs + g\dot{s}$. (c) Find the expression for specific acoustic impedance in (a) and (b) of the problem. ($\dot{s} = ds/dt$.)

2. Find the particle velocity amplitude in air for an acoustic pressure of 0.002 dyne/cm². Find the condensation, energy density, and acoustic intensity. Find the displacement amplitude if the frequency is 1,000 cycles.

3. Draw curves of the acoustic resistance and reactance of a water column of area 6.25 cm² as a function of column length if the column is terminated in an infinite reflector made of aluminium, density 2.7, velocity 5×10^5 cm/sec. Draw a curve of the force necessary to maintain a velocity of 0.1 cm/sec on a piston placed at the input of the column. Find the SWR.

4. A plane wave is propagated from a pipe of area S_1 into a pipe of infinite

length and of smaller area $S_2 = hS_1$. Find the intensity in S_2 compared to that which would be propagated in S_1 if it were of infinite length (that is, to the incident intensity in S_1). Find the pressure and volume velocity in S_2 compared to the incident pressure and volume velocity. Find the reflected pressure and volume velocity at the discontinuity. Find the SWR in S_1, and correlate it with the intensity and pressure values.

5. (a) An aluminum plate is used as a separator between water and mercury. Densities: water, 1; aluminum, 2.7; mercury, 13.6. Velocities: water, 1.5×10^5; aluminum, 5.15×10^5; mercury, 1.45×10^5 cm/sec. Find the thickness necessary to effect 100 per cent transmission from the water to the mercury, if the frequency is 20 kc. (b) Find the thickness necessary if the plate were of steel. Find the reflection coefficients at the water-metal surfaces and at the metal-mercury surfaces.

6. Find the velocity of sound in hydrogen at 127°C.

7. Show that a wave having an acoustic pressure of 1 dyne/cm² has an intensity level of 74 db in air. Find the intensity in erg/sec cm² corresponding to zero db intensity level. Find the intensity in watts/cm² corresponding to an acoustic pressure of 0.0002 dyne/cm² and to one of 1 dyne/cm². Find the intensity level corresponding to an acoustic pressure of 1 dyne/cm² in water. Find the acoustic pressure corresponding to an intensity level of 0 db in water.

8. Find the length of a closed pipe for which the input acoustic resistance equals the input acoustic reactance if the angular frequency of a wave is 2,000 radians/sec, and the terminating impedance of the pipe is twice the impedance of the fluid enclosed by the pipe.

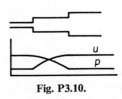
Fig. P3.10.

9. A pipe of area S_2 is used as a quarter-wave matching section between pipes of area S_1 and $S_3 = 9S_1$. Although the standing wave condition does not exist in pipes 1 and 3, it does exist in pipe 2. Show that the pressure-velocity relations in the three pipes is as given in Fig. P3.10 and that therefore the net power flow in pipe 2 is equal to that in pipes 1 and 3.

10. If absorption is present in a medium, the expression for input specific acoustic impedance of a fluid column becomes

$$Z_{In} = \rho c \frac{e^{\gamma L} + K e^{-\gamma L}}{e^{\gamma L} - K e^{-\gamma L}} \qquad \gamma = \alpha + j\beta$$

Show that this expression may be derived by the method used to derive the input specific impedance of a nonabsorbing fluid column in Art. 3.8.

11. Show that the expressions for specific acoustic resistance and specific acoustic reactance of an absorbing fluid column become

$$r_s = \frac{1 - K^2 e^{-4r\alpha}}{1 - 2K e^{-2r\alpha} \cos 2\beta r + K^2 e^{-4\alpha r}}$$

$$x_s = \frac{-2K e^{-2\alpha r} \sin 2\beta r}{1 - 2K e^{-2\alpha r} \cos 2\beta r + K^2 e^{-4\alpha r}}$$

12. Find the expressions for the maxima and minima of r_s. Show that $x_s = 0$ at both maxima and minima of r_s. Plot the first five maxima and the first five minima of r_s for the following values of K and α.

(a) $K = 1$, $\alpha = 0.1$.

(b) $K = 1$, $\alpha = 0.2$.

(c) $K = 0.9$, $\alpha = 0.2$.

(d) $K = 1$, $\alpha = 1$.

(e) $K = -1$, $\alpha = 0.2$.

(f) $K = -0.9$, $\alpha = 0.2$.

Chapter 4

SPHERICAL WAVES AND RADIATION

Plane waves are a special case of the transmission of sound in three-dimensional space. Although the plane wave derivations involved such three-dimensional concepts as pressure and volume, the ultimate equation was a function of only a single space variable and the time, and as such, was effectively a one-dimensional wave equation. If we consider a plane wave of unlimited extent proceeding in the direction of positive-x, we must assume it to be produced by an infinite piston in the y–z plane. By limiting the extent of the wave front we find that we can apply the plane-wave concept successfully to the study of propagation of sound in tubes, but this is certainly a limited application.

A far greater number of applications involve sound waves which *diverge* from a source that is small compared with the wavelength. An exact solution to such problems can be obtained by developing the wave equation directly in spherical coordinates, but both the geometry and the dynamics of this derivation are difficult. An alternative is to develop the wave equation in Cartesian form (which is relatively simple), and to convert to spherical coordinates by purely geometrical transformation equations. However, this transformation, while straightforward, is a very lengthy process.

Fortunately, the most important applications do not require the use of the wave equation in its full generality, and if we apply the restrictions which obtain in practice, we can perform the geometric part of the development for spherical waves without undue difficulty. But even with these restrictions, the dynamic portion of the problem, if attacked directly in spherical coordinates, would require mathematical forms more advanced than we care to introduce.

The "geometric" phase of the development comprises the derivation of an equation of continuity, to which we shall devote a good portion of the next article. The dynamic phase involves the reaction of a portion of a fluid medium to a pressure differential in the medium. It turns out that the dynamic equations, for the special assumptions of classical acoustics, are independent of the coordinate system, and if these equations are obtained in the Cartesian system, they can be carried over into the spherical system. The required equation of continuity can be derived with equal ease in either Cartesian or spherical coordinates. The development will consist of three steps:

1. Carrying through the derivation entirely in Cartesian coordinates, obtaining the three-dimensional wave equation.

2. Developing the necessary equation of continuity in spherical coordinates.

3. Combining the equation of continuity developed for spherical coordinates, and the dynamic equation which is valid for either system, to build up the desired equation for spherical waves.

4.1 The Cartesian Form of the Three-dimensional Wave Equation

In the development of the plane wave equation two basic laws were utilized, one an elastic law involving pressure and condensation, the second a dynamic law involving force and acceleration. In the present derivation we shall make use of the equation of continuity, which involves velocities, rather than an elastic law involving displacement. Newton's law will be used in exactly the same manner as previously, except that it will be extended to each of the three components of force and acceleration.

The equation of continuity is quite simple in concept. In words, it states that if there is a net rate of flow of mass into a fixed volume, the rate of change of density is proportional to the rate of change of mass. Or, more precisely, that the net rate of mass flow divided by the volume is equal to the rate of

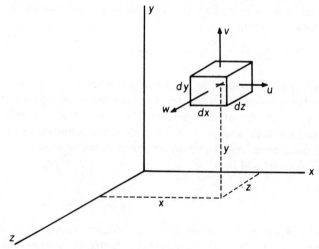

Fig. 4.11. Volume element in a continuous fluid, showing components of flow normal to faces.

change of density within the volume. Like the over-all development, this part is also divided into three sections: (1) the development of the equation of continuity, (2) the derivation of the dynamic equation, (3) the union of the two to produce the wave equation.

Let us consider a small cube with center at the point x, y, z (Fig. 4.11). Let u, v, and w be the components of particle velocity at this point, and ρ' the density. Then the mass flow through the left face of this cube will be

$$\left[\rho'u - \frac{\partial}{\partial x}(\rho'u)\frac{dx}{2} \right] dy\, dz,$$

and the mass flow through the opposite face,

$$\left[\rho'u + \frac{\partial}{\partial x}(\rho'u)\frac{dx}{2} \right] dy\, dz.$$

The net flow *out* of the cube through these two faces will be the difference between these two flows, or

$$\frac{\partial}{\partial x}(\rho'u)\, dx\, dy\, dz = \frac{\partial}{\partial x}(\rho'u)\, dV \tag{4.11}$$

where dV stands for the volume of the cube.

We obtain similar expressions for the y and z directions, so that net efflux of mass will be

$$\left[\frac{\partial}{\partial x}(\rho'u) + \frac{\partial}{\partial y}(\rho'v) + \frac{\partial}{\partial z}(\rho'w) \right] dV \tag{4.12}$$

Since the net rate of mass flow per unit volume is the rate of change of density with time, we have

$$\frac{\partial}{\partial x}(\rho'u) + \frac{\partial}{\partial y}(\rho'v) + \frac{\partial}{\partial z}(\rho'w) = -\frac{\partial \rho'}{\partial t} \tag{4.13}$$

This is the equation of continuity in Cartesian coordinates.

To obtain the dynamic equation for a mass element in a fluid, let p' be the pressure at the center of the element. Then $p' - (\partial p'/\partial x)\, dx/2$ is the pressure on the left face, and $p' + (\partial p'/\partial x)\, dx/2$ the pressure on the right. Since the two faces are of equal area, $dy\, dz$, the X component of the net force acting on this element will be

$$f_x = -\frac{\partial p'}{\partial x} dx\, dy\, dz = -\frac{\partial p}{\partial x} dx\, dy\, dz$$

The mass of this cube is $\rho'\, dx\, dy\, dz$ to a close approximation, because of our assumption of infinitesimal condensation. Similarly, u may with small error be taken as the x component of particle velocity throughout the cube. By Newton's second law,

$$\frac{\partial}{\partial t}(\rho'u)\, dx\, dy\, dz = -\frac{\partial p}{\partial x} dx\, dy\, dz \tag{4.15}$$

Therefore
$$\frac{\partial}{\partial t}(\rho'u) = -\frac{\partial p}{\partial x} \tag{4.16a}$$

Similar equations are obtained for the Y and Z directions:

$$\frac{\partial}{\partial t}(\rho'v) = -\frac{\partial p}{\partial y} \tag{4.16b}$$

$$\frac{\partial}{\partial t}(\rho'w) = -\frac{\partial p}{\partial z} \tag{4.16c}$$

Equations (4.13) and (4.16) are the equation of continuity and the dynamic equation from which we develop the wave equation. The remainder of the derivation consists of routine mathematical steps. First, the three equations of (4.16) are differentiated, respectively, with x, y, and z, and added:

$$-\frac{\partial^2 p}{\partial x^2} = \frac{\partial^2}{\partial t\,\partial x}\rho'u$$

$$-\frac{\partial^2 p}{\partial y^2} = \frac{\partial^2}{\partial t\,\partial y}\rho'v$$

$$-\frac{\partial^2 p}{\partial z^2} = \frac{\partial^2}{\partial t\,\partial z}\rho'w$$

$$-\left(\frac{\partial^2}{\partial x^2} + \frac{\partial^2}{\partial y^2} + \frac{\partial^2}{\partial z^2}\right)p = \frac{\partial}{\partial t}\left[\frac{\partial}{\partial x}(\rho'u) + \frac{\partial}{\partial y}(\rho'v) + \frac{\partial}{\partial z}(\rho'w)\right] \tag{4.17}$$

But considering Eq. (4.13), the right-hand member of Eq. (4.17) is simply $-\partial^2\rho'/\partial t^2$, so that

$$\nabla^2 p = \frac{\partial^2\rho'}{\partial t^2} \tag{4.17a}$$

where $\nabla^2 p$ is a shortened form of

$$\left(\frac{\partial^2}{\partial x^2} + \frac{\partial^2}{\partial y^2} + \frac{\partial^2}{\partial z^2}\right)p$$

It is called the Laplacian of p.

Using fundamental relations between the pressure, density, and condensation, we can readily obtain

$$B\nabla^2 s = \rho\frac{\partial^2 s}{\partial t^2}$$

which gives directly the wave equation for both the condensation and the pressure:

$$\frac{\partial^2 s}{\partial t^2} = \frac{B}{\rho}\nabla^2 s, \qquad \frac{\partial^2 p}{\partial t^2} = \frac{B}{\rho}\nabla^2 p \tag{4.18}$$

If we compare the derivation with that for the plane wave equation of the previous chapter, we note that we obtained three equations almost simultaneously in the previous chapter, those for displacement, condensation, and pressure; while in the present case, only the equations of pressure and condensation have been obtained. It might be thought that a minor addendum to the derivation is all that is needed to obtain the equation for the displacement, but this is not true. As a matter of fact, in the general case, there are three independent equations for the displacement, since the displacement has three components. The displacement equation is a *vector equation*, while the pressure and condensation equations are scalar equations. But *vector* here is being used in a sense entirely different from the sense in which it has been used up to this point. We therefore digress slightly to discuss a difficulty that exists in the subject of acoustics with regard to the term *vector*.

Without attempting the rigorous definitions required of a mathematical treatment, we may state that there exists a formal mathematical discipline called *vector analysis*, in which the *vector* is defined as a directed line segment in space, or, more abstractly, as a number triplet. Geometrically, the number triplet consists of the x, y, and z projections of the vector (assuming, for the moment, a Cartesian system). Time variation may enter into this scheme, in that each of the three *components* of a vector may be variable in time. As long as this time variation is expressed in terms of instantaneous values, it presents no difficulties.

Now, in circuit electricity, and in simple harmonic motion, as was seen in the first chapter, the basic equations involve variation of scalar quantities with a single variable, the time. There is no call whatever for the methods of *vector analysis*, as such. It turns out that with a very particular time variation, namely the sinusoidal, relations between the key quantities can be clarified by the adoption of a complex notation, and because of the superficial relation between the complex number and the two-dimensional vector, such notation has become known *within this special field* as *vector notation*. The term *phasor* is the proper term for the "*time*" *vector*, but this term has never become popular, so we have gone along with usage in effect among the majority of physicists and engineers.

If we adopt the correct term, we can clear up the difficulty nicely. Pressure, density, displacement, and particle velocity are all *phasors* in the sense that they are all in sinusoidal time variation. However, only the displacement and the particle velocity are *vectors*, the pressure and the condensation being *scalars*; that is, only a single number is required to give the pressure or the condensation at a point in a fluid, whereas three numbers are required to determine the displacement and the particle velocity. That is why the pressure and condensation equations, but *not* the displacement equation, were so readily obtained in three dimensions. Now it is possible to obtain a vector equation for the displacement or velocity, but there is an alternative which is preferable. This alternative makes use of the concept of *potential*. The potential to be introduced is very similar to that of the electrostatic potential. (It is interesting that in electromagnetic field theory one also makes use of phasors and vectors simultaneously.) Potential can be defined in many different ways, but for our purpose it will be considered a *scalar* function whose derivatives with respect to space coordinates give vector components corresponding to those coordinates. The potential which we shall use is the *velocity potential* ϕ, defined by the following trio of equations:

Instantaneous	*Phasor*	
$u = -\dfrac{\partial \phi}{\partial x}$	$u = -\dfrac{\partial \phi}{\partial x}$	
$v = -\dfrac{\partial \phi}{\partial y}$	$v = -\dfrac{\partial \phi}{\partial y}$	(4.19)
$z = -\dfrac{\partial \phi}{\partial z}$	$w = -\dfrac{\partial \phi}{\partial z}$	

The relation between the velocity potential and the velocity is thus analogous to that between the electrostatic potential and the electrostatic field intensity.

The velocity potential is of great value in the study of three-dimensional waves, since it enables one to work with a scalar, rather than a vector quantity, and to find vector values indirectly by simple differentiation. Obviously, the next step is to derive the wave equation for the velocity potential, since, having once found the expression for the velocity potential we can find the components of particle velocity. If desired, the displacement components can be derived from the particle velocity components, although this step is usually unnecessary.

Note that the velocity potential can be written as a *phasor*, although geometrically it is a scalar.

4.2 The Wave Equation for the Velocity Potential

Let us rewrite the equation of continuity on the assumption that the rate of change of density from point to point (not with time) is so small as to be negligible. We have

$$\rho\left(\frac{\partial u}{\partial x} + \frac{\partial v}{\partial y} + \frac{\partial w}{\partial z}\right) = -\frac{\partial \rho'}{\partial t} \tag{4.21}$$

Now introducing the velocity potential, from Eq. (4.19),

$$\frac{\partial^2 \phi}{\partial x^2} + \frac{\partial^2 \phi}{\partial y^2} + \frac{\partial^2 \phi}{\partial z^2} = \frac{1}{\rho}\frac{\partial \rho'}{\partial t} \tag{4.22}$$

Within this approximation, we can also show that Eqs. (4.16) may be written

$$\rho\frac{\partial u}{\partial t} = -\frac{\partial p}{\partial x}, \quad \text{etc.} \tag{4.23}$$

Multiplying these equations, respectively, by dx, dy, dz, and adding,

$$\rho \frac{\partial u}{\partial t} \, dx = - \frac{\partial p}{\partial x} \, dx$$

$$\rho \frac{\partial v}{\partial t} \, dy = - \frac{\partial p}{\partial y} \, dy$$

$$\rho \frac{\partial w}{\partial t} \, dz = - \frac{\partial p}{\partial z} \, dz$$

$$\rho \frac{\partial}{\partial t} \left(u \, dx + v \, dy + w \, dz \right) = - \left(\frac{\partial p}{\partial x} \, dx + \frac{\partial p}{\partial y} \, dy + \frac{\partial p}{\partial z} \, dz \right)$$

Now substituting from Eq. (4.19),

$$\rho \frac{\partial}{\partial t} \left(\frac{\partial \phi}{\partial x} \, dx + \frac{\partial \phi}{\partial y} \, dy + \frac{\partial \phi}{\partial z} \, dz \right) = \frac{\partial p}{\partial x} \, dx + \frac{\partial p}{\partial y} \, dy + \frac{\partial p}{\partial z} \, dz \qquad (4.24)$$

It will be noticed that this equation contains two perfect differentials in the space coordinates. *This is the major contribution of the velocity potential.* It is a feature that is lacking in the equations that appeared in our original development of the wave equation.

We may therefore write

$$\rho \frac{\partial}{\partial t} (d\phi) = dp = dp' \qquad (4.25)$$

$$\rho d \left(\frac{\partial \phi}{\partial t} \right) = dp'$$

(order of derivation being of no significance.)

Integrating,

$$\rho \frac{\partial \phi}{\partial t} = p' + C \qquad (4.26)$$

If there is no excess pressure, that is, if there are no acoustic waves, the velocity potential at a point is constant with time. Thus the constant C must equal the negative of the static pressure $-p_0$, and the right-hand member of Eq. (4.26) must be simply the acoustic pressure, that is,

$$\rho \frac{\partial \phi}{\partial t} = p \qquad (4.27)$$

Employing the fundamental relation $p = Bs$, we may obtain from Eq. (4.27),

$$\frac{B}{\rho} s = \frac{\partial \phi}{\partial t} \qquad (4.28)$$

and using the fundamental relation between density and condensation, we may rewrite Eq. (4.22) to obtain

$$\nabla^2 \phi = \frac{1}{\rho} \frac{\partial \rho'}{\partial t} = \frac{\partial s}{\partial t} \qquad (4.28a)$$

Differentiating Eq. (4.28) with respect to time, we obtain

$$\frac{B}{\rho}\frac{\partial s}{\partial t} = \frac{\partial^2 \phi}{\partial t^2} \tag{4.29}$$

Finally, comparing Eq. (4.28a) and Eq. (4.29), we obtain the *wave equation for the velocity potential*:

$$\frac{B}{\rho}\nabla^2\phi = \frac{\partial^2 \phi}{\partial t^2} \tag{4.210}$$

Once the velocity potential has been obtained, all the other dynamic variables can be obtained by routine computation. The particle velocity can be obtained by the defining Eqs. (4.19); the pressure, by the fundamental Eq. (4.27); the condensation is readily obtained from the pressure, and the displacement from the velocity.

Since u, v, and w are the components of the *vector velocity* (here *vector* is used rigorously in its geometric sense)

$$-\frac{\partial \phi}{\partial x}, \qquad -\frac{\partial \phi}{\partial y}, \qquad -\frac{\partial \phi}{\partial z}$$

must also be components of a vector $(-\partial\phi/\partial r)$. This is, of course, the total velocity V_r written as the *gradient of the velocity potential*. For spherical waves, it is easy to see that this expression is the (negative) rate of change of

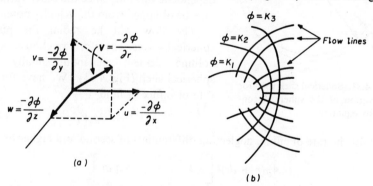

Fig. 4.21. (a) The vector velocity and its components; (b) flow lines and lines of equal velocity potential.

the velocity potential in the direction of lines of flow, which is also the direction of maximum rate of change of ϕ (Fig. 4.21).

We wish to stress at this point the two all-important relations which are true *in general* for spherical waves:

$$p = \rho \frac{\partial \phi}{\partial t} \qquad\qquad \text{(a)} \quad (4.211)$$

$$V = -\frac{\partial \phi}{\partial r} \qquad\qquad \text{(b)} \quad (4.211)$$

In the above equations, the velocity is *both* a *phasor* and a *vector*. However, it is not necessary to emphasize its vector properties for spherical waves, since its direction is always radial. With this tacit understanding, a single number is sufficient to determine the velocity, and effectively, it degenerates into a scalar.

4.3 The Wave Equation for Spherical Waves

In concluding the development of the wave equation for spherical waves we have only to obtain the equation of continuity for this special case, since we have already obtained the dynamic equation in Cartesian coordinates, and have pointed out that under the permissible

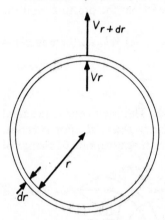

assumptions of classical acoustics, this equation is independent of coordinate systems. From these two equations we obtain the wave equation as a differential equation in a single dependent variable, the radial velocity V_r, with r and t as independent variables. We shall also obtain an equation with the velocity potential as dependent variable, since the other variables may be obtained from the velocity potential.

The flow will be radial for purely spherical waves. Therefore we choose as our volume element an infinitesimally thin spherical shell (Fig. 4.31). We have for the rate of influx of fluid

Fig. 4.31. Spherical shell used for derivation of the spherical continuity equation.

$$4\pi r^2 \rho_1 V_r \tag{4.31}$$

and for the rate of efflux, neglecting differentials of second and higher orders,

$$4\pi(r + dr)^2 \left[\rho' V_r + \frac{\partial}{\partial r} (\rho' V_r) \, dr \right]$$

$$= 4\pi \left[\rho' V_r r^2 + \frac{\partial}{\partial r} (\rho' V_r) r^2 \, dr + 2\rho' V_r r \, dr \right] \tag{4.32}$$

Thus the *net* rate of efflux will be

$$4\pi r^2 \, dr \left[\frac{\partial}{\partial r} (\rho' V_r) + \frac{2}{r} (\rho' V_r) \right] \tag{4.33}$$

If we divide this rate of mass flow by the volume of the shell, we shall have the equation for the rate of change of density:

$$\frac{\partial}{\partial r} (\rho' V_r) + \frac{2}{r} (\rho' V_r) = -\frac{\partial \rho'}{\partial t} \tag{4.34}$$

This is the equation of continuity for spherical waves.

The single dynamic equation needed for the development of the spherical wave equation is Eq. (4.211a). If we differentiate this equation partially with respect to r and use Eq. (4.211b), we obtain

$$\frac{\partial p}{\partial r} = \rho \frac{\partial}{\partial r} \frac{\partial \phi}{\partial t} = \rho \frac{\partial}{\partial t} \frac{\partial \phi}{\partial r} \tag{4.35}$$

Remembering that $\partial \phi / \partial r = V_r$, we can see that this equation resembles Eq. (4.23) so closely that we might think that it could be derived directly. However, if we tried to derive it directly in spherical coordinates, we would encounter unexpected difficulties, because the flow is *diverging*. As a matter of fact, our simple expression for the dynamic equation is not complete unless our quantities are infinitesimal in nature, which fortunately is usually true in acoustics.

We are now ready to unite the equation of continuity and the dynamic equation to obtain the wave equation. First, however, note that if we carry out the derivation of $\rho' V_r$ with respect to r (in Eq. 4.34), we obtain

$$\frac{\partial}{\partial r}(\rho' V_r) = \rho' \frac{\partial V_r}{\partial r} + V_r \frac{\partial \rho'}{\partial r}$$

Now the first of these terms involves the product of the finite instantaneous density by the infinitesimal space derivative of the particle velocity, and so is an infinitesimal of the first order. But the second is a product of the infinitesimal particle velocity and the infinitesimal space derivative of the density and so is an infinitesimal of the second order, and may be neglected. We also note that $\partial \rho' / \partial t$ in Eq. (4.34) may be replaced by $\rho(\partial s / \partial t)$. Rewriting the equation of continuity with these simplifications,

$$\frac{\partial^2 \phi}{\partial r^2} + \frac{2}{r} \frac{\partial \phi}{\partial r} = \frac{\partial s}{\partial t} \tag{4.36}$$

If we differentiate Eq. (4.35) partially with respect to t, we obtain

$$\frac{\partial}{\partial r}\left(\frac{\partial p}{\partial t}\right) = \rho \frac{\partial}{\partial r}\left(\frac{\partial^2 \phi}{\partial t^2}\right)$$

and, except for an unimportant constant, we have

$$\frac{\partial p}{\partial t} = \rho \frac{\partial^2 \phi}{\partial t^2} \tag{4.37}$$

from which we readily obtain

$$\frac{\partial s}{\partial t} = \frac{\rho}{B} \frac{\partial^2 \phi}{\partial t^2} \tag{4.38}$$

Substituting Eq. (4.36) we have

$$\frac{\partial^2 \phi}{\partial r^2} + \frac{2}{r} \frac{\partial \phi}{\partial r} = \frac{\rho}{B} \frac{\partial^2 \phi}{\partial t^2} \tag{4.39}$$

This is the *wave equation for spherical waves*.

Letting $B/\rho = c^2$, this equation may be put in the more convenient form,

$$\frac{\partial^2}{\partial r^2}(r\phi) = \frac{1}{c^2}\frac{\partial^2}{\partial t^2}(r\phi) \tag{4.310}$$

Let us try for the solution of Eq. (4.310):

$$r\phi = f_1(ct - r) + f_2(ct + r) \tag{4.311}$$

Differentiation with respect to r and t gives

$$\frac{\partial^2}{\partial r^2}(r\phi) = f_1'' + f_2''$$

$$\frac{\partial^2}{\partial t^2}r(\phi) = c^2(f_1'' + f_2'')$$

The solution for ϕ is therefore

$$\phi = \frac{1}{r}f_1(ct - r) + \frac{1}{r}f_2(ct + r) \tag{4.312}$$

This solution is analogous to the general solution of the plane-wave equation, in which the first term represents a wave moving in the direction of positive-x, and the second a wave in the direction of negative-x. A similar investigation shows that the first term of Eq. (4.312) represents a diverging wave, and the second term represents a wave converging toward a point. The second has little application in acoustics, and will be neglected. The first is such as would be produced by a small pulsating sphere completely isolated from reflecting surfaces. If the sphere pulsates harmonically, an exponential function can be assumed. As a consequence, in our study of spherical waves, we have as the fundamental form for the velocity potential:

$$\phi = \frac{A}{r}e^{j(\omega t - kr)} \tag{4.313}$$

where $|A|$ is the magnitude of the velocity potential at unit distance from the source. As we know, the initial value is often unimportant, so that it may occasionally be more convenient to use the equation

$$\phi = \frac{A}{r}e^{j(\omega t - kr)} \tag{4.313a}$$

where $A = |A|$.

4.4 Specific Acoustic Impedance for Progressive Spherical Waves

From Eq. (4.313) for the velocity potential, and Eq. (4.211) for the pressure and velocity in terms of the velocity potential, we obtain

$$p = \rho\frac{\partial\phi}{\partial t} = j\omega\rho\phi = j\omega\rho\,\frac{A}{r}e^{j(\omega t - kr)} \tag{4.41}$$

$$V = -\frac{\partial\phi}{\partial r} = -\left(-jk - \frac{1}{r}\right)\phi = jk\left(1 - \frac{j}{kr}\right)\phi \tag{4.42}$$

and therefore the specific acoustic impedance becomes

$$z = \frac{p}{V} = \frac{j\omega\rho}{jk(1 - j/kr)} = \rho c \left[\frac{1 + j/kr}{1 + (1/kr)^2} \right]$$

$$= \rho c \left(\frac{k^2 r^2}{k^2 r^2 + 1} + j \frac{kr}{k^2 r^2 + 1} \right) \qquad (4.43)$$

$$= \frac{\rho c k r}{\sqrt{k^2 r^2 + 1}} \bigg/ \tan^{-1} \frac{1}{kr} \qquad (4.44)$$

Thus we find that the specific acoustic impedance for spherical waves is equal to the characteristic impedance of the medium, multiplied by a factor which has both magnitude and phase.

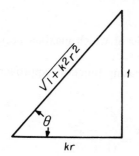

Fig. 4.41. Angle of z for spherical waves:

$\tan \theta = 1/kr$

$\cos \theta = kr/(1 + k^2 r^2)^{1/2}$

From the value of the tangent of the impedance angle (Fig. 4.41) we can find $\cos \theta$, which has many uses in the articles to come.

$$\tan \theta = \frac{1}{kr}, \quad \sec^2 \theta = 1 + \frac{1}{k^2 r^2} = \frac{k^2 r^2 + 1}{k^2 r^2}$$

$$\cos \theta = \frac{kr}{\sqrt{1 + k^2 r^2}} \qquad (4.45)$$

From (4.44) above, we note that

$$|z| = \rho c \cos \theta \qquad (4.46)$$

To get some idea of the meaning of the specific acoustic impedance, let $kr = 1$. This means that $\omega r/c = 2\pi r/\lambda = 1$, or that $r = \lambda/2\pi$.

Now the wavelength of a 180-cycle tone is approximately 2π ft. Thus for this frequency, at a distance of 1 ft from the center of a spherical disturbance ($kr = 1$), the ratio between pressure and particle velocity will have the value

$$z = (\tfrac{1}{2} + \tfrac{1}{2}j)\rho c$$

This is obtained from Eq. (4.43) by substitution $kr = 1$.

Thus if we have a sphere with a 1-ft radius pulsating at this frequency, each point on its surface will experience a ratio of pressure to velocity, such that its resistive and reactive components, r_s and x_s, are each equal to one-half of the characteristic impedance of the medium. For example, for a radial velocity of 1 cm/sec in air, the pressure is $21\sqrt{2}$ dynes/cm² and leads the velocity by $\frac{1}{8}$ cycle. It is also pertinent to note the limits of the resistive and reactive components of z.

$$\lim_{r\to 0} r_s = \lim_{r\to 0} \frac{k^2 r^2 \rho c}{1 + k^2 r^2} = 0 \qquad \text{(for small } r,\ x_s \approx k^2 r^2 \rho c)$$

$$\lim_{r\to\infty} r_s = \rho c$$

$$\lim_{r\to 0} x_s = \lim_{r\to 0} \frac{k r \rho c}{1 + k^2 r^2} = 0 \qquad \text{(for small } r,\ r_s \approx k r \rho c)$$

$$\lim_{r\to\infty} x_s = 0$$

We shall also compute the value of kr at which maxima occur. It will simplify the writing of equations to let $kr = x$.

Obviously r_s is a monotonically increasing function, approaching unity as x approaches infinity.

However, x_s has a definite maximum.

$$\frac{dx_s}{dx} = \frac{1 + x^2 - 2x}{(1 + x^2)^2} = \frac{1 - x^2}{(1 + x^2)^2}$$

If we equate dx_s/dx to zero, $x = 1$; i.e. $r = 1/k$. At this value of r, $x_s/\rho c = \frac{1}{2}$. The specific acoustic resistance and reactance of the spherical wave are plotted in Fig. 4.42.

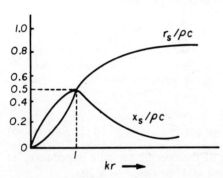

Fig. 4.42. Specific acoustic impedance of spherical wave.

Curves similar to these are obtained for the radiation impedance of a piston in Art. 4.11, but the derivation is much more difficult. The curves of Fig. 4.42 have been plotted so that the student will feel a certain familiarity with the curves derived for piston radiation. We note that a small sphere radiates sound poorly, since it has a small radiation resistance and a large phase angle.

4.5 Intensity of a Spherical Wave

For the intensity of the spherical waves we follow the method of Art. 3.5 for the plane wave, in which the intensity is defined as the average of the product of pressure and velocity over a cycle. That is,

$$I = \frac{1}{T} \int_0^T (P_0 \sin \omega t) \, V_0 \sin (\omega t - \theta) \tag{4.51}$$

$$= \frac{P_0 V_0}{2T} \int_0^T [\cos \theta - \cos (2\omega t - \theta)] dt = \frac{P_0 V_0}{2} \cos \theta \tag{4.52}$$

$$= PV \cos \theta$$

Since the magnitude of z, which is the ratio P/V, is given by $\rho c \cos \theta$ (Eq. 4.46), we can write for the intensity,

$$I = PV \cos \theta = PV \frac{P}{V\rho c} = \frac{P^2}{\rho c} = \rho c V^2 \cos \theta \tag{4.53}$$

or in terms of pressure and velocity amplitudes,

$$I = \frac{P_0^2}{2\rho c} = \frac{\rho c V_0^2 \cos^2 \theta}{2} \tag{4.54}$$

From the expression for intensity, we can readily find the power output of a source of spherical waves, since the intensity field is spherically symmetric about the source.

$$P_{Av} = \frac{4\pi r^2 P^2}{\rho c} = 2\pi r^2 \frac{P_0^2}{\rho c} = 2\pi k \omega \rho A^2 \tag{4.55}$$

where A in this equation is the velocity potential at unit distance from the source center. We should prefer to have the power output given in terms of quantities characteristic of the source itself. For this purpose we define the *source strength* in the next article.

4.6 Source Strength—Radiation from a Pulsating Sphere

So far, we have been concerned only with the "field theory" of spherical waves. Our equations have contained relations between field quantities (e.g. pressure and intensity), and have told us the type of variation to expect in these quantities with variation of distance from the source, but they have told nothing of the relation between the field quantities and the properties of the source itself. As the most convenient type of source we shall assume a pulsating sphere, and define the *strength of source Q* to be the product of the surface area of the source and the velocity amplitude of its surface U_0. That is,

$$Q = SU_0 = 4\pi a^2 U_0 \tag{4.61}$$

where a is the radius of the pulsating sphere.

Probably the most characteristic field quantity is intensity. Hence our key problem is: given a source of a certain strength, to find the intensity at a given distance from the source center. Such a problem is a *radiation* problem, and radiation from a pulsating sphere is the primary radiation problem in acoustics. To relate field quantities to the source, we must find one quantity that is common to both the source and the medium. This quantity is the particle velocity at the surface of the source. Thus if we express the intensity in terms of particle velocity, we have, in effect, the intensity in terms of strength of source. We shall follow through this line of reasoning in a quantitative manner in the following steps. It will be remembered that we made a similar assumption of continuity of velocity when we discussed the radiation of sound by a piston in a pipe.

We repeat Eq. (4.53b) for the intensity in terms of the particle velocity in the medium, since this expression is the foundation of the development, writing I_a as the intensity at the surface of the source.

$$I_a = \frac{V_a^2 \cos^2 \theta \rho c}{2} \tag{4.62}$$

where V_a is the velocity amplitude at the surface.

But by our assumption of continuity of velocity at the boundary, $V_a = U_0$ and we can now modify Eq. (4.62) to make it a function of source strength.

$$I_a = \frac{\rho c Q^2}{32\pi^2 a^4} \cos^2 \theta \tag{4.63}$$

We can now substitute for the cosine factor the expression

$$\frac{k^2 a^2}{1 + k^2 a^2}$$

which gives, finally,

$$I_a = \frac{\rho c Q^2 k^2}{32\pi^2 a^2 (1 + k^2 a^2)} \tag{4.64}$$

We can now write the important expression for the *power output* of the source in terms of strength of source.

$$P_{Av} = 4\pi a^2 I_a = \frac{\rho c Q^2 k^2 a^2}{8\pi a^2 (1 + k^2 a^2)} \tag{4.65}$$

We should also note that the specific acoustic resistance r_a at the surface is $\rho c k^2 a^2 / (1 + k^2 a^2)$ so that the power output may also be written

$$P_{Av} = \frac{U_0^2 S r_a}{2} \tag{4.66}$$

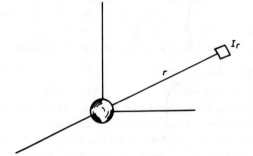

Fig. 4.61. Spherical source: $a \equiv$ radius of pulsating sphere; $Q = 4\pi a^2 U_0$.

This is a relation which is very generally true for the power output of a source. Finally, we obtain the intensity at any distance r in terms of the source strength (Fig. 4.61).

$$I_r = \frac{a^2}{r^2} I_a = \frac{\rho c k^2 Q^2}{32\pi^2 r^2 (1 + k^2 a^2)} \tag{4.67}$$

The equations which we have derived so far, when applied to a spherical source, do *not* demand that the source be small. They *do* simplify, however, if the source is assumed to be small compared with the wavelength, since the ka term then becomes small compared with unity, and can therefore be neglected in the bracket in the denominator. We then get the simpler expressions:

$$I = \frac{\rho c k^2 Q^2}{32\pi^2 r^2}, \qquad P_{Av} = \frac{\rho c k^2}{8\pi} Q^2 \tag{4.68}$$

Further, it is found by experiment that *any* source which is small compared with the wavelength of the sound emitted produces a wave which is approximately spherical and that the intensity of such a wave obeys Eq. (4.68). A source which gives the intensity expression (4.68) is called a *simple source*. We must note that the pulsating sphere, though it emits a purely spherical wave, is not strictly a simple source, because the term $k^2 a^2$ is not necessarily $\ll 1$. As we shall see when we compute the radiation field of a piston, any extended acoustic radiator can be analyzed as an assembly of simple sources, each obeying Eq. (4.68). The total radiation field then consists of the superposition of the radiation from all these sources.

In closing this article we rewrite the important equation for the velocity potential in terms of the source strength, for the case of a simple source—that is, where the factor $1 + k^2 a^2$ may be taken equal to unity. We rewrite Eq. (4.313a):

$$\phi = \frac{A}{r} e^{j(\omega t - kr)}$$

From Eq. (4.42), we can write, since $ka \ll 1$,

$$V_a e^{j\omega t} = U_0 e^{j\omega t} = \left(jk + \frac{1}{a} \right) \phi_a \approx \frac{\phi_a}{a} \approx \frac{A}{a^2} e^{j(\omega t - kr)}$$

and from Eq. (4.61),

$$U_0 = \frac{Q}{4\pi a^2}$$

so that

$$\frac{Q}{4\pi a^2} = \frac{A}{a^2} \quad \text{and therefore} \quad A = \frac{Q}{4\pi}$$

and finally,

$$\phi = \frac{Q}{4\pi r} e^{j(\omega t - kr)} \tag{4.69}$$

We shall use this expression in studying the radiation from a piston.

4.7 The Acoustic Doublet

The acoustic doublet consists of equal simple sources of opposite sign separated by a small distance l. By opposite sign we mean that there is a phase difference of $180°$ in the velocities.

We consider the positive source to be at the origin of a system of polar coordinates and the negative source a distance *l* to the right (Fig. 4.71); we compute the velocity potential, the acoustic pressure, and the intensity at the point $P(r, \theta)$, where the radius vector *r* is taken to be large compared with *l*.

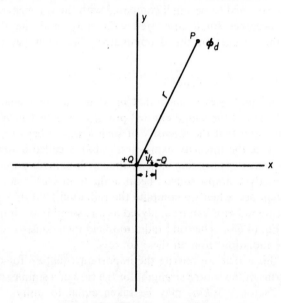

Fig. 4.71. The acoustic doublet.

The total potential at *P* will be a superposition of the potentials of the positive and negative sources.

For the source at the origin, we have as the potential at point *P*,

$$\phi_+ = \frac{Q}{4\pi r} e^{j(\omega t - kr)} \tag{4.71}$$

Now we suppose the source to move an infinitesimal distance *l* in the positive-*x* direction, and compute the differential of the potential at point *P* due to this motion. We have*

$$d\phi = -\frac{\partial \phi}{\partial x} l$$

Since the source at the distance *l* from the origin is of opposite sign to that at the origin, this differential is actually the net potential at point *P* due to the doublet. We call this difference ϕ_d, the potential of the doublet.

$$\phi_d = \frac{\partial \phi}{\partial x} l = \frac{\partial \phi}{\partial r} \frac{\partial r}{\partial x} l \tag{4.73}$$

---

* Motion of the charge to the right is the equivalent of motion of point *P* an equal distance to the left; hence the negative sign in the right-hand number of the equation.

Evaluating the partial derivatives,

$$\frac{\partial \phi}{\partial r} = \frac{Q}{4\pi}\left(-\frac{1}{r^2} - j\frac{k}{r}\right)e^{j(\omega t - kr)}$$

$$\frac{\partial r}{\partial x} = \frac{\partial}{\partial x}\left(x^2 + y^2\right)^{1/2} = \frac{1}{2}\left(x^2 + y^2\right)^{-1/2}2x = \frac{x}{r} = \cos\psi$$

which enables us to write ϕ_a in terms of r and ψ.

$$\phi_a = -\frac{Ql\cos\psi}{4\pi r}\left(\frac{1}{r} + jk\right)e^{(j\omega t - kr)} \tag{4.74}$$

We could find the velocity and pressure directly from Eq. (4.74) by taking derivatives with respect to r and t. The forms, however, become so involved that it is more useful to make approximations by taking the two extreme cases in which $r \gg \lambda$ and $r \ll \lambda$. When $r \gg \lambda$, then $k \gg 1/r$, so that we may neglect the first term in the brackets and write

$$\phi_a = \frac{-jQlk\cos\psi}{4\pi r}e^{j(\omega t - kr)} \qquad (r \gg \lambda) \quad (4.75)$$

We obtain the pressure from the velocity potential in the conventional manner. However, when we solve for the velocity we must take into account the fact that the velocity potential is a function of ψ as well as r, and consequently that there are two velocity components, one in the radial direction and one in the transverse direction. The differential distance in the transverse direction will be $rd\psi$, and therefore the velocity in this direction will be

$$u_\psi = -\frac{d\phi}{r\,d\psi} = -\frac{1}{r}\left(\frac{\partial\phi}{\partial\psi}\right) = \frac{jQkl\sin\psi}{4\pi r^2}e^{j(\omega t - kr)} \tag{4.76a}$$

while the velocity in the r direction is simply the partial with respect to r, as for a simple source:

$$u_r = -\frac{\partial\phi}{\partial r} = -\frac{jklQ\cos\psi}{4\pi r}\left(-\frac{1}{r} - jk\right)e^{j(\omega t - kr)}$$

$$\approx \frac{k^2lQ\cos\psi}{4\pi r}e^{j(\omega t - kr)} \tag{4.76b}$$

and for the pressure,

$$p = \rho\frac{\partial\phi}{\partial t} = \frac{\rho lQ\,k^2 c\cos\psi}{4\pi r}e^{j(\omega t - kr)}$$

and since $\omega = ck$,

$$p = \rho c\frac{\omega^2 lQ\cos\psi}{4\pi rc^2}e^{j(\omega t - kr)} \qquad (r \gg \lambda) \quad (4.77)$$

If we take the other extreme, where the wavelength is long compared with the distance r, we can omit jk in the bracket as being small compared with $1/r$, and we have for the potential,

$$\phi_a = -\frac{Ql\cos\psi}{4\pi r^2}e^{j(\omega t - kr)} \qquad (\lambda \gg r) \quad (4.78)$$

and for the velocity components and the pressure,

$$u_\psi = -\frac{1}{r}\frac{\partial \phi}{\partial \psi} = \frac{Ql \sin \psi}{4\pi r^3} e^{j(\omega t - kr)} \tag{4.79a}$$

$$u_r = \frac{Ql \cos \psi}{4\pi r^2}\left(-\frac{2}{r} - jk\right)e^{j(\omega t - kr)}$$

$$\approx \frac{Ql \cos \psi}{2\pi r^3} e^{j(\omega t - kr)} \tag{4.79b}$$

$$p = \frac{j\omega l Q \cos \psi}{4\pi r^2} e^{j(\omega t - kr)} \tag{4.710}$$

Doublet theory may be used, with qualifications, in cases where the distance l is not infinitesimal. We shall limit our considerations of finite l to the condition in which P is *distant* (i.e. $r \gg l$) and at the same time $\lambda \gg r$. Eq. (4.710) shows that the pressure obeys the inverse square law and the intensity obeys the inverse fourth-power law. Further, for any fixed distance, the pressure is frequency-sensitive, a halving of frequency causing a halving of pressure. This is usually stated in decibel terminology as a fall-off of 6 db per octave. Further investigation, which is beyond the scope of our treatment, shows that there is a rather sharp transition from singlet to doublet action at the frequency at which $\lambda = l$. Practically, this means that two sources with a finite distance between them and a phase difference of 180° will have very poor radiating properties at low frequencies. We shall see that this is an important consideration in loudspeaker design.

In general, doublets occur more naturally than singlet sources. Practically, it is easier to produce oscillation than pulsation. A tuning fork is an example of doublet operation, and it is known from experience that the acoustic output of a tuning fork is low. But often it is possible to prevent the radiation from one of the elements of the doublet from arriving at the listening point, thus effectively converting the doublet into a singlet. For example, if an infinite rigid plane were interposed between the two doublet elements in Fig. 4.71, the combination would no longer function as a doublet. Such an infinite rigid plane is called an *infinite baffle*. For further progress in this chapter it is necessary that we investigate the sound field that would be produced by a *pulsating hemisphere in an infinite baffle*.

The practical importance of doublet theory lies in its connection with the radiation of sound at low frequencies by piston radiators such as the loudspeaker.

4.8 The Hemisphere in an Infinite Baffle

If a pulsating hemisphere is enclosed in an infinite baffle, the sound field on the convex side of the hemisphere is *exactly similar* to that of a pulsating sphere of the same radius at the same location (Fig. 4.81). Were it not for the definition of strength of source, the difference between the two cases would be so trivial as to be hardly worthy of mention. However, if we consider only the convex surface as the active source, the source strength of the hemisphere is only one-half that of a pulsating sphere of equal velocity amplitude. Hence

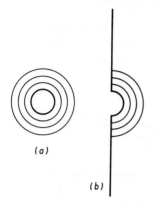

(a)

(b)

Fig. 4.81. (a) Radiation from a pulsating sphere; (b) radiation from a pulsating hemisphere in an infinite baffle.

the equations of velocity potential, pressure, and intensity,* in terms of the source strength, for the hemisphere set in an infinite baffle will be

$$\phi = \frac{Q}{2\pi r} e^{j(\omega t - kr)}$$

$$p = \frac{j\rho ck Q}{2\pi r} e^{j(\omega t - kr)} \tag{4.81}$$

$$I = \frac{\rho ck^2 Q^2}{8\pi^2 r^2}$$

Purely radial motion of a vibrating surface is seldom encountered in practice. A better approximation to actual practice is that of piston motion; that is, motion in which the source surface vibrates as a rigid plane, with velocity perpendicular to the plane. For wavelengths much greater than the perimeter of the piston, the source strength is given by the product of the surface area and the velocity amplitude, exactly as for the hemisphere set in an infinite baffle, and the same formulas for velocity potential, pressure, and intensity apply. This is not true when the perimeter of the piston becomes comparable with the wavelength, but we make use of Eqs. (4.81) nonetheless by considering the finite piston as a two-dimensional array of elementary sources, to which these equations apply. The radiation of sound by a finite piston in a rigid, infinite baffle is one of the fundamental problems of acoustics, and it will be treated in detail in the succeeding article. We limit the treatment

---

* The *average* intensity at any distance from the source is given as before in terms of the source strength, since average intensity is defined as the integrated power divided by the area of a *sphere* of equal radius.

to the computation of the radiation field at distances from the center of the piston which are large compared with the radius of the piston, and we assume the piston to be of circular shape.

4.9 Radiation from a Finite Piston in an Infinite Baffle

If we assume the boundary of a finite piston to be enclosed in an infinite baffle so that only radiation from the front surface will appear in the medium, we may consider the radiation at any point to be the superposition of spherical waves from the elementary areas of the finite piston, as long as these surface

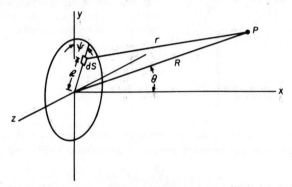

Fig. 4.91. Radiating piston. The piston is in the y-z plane; the point P in the x-y coordinate plane.

elements are small enough to act as simple sources. We then use the expression for the velocity potential at point P caused by the motion of elementary area dS (Fig. 4.91), considering this element a simple source in an infinite baffle.

$$d\phi = \frac{U_0\, dS}{2\pi r} e^{j(\omega t - kr)} \tag{4.91}$$

In this expression, r is the distance from any element to the point P.

The problem is, to find the integrated velocity potential at the point $P(r, \theta)$, where θ is the angle that the radius vector of P makes with the axis of the piston. We take P to be in the x-y plane. Then $r^2 = R^2 + \mathcal{R}^2 - 2R\mathcal{R} \cos \delta$, where R is the distance from the center of the piston to point P, $\mathcal{R}$ is the distance from the center of the piston to dS, and δ is the angle between R and $\mathcal{R}$. The angle δ can be expressed in terms of θ and ψ by a formula from solid analytic geometry giving the cosine of the angle between two lines in space in terms of the directional cosines of the lines.

$$\cos \delta = l_1 l_2 + m_1 m_2 + n_1 n_2$$

where
$$l_1 = \cos \theta, \qquad l_2 = 0$$
$$m_1 = \sin \theta, \qquad m_2 = \cos \psi$$
$$n_1 = 0, \qquad n_2 = \sin \psi$$

We see that $\qquad\qquad\qquad\qquad \cos\delta = \cos\psi\,\sin\theta$

and therefore

$$r = R\left(1 + \frac{\mathcal{R}^2}{R^2} - 2\,\frac{\mathcal{R}}{R}\cos\psi\,\sin\theta\right)^{1/2}$$

Since our investigation is limited to cases in which $R \gg \mathcal{R}$, $\mathcal{R}^2/R^2$ may be neglected as an infinitesimal of the second order as compared with the first-order infinitesimals, which are significant. The parenthetical factor is then of the form $(1 - \epsilon)^{1/2}$ where ϵ is an infinitesimal of the first order. By binomial expansion, the expression in parentheses is $1 - \epsilon/2$ through infinitesimals of the first order. Thus we have for r:

$$r \approx R - \mathcal{R}\cos\psi\,\sin\theta \qquad\qquad (4.92)$$

Now, though $\mathcal{R}\cos\psi\,\sin\theta$ is quite small compared with R, the smaller term cannot be neglected in the *phase factor* of Eq. (4.91). A numerical illustration may make this clear. Assume that kR has the value 2000π, and that $k\mathcal{R}\cos\psi\,\sin\theta$ has the value $\pi/2$. It is immediately clear that the second term has as great a significance as the first in the phase factor, and of course the conclusion springs from the fact that the phase factor is *cyclic*. As a result, no matter how great R becomes, the influence of the term $\mathcal{R}\cos\psi\,\sin\theta$ on the phase factor is the same.

However, the relative error caused by omitting the second term in the amplitude factor of Eq. (4.91) is simply the ratio of $\mathcal{R}\cos\psi\,\sin\theta$ to R, and since we have already stated that $R \gg \mathcal{R}$, we may replace r by R without affecting the results to any great degree. Therefore we have as a working formula for the differential velocity potential,

$$d\phi = \frac{U_0\,dS}{2\pi R}e^{j(\omega t - kR + k\mathcal{R}\cos\psi\,\sin\theta)} \qquad\qquad (4.93)$$

To find the velocity potential due to the entire piston, we integrate over the surface of the piston, with $\mathcal{R}$ and ψ as variables of integration, obtaining

$$\phi = \frac{U_0}{2\pi R}e^{j(\omega t - kR)}\int_0^a \mathcal{R}\,d\mathcal{R}\int_0^{2\pi}e^{jk\mathcal{R}\cos\psi\,\sin\theta}\,d\psi \qquad\qquad (4.94)$$

The variable of integration in the second integral is ψ. The integral is of the type

$$\int_0^{2\pi}e^{jx\cos\psi}\,d\psi$$

If this were an indefinite integral, it could not be evaluated, since there exists no explicit function which has $e^{jx\cos\psi}$ as its derivative. It could, of course, be expanded as a series, and integrated term by term, but this does not lead to any convenient solution of the problem. Since it is a definite integral, however, we can always find its value, if necessary by numerical methods. We can plot the curves $e^{jx\cos\psi}$ for each of many values of x, as the abscissa varies from 0 to 2π. Since each area represents a value of the integral, and each corresponds to a definite value of x, the value of the integral is a definite function of x.

This integral is a special case of the more general definite integral

$$\frac{(-j)^m}{2\pi}\int_0^{2\pi} e^{jx\cos\psi}\cos m\psi\,d\psi \qquad (m\text{ integral}) \quad (4.95)$$

which is a function of both x and m. It is called a *Bessel function* of the mth order $J_m(x)$. The values of these integrals have been computed for all important values of x and m, and are contained in tables. There are also relations between the Bessel function which facilitate the evaluation of integrals con-

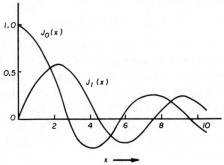

Fig. 4.92. Zero-order and first-order Bessel functions, $J_0(x)$ and $J_1(x)$.

taining them. One of these relations which is important for our present purpose is the following:

$$\int x\,J_0(x)dx = x J_1(x) \tag{4.96}$$

A plot of $J_0(x)$ and $J_1(x)$ as functions of x is shown in Fig. 4.92. The first few terms of the series expansion of $J_0(x)$ and $J_1(x)$ are

$$J_0(x) = 1 - \frac{x^2}{2^2} + \frac{x^4}{2^2\cdot 4^2} - \frac{x^6}{2^2\cdot 4^2\cdot 6^2} + \cdots$$

$$J_1(x) = \frac{1}{2}\left(x - \frac{x^3}{2\cdot 4} + \frac{x^5}{2\cdot 4\cdot 4\cdot 6} + \cdots\right)$$

A table of these and related functions is contained in Appendix 1, and a more thorough treatment of Bessel functions is contained in Appendix 2. However, the brief sketch we have given is sufficient to evaluate the integral of Eq. (4.94). By our definition of the Bessel functions,

$$\phi = \frac{U_0}{R}e^{j(\omega t - kR)}\int_0^a \mathcal{R}\,J_0(k\,\mathcal{R}\,\sin\theta)\,d\mathcal{R}$$

$$= \frac{U_0}{R}e^{j(\omega t - kR)}\frac{1}{k^2\sin^2\theta}\int_0^a k\,\mathcal{R}\,\sin\theta\,J_0(k\,\mathcal{R}\,\sin\theta)\,k\sin\theta\,d\mathcal{R}$$

We evaluate the integral by Eq. (4.96) to obtain

$$\phi = \frac{U_0 e^{j(\omega t - kR)}}{k^2 R \sin^2 \theta} \, ka \sin \theta \, J_1(ka \sin \theta)$$

(Equation 4.95 shows that $J_m(0) = 0$ for any m save $m = 0$.)
We can simplify the last expression to

$$\phi = \frac{Q e^{j(\omega t - kR)}}{2\pi R} \left[\frac{2J_1(ka \sin \theta)}{ka \sin \theta} \right] \qquad (4.97)$$

We note that this form is similar to that obtained for the pulsating sphere, except for the factor in the brackets, which is called the *directivity factor* of the piston. This factor is considered as a function of θ, with k and a as parameters. (For any problem we shall know the wavelength and the size of the piston, and the velocity potential will vary only with θ and R.) For simplicity of notation we make the substitution:

$$x = ka \sin \theta$$

and plot the directivity function $2J_1(x)/x$ as a function of x (Fig. 4.93).

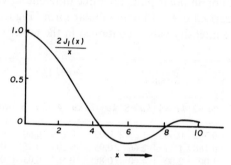

Fig. 4.93. Piston directivity function $2J_1(x)/x$.

The pressure equation is found from the equation of the velocity potential by differentiation, and the intensity is found from the pressure by use of the fundamental equation $I = P_0^2/2\rho c$. They are shown in Eq. (4.98) and (4.99).

$$p = \frac{\rho c k Q e^{j\omega t}}{2\pi R} \left[\frac{2J_1(ka \sin \theta)}{ka \sin \theta} \right] \qquad (Q = \pi a^2 U_0) \quad (4.98)$$

$$I = \frac{\rho c k^2 S^2 U_0^2}{8\pi^2 R^2} \left[\frac{2J_1(ka \sin \theta)}{ka \sin \theta} \right]^2 \qquad (S = \pi a^2) \quad (4.99)$$

The plot of the directivity function is used to find the relative values of the pressure and intensity at points equidistant from the piston, but at different angles with respect to the piston axis. We must remember that both the radius of the piston and the wavelength of the emitted sound must be known to use the directivity function.

Illustrative Example: Given a piston of radius 10 cm radiating sound at a wavelength of 15.7 cm, find the pressure at a point whose radius vector makes an angle of 30° with respect to the piston axis, compared with the pressure on the piston axis at a point equidistant from the piston.

Solution:

$$k = \frac{2\pi}{\lambda} = \frac{6.28}{15.7} = 0.40; \quad ka = 4$$

$$x = ka \sin \theta = 2.0$$

$$\frac{P_{30°}}{P_{0°}} = \frac{2J_1(x)}{x} = 0.60 \quad Ans. \text{ (from Fig. 4.93 or from tables)}$$

In decibels, $P_{30°}/P_{0°} = -4.44$ db

4.10 Directivity Patterns and Directivity Index

It is conventional to show the directivity of a radiator by means of a polar plot, which may be derived from the directivity function of Fig. 4.93. As an example, we shall obtain polar plots for three different ka values. The computations can be carried out readily in tabular form. Figure 4.101 is a polar plot of the relative intensity values contained in the table.

θ	$\sin \theta$	$x = ka \sin \theta$			$\dfrac{2J_1(x)}{x}$			$\left[\dfrac{2J_1(x)}{x}\right]^2$		
		$ka{=}2$	$ka{=}4$	$ka{=}8$	$ka{=}2$	$ka{=}4$	$ka{=}8$	$ka{=}2$	$ka{=}4$	$ka{=}8$
10°	0.166	0.332	0.666	1.33	0.99	0.95	0.80	0.98	0.89	0.64
20°	0.332	0.166	1.33	2.66	0.95	0.80	0.35	0.90	0.64	0.13
30°	0.500	1.00	2.00	4.00	0.88	0.58	0.03	0.77	0.33	0.001
45°	0.707	1.41	2.82	5.64	0.77	0.29	−0.12	0.59	0.08	0.015
60°	0.866	1.73	3.46	6.92	0.67	0.10	−0.001	0.44	0.007	0.000
90°	1.000	2.00	4.00	8.00	0.58	−0.03	−0.09	0.33	0.001	0.008

A study of the directivity function values in Appendix 1 will show that the strength of radiation may become zero at certain angles, beyond which the radiation will again approach a maximum, though second, third, and higher order maxima are always much weaker than the maximum at zero degrees. These secondary maxima (side lobes) show up better on a decibel plot, but the linear plot of Fig. 4.101 gives a better idea of the directivity as a whole. It must be admitted, however, that the decibel plot is more conventional for plotting directivity in practical application.

The directivity function and the polar plot contain in detail the pressure and intensity distribution of the piston source. (The polar plot is actually a three-dimensional representation of directivity. A three-dimensional figure may be obtained by rotating the curves of Fig. 4.101 about the piston axis.) However, one often desires a more concise characterization of the directivity.

A simple method is to specify the angle at which the *intensity* is down to one-half its axial value (down 3 db) in analogy to the half-power points which define the band width of the electric and mechanical oscillators. The 3 db specification is not the only one employed to specify beam width, 6 db and

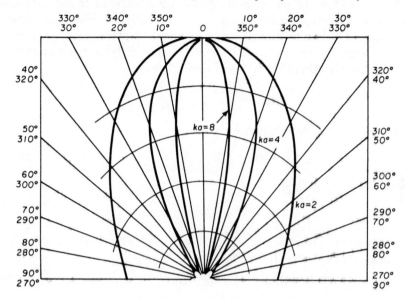

Fig. 4.101. Polar plot of directivity for three *ka* values. (Note presence of "side lobes" when *ka* = 8. These lobes are exaggerated in the drawing.)

10 db drops being also in use (although 6 db and 10 db drops will not occur unless the wavelength is fairly short compared with the radius of the piston. For example, a 10-cm piston radiating into air will be down less than 6 db at 1,000 cycles at an angle of 90° with respect to the axis.)

A second method is similar to that used to specify "antenna gain" in the theory of electromagnetic radiation. We define the *directivity ratio D* as the ratio of the intensity at any point on the axis of the piston to the intensity that would be produced at the same point by a simple source of strength equal to that of the radiating piston. This is equivalent to the definition

$$D = \frac{I_0}{I_{Av}} \tag{4.101}$$

where I_{Av} is the total power output divided by the surface area of a sphere of radius equal to the radius vector of the point of measurement. One finds the total power by integrating over infinitesimal *zones*, since the distribution is symmetrical about the piston axis. Since we have

$$I_\theta = I_0 \frac{4J_1^2(ka \sin \theta)}{(ka \sin \theta)^2} \tag{4.102}$$

and $$dS = 2\pi R^2 \sin\theta\, d\theta,$$

$$I_{Av} = \frac{8\pi R^2 I_0}{4\pi R^2} \int_0^{\pi/2} \frac{J_1^2\,(ka\sin\theta)}{(ka\sin\theta)^2}\sin\theta\, d\theta \qquad (4.103)$$

Again we have an integral containing a Bessel function. In much the same way that we introduced the Bessel function initially, we simply state that if necessary, this definite integral can be evaluated by plotting the area under a curve. Actually, the expression integrates simply, giving a Bessel function of the same order. Omitting details of integration,

$$I_{Av} = \frac{I_0}{k^2 a^2}\left[1 - \frac{2J_1(2ka)}{2ka}\right] \qquad (4.104)$$

Thus we have for the directivity ratio,

$$D = \frac{k^2 a^2}{1 - 2J_1(2ka)/2ka} \qquad (4.105)$$

When ka becomes large,

$$D \approx k^2 a^2 = \frac{4\pi^2 a^2}{\lambda^2} \qquad (4.105a)$$

since $J_1(x)/(x) \to 0$ as $x \to \infty$. The *directivity index d* is a decibel expression of the directivity ratio. It is defined as

$$d = 10\log_{10} D \qquad (4.106)$$

4.11 Radiation Impedance of a Piston

A vibrating piston whose surface is in contact with an elastic medium sets up pressure at all points of the medium, including those points at the bounding surface of the piston. The pressure is not constant over the piston surface, however (as it is in the case of the pulsating sphere), so that we must integrate over the surface of the piston to get the total reactive force. This total reactive force divided by the velocity of the piston is called the *radiation impedance of the piston*. Two separate integration processes are involved: the first is entirely similar to the derivation of the pressure at a point in the medium by integration of the velocity potentials of the simple sources that make up the piston; the second is the integration of the forces on each element of area to find the total force. In the first, we build up an expression for the force at the general point (r, θ) of the piston; in the second, we sum up over the piston face with r and θ as variables (Fig. 4.111).

We shall be dealing with pairs of elements, one of which we shall call the elementary source, and the other, the elementary receiver. Now every pair of elements occurs twice in the generation of the reactive force, once as the source, and once as the receiver. Our problem is to add up the elementary forces produced by these pairs. One way is to consider the receiving elements arranged in *rings*, and to sum the effects of all the source elements within a certain ring on the elements of that ring. As we allow the elementary rings to expand from a radius of zero to a radius of a (the radius of the piston) we shall have taken into account the action of each element as source on each element as receiver (though we shall not have considered the converse, in

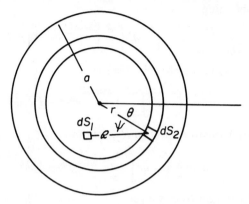

Fig. 4.111. Integration of the force on a vibrating string. $dS_1 = \mathcal{R}\,d\mathcal{R}\,d\psi$ and $dS_2 = r\,dr\,d\theta$.

which the source elements and receiving elements are transposed). However, this transposition simply doubles the value of the integral.

Taking $\mathcal{R}$ as the distance between any two elements, we find the pressure on a receiving element dS_2 caused by a source element dS_1 by the fundamental expression for pressure,

$$dp_2 = j\frac{\rho ck}{2\pi\mathcal{R}}\,U_0\,dS_1 e^{j(\omega t - k\mathcal{R})} \qquad (4.111)$$

We set up a system of polar coordinates with pole at dS_2 and with axis drawn through 0, the center of the piston. Since the area of the source element dS_1 is given by $\mathcal{R}\,d\mathcal{R}\,d\psi$ (Fig. 4.111), we have for the pressure on any element dS_2 as caused by the entire area within the ring of radius r the expression,

$$\frac{j\rho ck\,U_0}{2\pi}\int_{-\pi/2}^{\pi/2}\int_0^{2r\cos\psi}\frac{1}{\mathcal{R}}e^{j(\omega t - k\mathcal{R})}\mathcal{R}\,d\mathcal{R}\,d\psi \qquad (4.112)$$

By symmetry, the pressure on any one element of the ring is the same as that on any other element (this is *not* true for the piston in general). Therefore the total force on the ring caused by the interior elements is

$$dF = j\rho ck\,U_0 e^{j\omega t}\,r\,dr\int_{-\pi 2}^{\pi 2}\int_0^{2r\cos\psi}e^{-jk\mathcal{R}}d\mathcal{R}\,d\psi \qquad (4.113)$$

We have now only to integrate the forces on the elementary rings and multiply by 2. Thus we have for the total force on the piston,

$$F = 2j\rho ck\,U_0 e^{j\omega t}\int_0^a r\,dr\int_{-\pi/2}^{\pi/2}\int_0^{2r\cos\psi}e^{-jk\mathcal{R}}\,d\mathcal{R}\,d\psi \qquad (4.114)$$

The formal evaluation of this integral is rather lengthy. The student may proceed immediately to the result, which is given in Eq. (4.115). For those who wish to follow the mathematical process, the evaluation is given in detail.

For convenience, we take the multiplier of the integral to the left side of the equation, obtaining

$$\frac{F}{2jpck U_0 e^{j\omega t}} = \int_0^a r \, dr \int_{-\pi/2}^{\pi/2} \int_0^{2r \cos \psi} e^{-jk\mathcal{R}} \, d\mathcal{R} \, d\psi \qquad \text{I}$$

and call the right-hand member $\mathscr{I}$. That is,

$$\mathscr{I} = \int_0^a r \, dr \int_{-\pi/2}^{\pi/2} \int_0^{2r \cos \psi} e^{-jk\mathcal{R}} \, d\mathcal{R} \, d\psi \qquad \text{II}$$

Integrating partially with respect to $\mathcal{R}$, we obtain

$$\mathscr{I} = \frac{j}{k} \int_0^a r \, dr \int_{-\pi/2}^{\pi/2} (e^{-2jkr \cos \psi} - 1) d\psi \qquad \text{III}$$

Integrating with respect to ψ, we get

$$\mathscr{I} = \frac{2j}{k} \int_0^a r \, dr \left[\int_0^{\pi/2} (e^{-2jkr \cos \psi} \, d\psi) - \frac{\pi}{2} \right] \qquad \text{IV}$$

The integral in ψ of IV is similar to that of Eq. (4.94). The only difference is in the limits. We again obtain a Bessel function, but in this case the function has both real and imaginary parts. This is not surprising, for $e^{-2jkr \cos \psi}$ is a complex number; it was the integral of (4.94) that was a special case. Thus we have

$$\int_0^{\pi/2} e^{-2jkr \cos \psi} d\psi = \frac{\pi}{2} [J_0(2kr) + jK_0(2kr)] \qquad \text{V}$$

Both terms are functions of zero order. The first we have already encountered. The second is called a Bessel function of the second kind, and as for J_0, we can find its value for any value of kr in tables. No further understanding of these functions is needed for our applications. We therefore have

$$\mathscr{I} = \frac{\pi j}{k} \int_0^a [J_0(2kr) - 1 - jK_0(2kr)] \, r \, dr$$

$$= \frac{\pi}{jk} \int_0^a [1 - J_0(2kr) + jK_0(2kr)] \, r \, dr \qquad \text{VI}$$

$$= \frac{\pi}{jk} \left[\int_0^a r \, dr - \frac{1}{(2k)^2} \int_0^a 2kr J_0(2kr) \cdot 2k \, dr + \frac{1}{2k^2} \int_0^a 2kr K_0(2kr) \cdot 2k \, dr \right] \quad \text{VII}$$

The first of these integrals is elementary. The second is integrated by use of Eq. (4.96). The third also integrates readily. We get, finally,

$$\mathscr{I} = \frac{\pi}{jk} \left[\frac{a^2}{2} - \frac{2ka J_1(2ka)}{(2k)^2} + \frac{K_1(2ka)}{(2k)^2} \right] \qquad \text{VIII}$$

(It happens that both $J_1(x)$ and $K_1(x)$ vanish for $x = 0$). After a little algebra, we obtain as the ultimate expression for the force,

$$F = \rho c \pi a^2 U_0 e^{j\omega t} \left[1 - \frac{2J_1(2ka)}{2ka} + j\frac{2K_1(2ka)}{(2ka)^2} \right] \qquad (4.115)$$

The ratio between this force and the velocity is called the *radiation impedance of the piston* Z_r. The real part is called the *piston radiation resistance*, and the imaginary part, the *piston radiation reactance*. In addition to these terms, we also define the *piston resistance function* R_1, and the *piston reactance function* X_1. These terms are defined in the following equations:

$$R_1 = 1 - \frac{2J_1(2ka)}{2ka}, \qquad X_1 = \frac{K_1(2ka)}{(2ka)^2}$$

$$F = Z_r U_0 e^{j\omega t}, \qquad Z_r = R_r + jX_r \qquad (4.116)$$

$$R_r = \rho c \pi a^2 R_1, \qquad X_r = \rho c \pi a^2 X_1$$

These impedance functions are used to find the power output of a piston radiator in terms of the driving force and the mechanical impedance of the piston vibrator. The functions $R_1(x) = 1 - 2J_1(x)/x$ and $X_1(x) = 2K_1(x)/x_2$ are shown in Fig. 4.112. The use is entirely similar to that of the characteristic

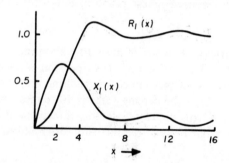

Fig. 4.112. Piston resistance and reactance functions.

impedance of the driven string in Art. 2.8, Eq. (2.82), except that the piston radiation impedance contains a reactive, as well as a resistive component. Again assuming an electromagnetic driving force, DI, we have for the velocity of the piston in terms of this driving force:

$$U = \frac{DI}{Z_m + Z_r} \qquad (4.117)$$

where $Z_m + Z_r$ can be considered the *total mechanical impedance* Z'_m, and therefore the power output of the piston, will be

$$P_{Av} = U^2 R_r = \left| \frac{DI}{Z_m + Z_r} \right|^2 R_r \qquad (4.118)$$

In most cases (in air) a good approximation for the velocity of the piston can be found by neglecting the radiation impedance term in the denominator of Eq. (4.117). Because of the importance of piston radiation, we shall illustrate with the solution of a complete design problem.

It was remarked in Art. 4.9 that the Bessel functions can be developed by expansion in series. It is sometimes useful for the purpose of making approximations to have the series expansion $R_1(x)$ and $X_1(x)$. For these functions,

$$R_1(x) = 1 - \frac{2J_1(x)}{x} = \frac{x^2}{2 \cdot 4} - \frac{x^4}{2 \cdot 4^2 \cdot 6} + \frac{x^6}{2 \cdot 4^2 \cdot 6^2 \cdot 8}$$

$$X_1(x) = \frac{4}{\pi} \left(\frac{x}{3} - \frac{x^3}{3^2 \cdot 5} + \frac{x^5}{3^2 \cdot 5^2 \cdot 7} - \cdots \right) \qquad (4.119)$$

If $x < 1$, we can take as permissible approximations:

$$R_1(x) \approx \frac{x^2}{8}, \qquad X_1(x) \approx \frac{4x}{3} \qquad (4.119a)$$

For large x, $R_1(x) \to 1$ as does the resistive component of the radiation impedance of a sphere, and $X_1(x) \to 4/(\pi x)$. The proof of these relations necessitates a more extensive investigation of Bessel functions, and need not concern us here.

Illustrative Problem: A piston of mass 10 g and radius 10 cm is mounted in an infinite baffle. The stiffness of the suspension is 10^6 dynes/cm and the mechanical resistance is 500 mechanical ohms. Find the following at 400, 800, 1,600, and 2,400 cycles if the driving force is 10^5 dynes rms: power output, axial intensity at 300 cm, directivity factor, directivity index, beam width 3 db down. Draw polar plots of the intensity distribution.

Solution:

The procedure is to find first the mechanical impedance of the piston suspension, Z_m, from the mechanical constants $m = 10$ g, $a = 10$ cm, $s = 10^6$ dynes/cm, $R_m = 500$ g/sec (Eq. 1.75); then the radiation impedance from Eq. (4.116), assuming $c = 34,500$ cm/sec to find k. The total mechanical impedance against which the force is exerted is the sum of the two, i.e.

$$Z'_m = Z_m + Z_r$$

The ratio of the rms force to the magnitude of the total impedance gives the rms velocity, and the power output can be found from the equation

$$P_{Av} = U^2 R_r \text{ ergs/sec} = 10^{-4} U^2 R_r mw$$

The power calculations are shown in tabulated form.

f	ω	$k=\omega/c$	$2ka$	$\dfrac{R_1}{(2ka)}$	$\dfrac{x_1}{(2ka)}$	ωm	s/ω	$\dfrac{|Z_m'|}{(\text{appr.})}$	$\dfrac{U_{rms}}{(cm/\ sec)}$	R_r	$\dfrac{P_{Av}}{(mw)}$
400	2,514	0.0732	1.464	0.240	0.535	25,000	398	30,000	3.33	3,120	3.45
800	5,028	0.1467	2.928	0.755	0.685	50,000	199	60,000	1.66	7,800	2.60
1,600	10,056	0.2928	5.956	1.10	0.162	100,000	100	114,000	0.88	14,300	1.07
2,400	15,084	0.4392	8.784	0.940	0.155	150,000	67	162,000	0.61	12,000	0.445

Equations 4.105 and 4.106 are used to compute directivities. To find the angle θ_3 at which the intensity is 3 db less than the axial intensity, note that

$$\left[\frac{2J_1(x)}{x}\right]^2 = 0.5 \quad \text{for} \quad x = ka \sin \theta_3$$

From the directivity tables in Appendix 2, it is found that the corresponding value of $ka \sin \theta_3 \approx 1.6$. The angle of the 3 db fall-off may then be found from the ka values for any frequency. If it is found that $\sin \theta_3 > 1$, there is no angle at which the fall-off is as great as 3 db. This condition holds at 400 and 800 cycles.

Directivity Calculations

f	ka	$(ka)^2$	$\dfrac{2J_1(2ka)}{(2ka)}$	D	d	$\sin \theta_3$
400	0.732	0.54	0.73	$\dfrac{0.54}{0.27}=2$	3 db	$\dfrac{1.6}{0.732}$ (none)
800	1.464	2.14	0.24	$\dfrac{2.14}{0.76}=2.8$	4.4 db	$\dfrac{1.6}{1.464}$ (none)
1,600	2.928	8.6	0.10	$\dfrac{8.6}{0.9}=9.6$	9.6 db	$\dfrac{1.6}{2.928}=0.545,\ \theta=33°$
2,400	4.392	19.4	0.057	$\dfrac{19.4}{0.943}=21.0$	13.2 db	$\dfrac{1.6}{4.392}=0.362,\ \theta=21°$

Axial intensity:

$$I_{Av} = \frac{P_{Av}}{4\pi r^2}$$

At $r = 300$,

$$I_{Av} = \frac{P_{Av}}{1.14 \times 10^6}, \qquad I_0 = DI_{Av}$$

f	D	P_{Av}(erg/sec)	I_{Av}(erg/sec cm²)	I_0(erg/sec cm²)	I_0 (db)
400	2	34,500	0.031	0.062	77.8
800	2.8	26,000	0.023	0.064	78.2
1,600	9.6	10,700	0.0094	0.090	79.5
2,400	21.0	4,450	0.0039	0.082	79.0

(I_0 in db re 10^{-9} erg/sec cm²)

Polar curves are plotted (Fig. 4.113) as in Art. 4.10.
Example for 1,600 cycles, $ka = 2.928$.

θ	$ka \sin \theta$	$[2J_1(x)]^2/x$
0	0	1.000
10°	0.468	0.945
20°	0.936	0.805
30°	1.464	0.570
60°	2.52	0.155
90°	2.928	0.062

$(x = ka \sin \theta)$

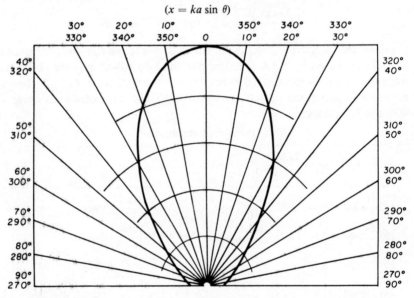

Fig. 4.113. Polar plot of relative intensity in erg/sec/cm² for 10 cm piston
radiating at 1,600 cycles.

References

Kinsler and Frey, *Fundamentals of Acoustics*, Wiley, New York, 1950.
Morse, *Vibration and Sound*, 2nd ed., McGraw-Hill, New York, 1948.

Problems

1. Show that the function $(1/r)(ct - r)$ is a solution to the spherical wave
equation. Find the expression for pressure, particle velocity, and condensation for this function. Does the concept of specific acoustic impedance have
meaning for this wave?

2. Plot the phase angle of the specific acoustic impedance as a function
of kr. What is the specific acoustic impedance at the source boundary of a

pulsating sphere in which $ka = 0.1$? For the above sphere, find the power output if the velocity amplitude is 10 cm/sec. Find the intensity at the surface if the sphere is vibrating in air, and plot the intensity as a function of r up to a value of r at which $kr = 10$.

3. Obtain a series expansion of Eq. (4.95) with $m = 0$. Then use Eq. (4.96) to find a series expansion for $J_1(x)$. By taking the first three terms of the series of $J_0(x)$ and $J_1(x)$, check the graphs of these two functions as given on Fig. 4.92.

4. From Eq. (4.105), find the directivity factor for $ka = 0.1$, $ka = 1.0$, $ka = 10$.

5. Find the reactive force on a circular piston of 2 cm radius in air at a frequency of 5,000 cycles if U_0 is 10 cm/sec. Find the power output.

6. Compare the power outputs of pulsating spheres of radius 0.1 cm, 1 cm, and 10 cm, respectively, if the wavelength is 10 cm and the velocity amplitude is 0.001 cm/sec. In each case, find the velocity potential and pressure at a distance of 1 m from the source. In each case, find the specific acoustic impedance at the surface of the sphere and at a distance from the source center equal to three times the radius.

7. In Chapter 1, Eq. (1.211), an expression is given for the differential equation of a Helmholtz resonator. Show that one can get $R_A = \rho c k^2/2\pi$ by considering radiation to take place from the resonator as if the mass of air in the plug acted as a piston of surface area S, where the radius of the piston is much smaller than the wavelength. Find the effective Q of the Helmholtz resonator, and draw the response curve of a resonator in which V is 1,000 cm³, L is 4 cm, and S is 2 cm², assuming that radiation is the only source of energy loss in the resonator.

8. If the above resonator is exposed to a sound field of 5 dynes/cm² rms pressure, what will be the acoustic power radiated by the resonator at its resonance frequency? Compare the intensities of the driving field and that of the radiated sound in the vicinity of the orifice.

9. Find the strength of a spherical source of 5 cm radius if the intensity level is 70 db at a distance of 1 m at (a) 400 cycles, (b) 3,000 cycles.

10. Solve Problem 9 if the intensity level is 70 db at a distance of 10 cm.

11. Find the strength of a spherical source of radius 1 cm if the intensity level is 10 db at a distance of 2 cm.

12. Find the velocity of vibration of a circular piston of radius 5 cm if the axial intensity is 70 db at a distance of 1 m at (a) 400 cycles, (b) 3,000 cycles.

13. A small speaker operating in open air acts approximately like a doublet with equal and opposite sources of equal numerical strength SU_0 separated by a distance equal to the diameter of the cone. In addition, the cone can be assumed to vibrate as a piston. Obtain an approximate solution for the acoustic pressure and the components of particle velocity at a point 30° off the axis of the speaker and at a distance of 1 m from the center of the cone (a) when the wavelength is 3 m (use condition $L \ll r \ll \lambda$; (b) when the

wavelength is 25 cm (use condition $L \ll \lambda \ll r$). Although the solution is only approximate, since the conditions are not closely fulfilled, the problem gives an idea of doublet action in a practical case. (Let diameter equal 5 cm.).

14. Find the pressure and particle velocity if the speaker of Problem 13 is surrounded by an infinite baffle, or enclosed in a cabinet which shuts out radiation from the rear of the speaker.

15. Show that the relation $\phi = c\xi$ holds for a plane wave. Comment on the relation between equations giving pressure and particle velocity in terms of displacement in Chapter 3, and those giving pressure and particle velocity in terms of velocity potential in Chapter 4.

Chapter 5

LOUDSPEAKERS

One of the milestones in the history of acoustics is the development in 1876, by Alexander Graham Bell, of an *electroacoustic transducer*, that is, a device which converts the variations of instantaneous sound pressure into similar variations of electric current or electric voltage. Bell's primary objective was to transmit the voice over greater distances than those possible with direct sound transmission. Because the attenuation of the electric current in a wire with distance is much less than the corresponding sound attenuation, Bell saw the utility of an electroacoustic transducer. Obviously a second electroacoustic transducer was required at the terminus of the electric circuit to reconvert the electric energy into acoustic energy. In modern terminology these two transducers are called the microphone and the loudspeaker. (In the special field of telephony, they are called the transmitter and the receiver.)

With the development of the vacuum tube (about 1915), a new element entered into the employment of the electroacoustic transducer, namely, *amplification*. With the aid of the vacuum tube, it is possible to convert the most minute electric variation into exactly similar variations of greater power, thus overcoming lack of sensitivity in the transducer. When one speaks of a *sound system*, then, one has in mind a microphone input, an electronic amplification system, and a loudspeaker output.

The loudspeaker is a development of the piston radiator. In the previous chapter we discussed in some detail the problem of piston radiation, particularly in the illustrative example at the end of the chapter. It will be remembered that mechanically the piston could be considered a driven vibrator and the velocity of motion could be solved for. The radiated sound power is a function of this velocity and the radiation resistance, which is in turn a function of the frequency and surface area of the piston. In a sound system the driving electromagnetic force of the speaker is controlled by some original source of sound which is converted into an electric variation by the input microphone. The output of the loudspeaker must be such that the sound variations are an acoustical facsimile of the driving force. For example, if the loudspeaker output contains frequency components which are not present in the driving force, it is said to have *harmonic distortion*; if it radiates more strongly at some frequencies than at others, it is said to have frequency discrimination. Although both of these faults are at times called distortion, *harmonic distortion is the more serious*, as frequency discrimination may be compensated for by introducing an opposing discrimination elsewhere in the system. In addition to fidelity of response (lack of distortion), the loudspeaker must be capable of producing the output power necessary for its application. Thus in a large auditorium, it might be necessary for the loudspeaker to provide several watts of acoustic power. Thirdly, the speaker must have a favorable directivity. As an example of an imperfect directivity, we have the piston radiator of the previous chapter, in which the low frequencies are distributed homogeneously throughout the hemisphere subtended by the piston, while the high frequencies are concentrated along the axis. Such a directivity tends to give a boomy response at points far removed from the axis. If the sound system is used for speech reproduction, this impairs the intelligibility, for the high frequencies are important in the recognition of phonetic sounds. *Efficiency*, though not of primary importance as it is in electric machinery, is nevertheless taken into account, since needless weight and bulk are disadvantageous in some applications; and in large installations, the cost of electric power may be appreciable. In modern loudspeaker construction, much consideration is also given to the design of the speaker so that it will faithfully reproduce transients. For example, in the reproduction of orchestral music the sudden impulse of a percussion instrument may cause "hangover," which blurs the passages immediately following the impulse. Since this text has developed only the mathematics of the steady state, it will not be possible to discuss the reproduction of transients.

In the preceding paragraph we have mentioned most of the factors which are important in speaker design. We shall discuss in detail only those which lend themselves primarily to acoustic treatment. The elimination of harmonic distortion, for example, is primarily a constructional problem. The two primary acoustic problems are the development of sufficient power output and the attainment of a "flat" frequency response throughout the desired frequency range.

Since the driving system has as its object the conversion of electric energy into mechanical energy (and the transduction of the mechanical energy into acoustic energy) it can be considered as an electromechanical network which has an electric impedance at the input and a mechanical impedance at the output. The relation between the electric and mechanical impedances is expressed by an *electromechanical coupling coefficient*. By the employment of this coupling coefficient, the electroacoustic transducer may be treated equivalently as a purely electrical problem or as an entirely mechanical problem. Since the preceding chapters have covered the mechanical and acoustic considerations, we shall devote the first part of this chapter to the electrical side of the investigation.

5.1 Construction of the Dynamic Loudspeaker

The constructional details of the dynamic loudspeaker are shown in Fig. 5.11. The radiating element is in the shape of the frustrum of a cone, and is elastically suspended at both the upper and lower bases of the frustrum. The cone is surrounded by an open-ribbed metallic structure called the "basket," which serves as the main framework to which are attached the working parts of the speaker. The motive force for the cone is supplied by a current-carrying coil attached to the apex of the cone, the coil moving in the radial induction

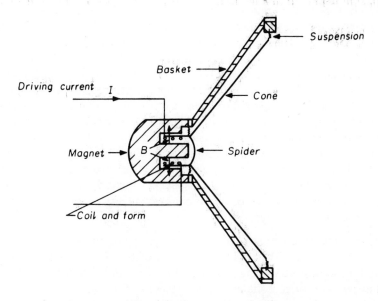

Fig. 5.11. Constructional details of the dynamic loudspeaker.

field of a "pot" magnet. The stiffness element which retains and centers the moving coil is called a *spider*. It is advantageous to have the air gap as small as possible, especially in small loudspeakers, where a gap width of 1 mm is used. The length of the air gap is usually made somewhat less than the length of the coil; the coil then invades the stray field at both ends, and as a result, nonlinearity of response is diminished. In our analysis, we shall assume that the coil moves in a homogeneous field. In the past, high-resistance coils have been used to match the impedance of the driving circuit, but there are several electrical advantages to be derived from the use of a low-resistance coil of from 4 to 20 ohms. Modern loudspeakers are manufactured with such low-resistance coils, employing a transformer to match the higher impedance of the driver. In order to emphasize the fundamental points of loudspeaker theory we shall assume at the start that the loudspeaker cone behaves as a rigid piston of diameter equal to the outer diameter of the cone.*

One important practical problem is the choice of the resonant frequency. This frequency should not fall within the range of reproduction because of the unduly large amplitude of vibration in the vicinity of resonance and the

---

* A paper cone, of course, does not.

consequent possibility of harmonic distortion, as well as the obvious frequency discrimination. The alternatives are, therefore, mass control and stiffness control. Since there is a practical lower limit to the mass of the cone and coil, extremely large stiffness constants are required to place the resonant frequency above the upper limit of the typical range of reproduction, and following from this, very high mechanical impedances within the range of reproduction. The result would be exceedingly small radiated power at the lower frequencies. On the other hand, the example of Art. 4.11 has shown that the rise in radiation resistance with frequency tends to compensate for the rise in the mechanical impedance of a mass-controlled system. We may take it as a general rule, then, that the loudspeaker is designed as a mass-controlled system. We exert every effort to achieve as light a cone as possible, while still retaining the necessary rigidity to approximate a rigid piston. Once this mass is known, the stiffness of the suspension can be made low enough so that the resonant frequency is below the limit of reproduction. Since the computation of this stiffness is a fairly obvious procedure, we shall hitherto make little reference to the resonant frequency of the loudspeaker. Instead we shall assume that it is always possible to reduce the resonant frequency to whatever low value is necessary for the design.

Illustrative example : Assume the range of reproduction to be from $\omega = 300$ to $\omega = 30,000$. Assume the mass of the cone plus coil to be 1 g. Solve for the necessary stiffness to place the resonant frequencies at the lower and upper limit of reproduction. With these stiffnesses, find the mechanical impedances at angular frequencies of 300, 3,000, and 30,000.

5.2 Electromechanical Theory of the Loudspeaker

If we suppose that the drive coil of the loudspeaker has a total length of L cm, and carries a sinusoidal current I amp in a field of B gausses, we have from elementary electrical theory for the driving force:

$$F = DI = \frac{BLI}{10} \text{ dynes} \tag{5.21}$$

where B is in gausses, L in centimeters, I in amperes. In this equation D is an *electromechanical coupling constant*.

If this coil is rigidly coupled to a mechanical system of mechanical impedance Z'_m we have also

$$F = Z'_m V \text{ dynes} \tag{5.22}$$

where V is the velocity of motion of the mass and Z'_m includes not only the mechanical constants of the vibratory system, but the resistive and reactive radiation loading; that is,

$$Z'_m = Z_m + Z_r = R_m + R_r + j\left(\omega m + X_r - \frac{s}{\omega}\right) \tag{5.23}$$

Actually, the radiation loading often has only a minor influence on the vibrational characteristics of the system, and in addition, over the greater portion of the frequency range, the mass of the system is the controlling factor, as we saw in the illustrative problem of Art. 4.11. However, we shall carry through the analysis of the electromechanical system in a fairly general manner in this article in order to gain a clearer insight into the action. In addition, the findings are useful in the prediction of the performance of other transducers.

We know from electrical theory that a conductor moving in a magnetic field generates a voltage, which we shall call the motional voltage E_M. We have, from Faraday's law,

$$E_M = BLV \times 10^{-8} \text{ volts} \tag{5.24}$$

and from our definition of the electromechanical coupling constant, this may be written

$$E_M = 10^{-7} DV \text{ volts} \tag{5.25}$$

The presence of the same coefficient in Eqs. (5.21) and (5.25) indicates that the dynamic speaker is of a class known as *reciprocal transducers*.

The ratio between the voltage E_M and the driving current I is known as the *motional impedance* Z_M of the transducer. It is a true electric impedance, unlike the mechanical impedance, in which the unit *mechanical ohm* is used only in an analogous sense. We have

$$Z_M = E_M/I = \frac{D^2}{10^7} \frac{1}{Z'_m} \tag{5.26}$$

If we define γ as a second coupling constant equal to $D^2/10^7$, we have

$$Z_M = \frac{\gamma}{Z'_m} \tag{5.27}$$

Similarly, we may define the *motional admittance* Y_M as Z'_m/γ. This gives for the motional admittance,

$$
\begin{aligned}
Y_M &= \frac{1}{\gamma}\left[R_m + R_r + j\left(\omega m + Xr - \frac{s}{\omega}\right)\right] \\
&= \frac{1}{\gamma}\left[R_m + R_r + j\omega\left(m + \frac{X_r}{\omega}\right) - j\frac{s}{\omega}\right]
\end{aligned}
$$

The resistive and reactive electric elements which would comprise such an admittance are shown within the enclosed rectangle in Fig. 5.21. The electric driver "sees" such an equivalent electric network "looking into" the speaker, plus the purely electric resistances and inductance of the voice coil. The loudspeaker problem has thus been reduced to the purely electrical problem of finding the power which flows into the radiation resistance. The efficiency is the ratio of this useful output to the total resistive power provided by the generator. We should not get the impression that such an equivalent circuit is necessary, or even particularly useful in solving an actual speaker design problem. (We solved the problem of piston radiation in the previous chapter by finding the force from the current, the velocity from the force, and the radiated power from the velocity and the radiation impedance, a method

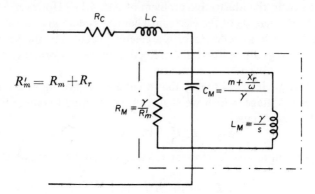

$$R'_m = R_m + R_r$$

Fig. 5.21. Equivalent electric circuit of loudspeaker.

that was primarily mechanical.) But such equivalent circuits do enable one to obtain a deeper understanding of the mechanism.

Since the development of high-quality electroacoustic radiators has occurred alongside the development of the vacuum tube, it is appropriate to consider in the next article the electronic driving circuit of the speaker. It is not necessary for us to treat the actual construction and theory of the vacuum tube for this purpose, since a theorem exists by which we can consider the vacuum tube as a circuit element consisting of a constant-voltage generator in series with a purely resistive internal impedance. We have already mentioned Thevenin's theorem in the second chapter. We shall find this theorem extremely useful again in the ensuing electrical analysis.

5.3 The Driving Circuit of the Loudspeaker

In Fig. 5.31 we show the schematic diagram of the speaker and its driving vacuum-tube stage. The circuit in this form shows merely the physical hookup of the two devices. Now employing Thevenin's theorem in the special form called the *equivalent plate circuit theorem*, we replace the vacuum tube by a generator of constant output voltage μE_g (where E_g is the voltage input applied to the vacuum tube and μ is a constant of the tube called the *amplification* factor), in series with the resistor r_p (which is another tube constant called its *plate resistance*). This gives the circuit of Fig. 5.32(a). We can simplify further by employing Thevenin's theorem again. Considering the circuit broken at A and B, and looking to the left with the generator short-circuited, we would measure an impedance $(1/a^2)r_p$, where a is the turns ratio of the transformer, and the open-circuit voltage between A and B would be $(\mu E_g)/a$.

Therefore we can replace the circuit between A and B by the equivalent circuit shown in Fig. 5.32(b). We have already analyzed the dynamic loudspeaker from the point of view of its equivalent electric circuit, and we use this

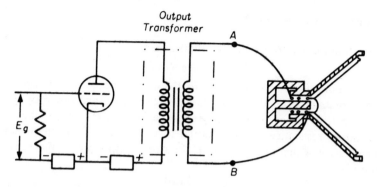

Fig. 5.31. Diagram of the loudspeaker and its driving vacuum-tube stage.

equivalent circuit between A and B looking to the right. Figure 5.32(c) shows the equivalent circuit in its final form. With this equivalent circuit, we can theoretically design a speaker to meet any specifications for power output and frequency response, *unless these specifications are contradictory.* Before solving a difficult theoretical problem, however, it is wiser to gain some insight into the practical problems of loudspeaker design. We shall find that it is

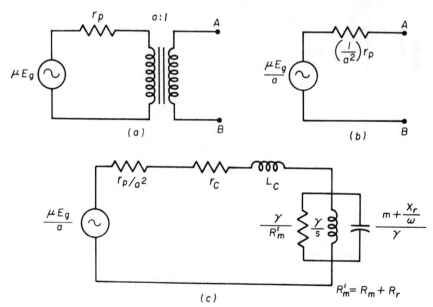

Fig. 5.32.

neither necessary nor gainful to solve the theoretical problem in all its generality, though the equivalent circuit remains a useful framework on which to build the analysis.

5.4 Practical Loudspeaker Design

The sound power radiated by a loudspeaker is

$$P_R = \tfrac{1}{2}\pi a^2 \rho c R_1 U_0^2 \tag{5.41}$$

This equation was developed in the treatment of the radiation of a piston.

For a mass-controlled system, the velocity will be inversely proportional to the frequency for a constant driving force. Equation (4.119a) shows that the radiation resistance is proportional to the square of the frequency for frequencies for which $2ka < 1$, i.e. $f = c/4\pi a$. In this region the resistance function is

$$R_1 = \frac{(2ka)^2}{8} \tag{5.42}$$

Up to this frequency, therefore, we have perfect compensation and can achieve a "flat" response. It follows that design begins by choosing the lowest frequency for reproduction and the acoustic power desired at that frequency.

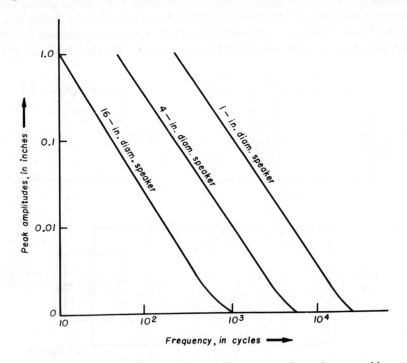

Fig. 5.41. Displacements required to radiate 1 watt of sound power with pistons of 1, 4, and 16 in. diameters.

We can then solve for the product $a^2 R_1 U_0^2$, which must be kept constant. The individual factors must be arrived at by a series of compromises. As an example, decreasing a will raise the frequency which is the upper limit of flat reproduction, but will lower the value of R_1 for any frequency. The $a^2 R_1$ product therefore decreases greatly with decreasing a, and the velocity must be increased to make up for this decrease. The velocity is proportional to the amplitude, and at low frequencies, large amplitudes are needed to develop large power output with speakers of small radius, and it becomes impractical, or even impossible, to provide the suspension necessary for the required amplitude of vibration. The curves of Fig. 5.41 show the displacements necessary to radiate 1 watt of sound power with pistons of 1 in., 4 in., and 16 in. diameters. If we remember that amplitude is proportional to the square root of the power, we can find the displacements necessary for any power output from this figure.

The singing voice can produce a sound power of the order of 0.01 watt, and musical instruments can approach an output of 0.1 watt. Let us place the desired sound power output somewhere in this region and choose, for best all-round performance, one of the three speakers listed. Without formal computation, it appears from Fig. 5.41 that the 1-in. speaker is incapable of producing the necessary power at the low-frequency end (say 100 cycles). The 16-in. speaker is of course to be preferred at 100 cycles, but the transition frequency at which $2ka$ becomes equal to unity may be fairly low. Actually, this frequency turns out to be 100 cycles, which is our lower limit of reproduction. For the 4-in. speakers the flat region extends to 400 cycles. It appears that of the three speakers, the 16-in. is capable of radiating only low frequencies, and the 1-in., only high frequencies. We are therefore led to the choice of the 4-in. speaker by a process of elimination. These speakers are typical of those employed in modern triple-speaker systems for highest quality reproduction, each one of them serving a portion of the sonic spectrum. For this reason, we show typical mechanical constants and impedance curves of these speakers in Figs. 5.42 and 5.43. We are now in a position to choose a *tentative* range of reproduction.

The range 80–4,000 cycles is often used for a moderately high quality of reproduction. Reference to the 4-in. speaker curves of Fig. 5.42 enables us to solve for the resonant frequency as the frequency at which $X_m + X_r = X_s$. The resonant frequency turns out to be about 100 cycles, not too far above the tentatively chosen lower limit.

If one considers the variation of mass reactance and radiation resistance with frequency, one can readily construct a curve of relative power output against frequency for a mass-controlled system (as in many similar cases, the abscissa is ka, rather than f.) Such a curve is shown in Fig. 5.44. We find from this curve that the relative power is one-half at $2ka = 4$ (about 2,200 cycles for a 4-in. speaker) and that the relative power is about one-tenth at the 4,000 cycles upper limit of reproduction.

The result is of course discouraging. Starting with only a moderately wide band for reproduction, and considering only a few of the factors of the ultimate design, we have utterly failed to achieve anything approaching flat reproduction. As we remarked, high-quality reproduction necessitates three

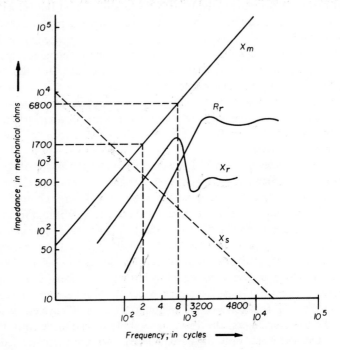

Fig. 5.42. Variation of mass reactance and radiation impedance with frequency for 4-in. diameter speaker. These curves are used to find the performance of the speaker of Art. 5.6. *Speaker constants:*

Diameter	4 in.
Mass of cone..	1.0 g
Mass of coil...	0.35 g
Air gap flux...	10,000 gauss

Note: Compliance of suspension is omitted since mass-control is assumed. The values producing these curves are computed and tabulated in Table 5.61, page 181.

speakers. These are fed from a common vacuum-tube stage through electric "cross-over" networks which consist of a low-pass filter for the 16-in. speaker, a high-pass filter for the 1-in. speaker, and a band-pass filter for the 4-in. speaker.

Our general consideration of loudspeaker design has shown that from the standpoint of high fidelity only fair results can be obtained with a single speaker. The 4-in. speaker is capable of reproducing very intelligible speech

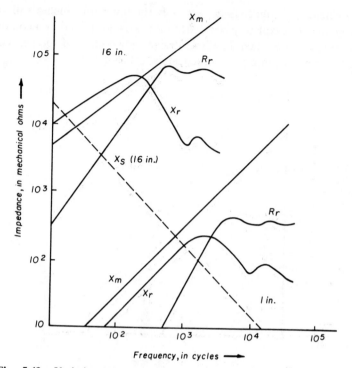

Fig. 5.43. Variation of mass reactance and radiation impedance with frequency for 1-in. and 16-in. speakers. *Speaker constants:*

Diameter, inches	1.0	16.0
Mass of cone, grams	0.015	40.0
Mass of coil, grams	0.015	4.0
Flux, gauss	10,000	10,000
Compliance, cm/dyne	5.3×10^{-7}	3.2×10^{-7}

Note: The stiffness-reaction variation is only shown for the 16-in. speaker. However, since the compliances do not differ greatly, the resonant frequencies can be determined approximately from the points of intersection of the X_s curve with the X_m curves.

and enjoyable music. Its power output is quite adequate for residences. For high-fidelity reproduction we have found a triple-speaker assembly to be practically a necessity. We have not mentioned one important problem at low frequencies, namely, the problem of baffling, which will be treated in the next article. In the article subsequent to that, we shall follow through on the design and performance of the 4-in. speaker. Before concluding this article, it is necessary to mention that modifications in single loudspeakers can be made which, in effect, produce results similar to those obtained with multiple speakers. As an example, a 4-in. cone may be attached by a compliance to a truncated 16-in. cone. At low frequencies the assembly vibrates as a rigid cone, whereas at a higher frequency only the inner four inches will vibrate. Similarly, the drive coil may be divided into two coils joined by a compliance. The consideration of such details of design, however, is of too specialized a nature for inclusion in a general acoustics text.

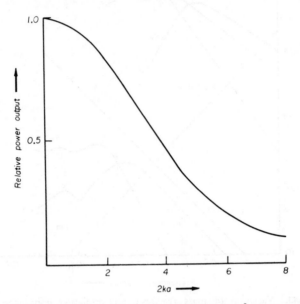

Fig. 5.44. Universal curve of relative power output of a mass-controlled piston radiator compared to the output at lower limit of mass-control.

5.5 The Cabinet Problem for Loudspeakers

In the problem of the piston in the rigid wall, we were concerned only with the emission from the front surface of the piston. If the piston were vibrating in the open, since the waves emitted from the rear are in opposite phase to those from the front, the piston for wavelengths comparable with its radius would constitute essentially an acoustic doublet with consequent poor radiating characteristics. While we could conceivably install the loudspeaker in a wall, and achieve the simplicity of the initial case, it is an understatement to say that this is not usually done. We might first effect a compromise by installing the speaker in a *finite* baffle, a plane surface of area as large as possible so that the waves leaving the rear would have a larger distance to travel than those leaving the front. For higher frequencies, the action is then practically that of a piston in an infinite baffle, but there is a rather sharp transition frequency at which the speaker changes over to a doublet. Theoretical considerations and experimental results show that the transition frequency occurs where the size of the baffle is about that of the wavelength of the sound.

If we consider that the wavelength at 128 cycles is approximately 8 ft, it is seen that a plane baffle is rather impractical for low-frequency radiation for any but large rooms, and we look for other solutions.

The thought occurs that if we completely enclose the rear, there will be no emission therefrom. This turns out to be true, but this solution presents additional problems. For high frequencies we now have behind the speaker a multiply resonant column (actually a resonant volume); for low frequencies, an acoustic compliance, $V/\rho c^2$ or an acoustic reactance $\rho c^2/V\omega$. The high-frequency standing waves can be overcome by lining the interior with absorbing material, but this has little effect on the compliance, and the added acoustic reactance raises the resonant frequency of the system.

However, complete closure of the space behind the loudspeaker is not necessary. If an opening is made in the front of the cabinet, it becomes a Helmholtz resonator, the natural frequency of which can be tuned to any desired value. For best results, the natural frequency of the resonator is chosen safely below the lowest frequency to be reproduced, and the mechanical resonant frequency still lower. The displacement of the air in the opening will then be in phase with the front face of the speaker at the lower limit of reproduction and 180° out of phase with the front face at the mechanical resonant frequency. Both are advantageous, since the former increases the radiation and the latter helps to counteract the objectionable rise at resonance. Such a cabinet is called a bass-reflex cabinet (Fig. 5.51).

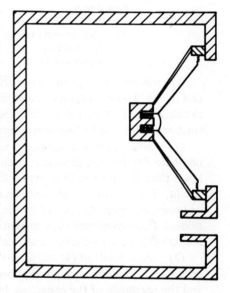

Fig. 5.51. Bass-reflex cabinet.

Only one more word need be said on the subject of cabinets: by the time a designer begins to consider a bass-reflex cabinet it is almost certain he has already decided to use more than one speaker, for a cabinet would be of little use unless the speaker itself were capable of delivering power at very low frequencies. But this means that the speaker must be large, and a large speaker cannot be driven for radiation at high frequencies.

5.6 Performance of a Typical Loudspeaker

In the two previous articles, we have discussed in a broad way the factors that enter into the design of a loudspeaker. Since these were so varied in nature, it was rather difficult to be quantitative about the discussion. We shall now take a set of design parameters, perhaps arrived at by a series of compromises, and study the performance of a speaker having such parameters, making several simplifying assumptions, lest the main points tend to be obscured by the detail. We shall neglect the low frequencies, since we have already discussed the cabinet problem and the mechanical resonant frequency. We can therefore assume mass control and calculate the acoustic power output at frequencies of 200, 400, 1,000, 2,000, 4,000, 8,000 cycles for a speaker circuit having the parameters and the voltage input given below.

Mass of cone and coil	1.35 g
Diameter of cone	4 in. (radius, $a = 5$ cm)
Resistance of coil	4 ohms
Inductance of coil	neglected
Length of coil wire............	200 cm
Flux density	10,000 gausses
Transformer turns ratio	10:1
Vacuum tube input voltage	14.1 v
plate resistance	1,000 ohms
amplification factor	10

The solution of the problem is carried out with the aid of the equivalent circuit of Fig. 5.32(c). Much of the difficulty of solving the complete equivalent circuit is obviated by permissible approximation. We shall now outline the treatment that will be followed, using these approximations:

(1). Since we are assuming mass control, the inductive branch can be omitted. Further, the capacitive branch of the circuit has an impedance much lower than the resistive branch and therefore is the controlling element in the circuit. The total motional impedance is very much less than that of the voice-coil resistance plus that caused by the driving vacuum tube. (This will become evident if one computes the constant γ.) The coil current, therefore, is determined by two fixed resistances, and can be considered constant with frequency.

(2). As a result of (1) above, the voltage E_M across the motional impedance part of the circuit is given approximately by the product of the current and the reactance of the capacitive branch, C_M.

(3). The power is computed from the motional voltage E_M and the radiation resistance by the formula $E_M^2 R_r/\gamma$. It will be noted that all power dissipated in this branch goes into radiation, since we have neglected the mechanical resistance of the suspension. Actually, this approximation does not cause a serious error in the calculations.

We have based the problem on the constants for the 4-in. speaker of Fig. 5.42. The curves for this figure are plotted from the following expressions:

$$X_m = \omega m = 1.35\omega$$

$$X_r = \pi a^2 \rho c X_1 = 3360 X_1$$

$$R_r = \pi a^2 \rho c R_1 = 3360 R_1$$

The method of computing these values is similar to that employed in Art. 4.11.

We have for the electromagnetic coupling constant

$$\gamma = \frac{B^2 L^2}{10^9} = 4,000$$

TABLE 5.61
Computation of Power Output of 4-in. Direct Radiator Speaker

(1)	(2)	(3)	(4)	(5)	(6)	(7)	(8) X_m
f	ω	$2ka$	R_1	X_1	R_r	X_r	ωm
200	1,260	0.37	0.0172	0.15	58.0	500	1,700
400	2,520	0.74	0.069	0.30	232	1,000	3,400
800	5,040	1.48	0.25	0.54	840	1,810	6,800
1,600	10,080	2.96	0.77	0.68	2,590	2,280	13,600
3,200	20,160	5.92	1.1	0.16	3,700	540	27,200
4,800	30,240	8.88	0.94	0.16	3,160	540	40,800

	(9)	(10)	(11)	(12)	(13)	(14)
f	$\omega m + X_r$	$\dfrac{\gamma}{\omega m + X_r}$	E_M	R_r/γ	$E_M^2/R_r/\gamma$	Eff. (%)
200	2,200	1.82	1.82	0.0145	0.048	1.2
400	4,400	0.91	0.91	0.058	0.048	1.2
800	8,610	0.465	0.465	0.021	0.046	1.15
1,600	15,820	0.253	0.253	0.638	0.041	1.05
3,200	27,740	0.144	0.144	0.93	0.0193	0.5
4,800	41,340	0.0968	0.0968	0.79	0.0075	0.01

Columns (6), (7), and (8) are plotted in Fig. 5.42.
Column (13) is plotted in Fig. 5.62.
For efficiency, total electric power to speaker $\approx$ 4 watts (Fig. 5.61).

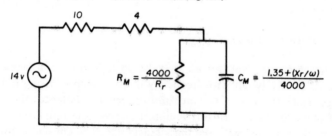

Fig. 5.61.

The special equivalent circuit for this problem is shown in Fig. 5.61. The procedure for computation of power output is:

1. For any frequency find X_m, X_r, and R_r from Fig. 5.42.
2. Compute the corresponding motional impedance from the relation $Z_M = 4,000/(\omega m + X_r)$.

3. Compute the motional voltage from the relation $E_M = IZ_M$.

4. Compute the acoustic power output from the relation $E_M^2 R_r/4{,}000$.
The computations are tabulated in Table 5.61.

We should also check the amplitude of vibration for the radiated power
at the lowest frequency. Figure 5.62 gives about 0.05 watt at 200 cycles, and
Fig. 5.41 gives approximately 0.2 in. as the required amplitude A for radiation
of 1 watt by a 4-in. speaker at 200 cycles. Since power is proportional to
amplitude squared, for our figure of about 1/25 watt we have $A = (1/\sqrt{25})$
$\times$ 0.2 or 0.04 in., an entirely reasonable value.

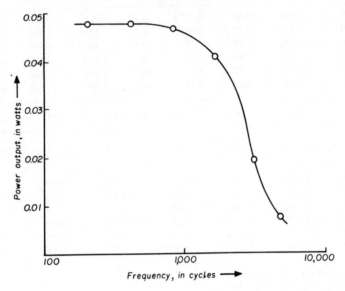

Fig. 5.62. Acoustic power output of 4-in. loudspeaker as a function of
frequency.

5.7 The Horn Loudspeaker

In Art. 5.4, the point is made that the power output of a mass-controlled
speaker is relatively flat with frequency in the region of rising radiation impedance, since the rise in the radiation impedance balances the continuous
rise of mass reactance. In this region, however, the radiation resistance is
quite small compared with the mass reactance. The efficiency, for example,
though steady with frequency, has a low value of about 1 per cent. Let us
now consider the effect upon speaker performance if it were possible to hold
the radiation resistance constant at its limiting value (about 3,360 ohms
mechanical for the 4-in. piston) as the frequency is reduced down to the lower
limit of mass control. As is clear from Fig. 5.42, the radiation resistance
would then exceed the mass reactance over a portion of the frequency range,
and we should obtain a very great increase in acoustic output over this range.

It is actually possible to obtain efficiencies of 50 per cent and greater by increasing the radiation impedance at the lower end of the frequency range. (Note that "low-frequency end" is a *relative* term, depending on the piston radius.) To understand how this increase in radiation impedance is possible, we must consider the *horn*, the device which accomplishes this increase.

5.8 Waves in the Horn

In Chapter 4, it was found that for a spherical wave, the velocity is radial, and that any spherical surface concentric with a spherical source is a surface of equal velocity potential. The same is true of a hemispherical source in an infinite baffle, except that there now exist boundary conditions—the equipotential surfaces and lines of flow end abruptly at the boundary of a hemispherical solid angle. If this solid angle is reduced, the sound field is such as exists within a *conical horn*. If we use spherical coordinates, we obtain a one-parameter wave equation *within the horn*, since all points that are equidistant from the source have the same velocity potential, pressure and so forth. For any other shape of horn there will be a corresponding coordinate system consisting of *streamlines*, or lines of flow, perpendicular to which are the *equipotential* surfaces. If we apply the equation of continuity to the infinitesimal shell included between two equipotential surfaces (Fig. 5.81) we shall derive the wave equation of the horn much as we derived the equation of the spherical wave in

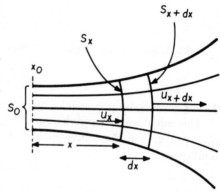

Fig. 5.81. Streamlines and equipotential surfaces in a horn.

Art. 4.3. Our initial equations will be somewhat more general than in Art. 4.3, since we may have any rate of increase of surface area with distance along the horn. Thus we have for the equation of continuity,

$$-\frac{\partial}{\partial x}(\rho' S u) = \frac{\partial}{\partial t}(S\rho') \qquad (5.81)$$

In this equation, x is the distance along a streamline.

Carrying out the differentiation, introducing condensation, pressure, and velocity potential, and making permissible approximations, we obtain

$$-\rho\left(S\frac{\partial u}{\partial x} + u\frac{\partial S}{\partial x}\right) = S\rho\frac{\partial s}{\partial t} = \frac{S}{B}\rho\frac{\partial p}{\partial t}$$

Referring to Eq. (4.211), we have

$$S\frac{\partial^2\phi}{\partial x^2} + \left(\frac{\partial S}{\partial x}\right)\left(\frac{\partial \phi}{\partial x}\right) = \left(\frac{S}{B}\right)\rho\frac{\partial^2\phi}{\partial t^2}$$

$$\frac{\partial^2\phi}{\partial x^2} + \left(\frac{1}{S}\right)\left(\frac{\partial S}{\partial x}\right)\left(\frac{\partial \phi}{\partial x}\right) = \frac{\rho}{B}\frac{\partial^2\phi}{\partial t^2} \tag{5.82}$$

For a formal solution of Eq. (5.82), we must know the law of variation of the cross section of the horn. The bounding curve of the horn may be exponential, hyperbolic, parabolic, or other shape, each having a different law of variation. In the exponential case, we have the law

$$S = S_0 e^{a(x-x_0)} \tag{5.83}$$

In this equation $S = S_0$ where $x = x_0$. We may, without loss of generality, take the origin at $x = x_0$ so that $x_0 = 0$. By differentiation, we obtain

$$\frac{\partial S}{\partial x} = aS_0 e^{ax}$$

and

$$\frac{1}{S}\left(\frac{\partial S}{\partial x}\right) = aS_0 e^{ax}/S_0 e^{ax} = a$$

Substituting in Eq. (5.82), we obtain the *wave equation of the horn*:

$$\frac{\partial^2\phi}{\partial x^2} + a\frac{\partial \phi}{\partial x} = \frac{1}{c^2}\frac{\partial^2\phi}{\partial t^2} \tag{5.84}$$

(In the wave equation, we take $c^2 = B/\rho$.)

This equation is somewhat similar in form to the equation of damped plane waves which we derived in Art. 3.18. Therefore we shall try as a solution

$$\phi = Ae^{-\alpha x}e^{j(\omega t - \beta x)} \tag{5.85}$$

We do not make the assumption that the wavelength constant β necessarily has the value $k = \omega/c$ in Eq. (5.85). We have for the derivatives,

$$\frac{\partial \phi}{\partial x} = -(\alpha + j\beta)\phi, \quad \frac{\partial^2\phi}{\partial x^2} = (\alpha + j\beta)^2\phi, \quad \frac{\partial^2\phi}{\partial t^2} = -\omega^2\phi$$

Making the substitutions in Eq. (5.84),

$$(\alpha + j\beta)^2 - a(\alpha + j\beta) = -\frac{1}{c^2}\omega^2$$

$$\alpha^2 - \beta^2 - a\alpha + j(2\alpha\beta - a\beta) = -k^2$$

We must solve this equation for α and β. Separating real and imaginary parts:

$$2\alpha\beta = a\beta, \quad \alpha = \frac{a}{2} \tag{5.86}$$

$$\beta^2 = k^2 + \alpha^2 - a\alpha, \quad \beta^2 = k^2 - \frac{a^2}{4} \tag{5.87}$$

With Eqs. (5.86) and (5.87) as conditions, Eq. (5.85) is a solution of Eq. (5.84).

Equation (5.85) indicates that there will be an attenuation per unit distance equal to $a/2$ and a wavelength constant $\beta = \sqrt{k^2 - a^2/4}$. That is, the wavelength in the horn is now given by the equation $\lambda = 2\pi/\beta$ and no longer by $\lambda = 2\pi/k$ as in previous cases (plane and spherical waves).

It can readily be shown that the complete solution of Eq. (5.84) has the form

$$\phi = A e^{-\alpha x} e^{j(\omega t - \beta x)} + B e^{\alpha x} e^{j(\omega t + \beta x)} \tag{5.85a}$$

We have seen several instances of this in previous chapters, the second term representing a wave in the negative-x direction.

The incoming wave arises by reflection at the *mouth* end of the horn. A very simple assumption which eliminates the incoming wave is that the horn is of infinite length. For a *finite* horn, there is a convenient criterion for judging the expected strength of the reflected wave. We may consider the shell of air at the mouth of the horn as a radiating piston. Reference to the curve of the radiation impedance of a piston shows that with a mouth diameter d such that $kd > 10$, the change in acoustic impedance at the mouth is sufficiently small that the reflection coefficient is negligible.

It appears that for a wide mouth, a very sharp flare (large a) should be used on horns. However, in deriving the wave equation of the horn, we have in effect made the assumption that the horn has a very gradual flare. The

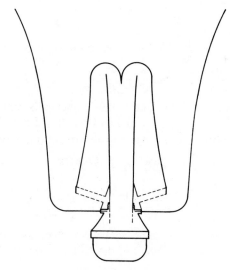

Fig. 5.82. Re-entrant horn.

combination of gradual flare and wide mouth means that the horn must be very long or it will contain serious low-frequency resonances such as are present in an open tube. For example, a commercial horn which radiates down to a frequency of 115 cycles is 6 ft long. To preserve the acoustic length while cutting down on the actual physical dimensions, horns are often made *re-entrant*, or *folded* (Fig. 5.82).

Each horn has a lower cutoff frequency below which only very weak radiation takes place. The theoretical cutoff frequency is the frequency at which β in Eq. (5.87) becomes imaginary. It is to be noted that the cutoff frequency is a function of the flare of the horn.

In the next article we shall treat the subject of the throat impedance of the horn, which indeed is our main reason for the study of the horn. The discussion will be simplified by the assumption that the horn is effectively infinite in length.

5.9 The Throat Impedance of the Horn

From the expression for the velocity potential of the infinite exponential horn,

$$\phi = Ae^{-\alpha x}e^{j(\omega t - \beta x)} = Ae^{-(\alpha + j\beta)x}e^{j\omega t} \tag{5.91}$$

we have for the pressure,

$$p = \rho\frac{\partial\phi}{\partial t} = j\omega\rho\phi \tag{5.92}$$

For the particle velocity we have

$$u = -\frac{\partial\phi}{\partial x} = (\alpha + j\beta)\phi \tag{5.93}$$

We have, therefore, for the specific acoustic impedance,

$$z = \frac{\rho j\omega}{a + j\beta} = \rho j\omega\,\frac{\alpha - j\beta}{\alpha^2 + \beta^2} = \frac{\rho\omega\beta}{\alpha^2 + \beta^2} + j\frac{\rho\omega\alpha}{\alpha^2 + \beta^2} \tag{5.94}$$

If the flare constant a is small, and if the frequency is well above the cutoff frequency, β will be very closely equal to k (see Eq. 5.87). If we restrict our consideration to this frequency range, we can write the approximate expression,

$$\begin{aligned} z &= \frac{\rho\omega k}{\alpha^2 + k^2} + j\frac{(\omega/k)\alpha\rho}{(\alpha^2 + k^2)/k} \\ &= \rho c\left(\frac{1}{1 + \alpha^2/k^2} + j\frac{k\alpha}{\alpha^2 + k^2}\right) \end{aligned} \tag{5.95}$$

From the equation for specific acoustic impedance, we can obtain the acoustic impedance Z_A at the throat of the horn in terms of the throat area S_1.

$$Z_A = \frac{\rho c}{S_1}\left(\frac{1}{1 + \alpha^2/k^2} + j\frac{k\alpha}{\alpha^2 + k^2}\right) \tag{5.96}$$

The specific acoustic impedance of the infinite exponential horn is plotted as a function of frequency in Fig. 5.91, together with the piston resistance and reactance functions, to show the great superiority of the horn in the lower part of the frequency range. The simple attachment of a horn to the direct-radiator cone speaker increases the lower-frequency output because of the great increase in radiation resistance.

However, the optimum results with horns are obtained by reducing the throat area to a value much less than that of the radiating piston (to get a high Z_A), and coupling the piston to the horn by means of a small cavity, as shown in Fig. 5.82. As a result, the radiation resistance presented to the piston of

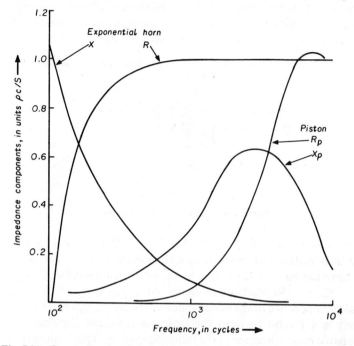

Fig. 5.91. Curves showing the acoustic resistance and reactance at the throat of an infinite exponential horn. Values are expressed relative to $\rho c/S$, the acoustic resistance of an infinite pipe of area S.

area S_p by a throat of area S_0 is effectively increased by a factor $(S_p/S_0)^2$ over that which would be obtained with the piston radiating from a throat equal in area to the piston. This effect will be analyzed in the next article. The important thing at this point is to note the two means by which the radiation resistance is greatly increased by the horn over the direct-radiator piston loudspeaker:

1. The resistive term of the characteristic impedance has a much higher value over the lower frequency range than that of the piston radiator.

2. An impedance step-up is obtained proportional to the square of the ratio of piston area to throat area.

Since, other things being equal, power output is directly proportional to radiation impedance, it is not surprising that horn efficiencies are many times greater than those efficiencies obtained with the piston radiator.

5.10 Elementary Horn Speaker

The following example is chosen to illustrate the major principles of horn speaker design. A horn of throat area 1 sq cm is coupled to a piston of surface area 15 sq cm by a small cavity as shown in Fig. 5.101. Let us assume a total mass of cone and coil equal to 1 g. Let us also assume that the horn is working in a frequency range in which the throat acoustic impedance has attained its maximum value, which for a 1 sq cm throat will be approximately 42 acoustical ohms resistive. The piston sees this acoustic impedance in parallel with

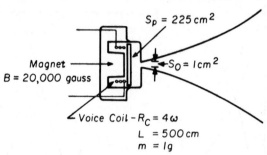

Fig. 5.101. Elementary horn speaker.

the acoustic impedance of the cavity (Art. 3.15), and if the cavity is kept small, its acoustic impedance will be high enough to neglect it in the first approximation. The radiation impedance seen by the piston will therefore be $Z_r = S_p^2 Z_A$ or $225 \times 42 = 9,450$ mechanical ohms. At a frequency of 400 cycles, the mechanical impedance of the piston mass will be only 2,500 mechanical ohms, and there is 4:1 ratio between the desirable radiation impedance and the objectionable mass reactance of the radiating system. This is quite the reverse of the direct-radiator speaker, in which the mass reactance predominates at all frequencies. In the design of horn speakers the *initial efficiency* is computed on the assumption that the mass reactance is *negligible* and that the mechanical impedance of the system is contributed entirely by the radiation impedance. Thus,

$$Z_m' \approx Z_r = 42 \times \frac{S_p^2}{S_0}$$

In the above equation S_p is the area of the piston and S_0 is the throat area.

To compute the initial efficiency, we must find the electric and motional impedances of the system. If we choose a 500 cm length of aluminium wire for the voice coil having a mass of $\frac{1}{2}$ g, we find its electric resistance from wire tables to be 4 ohms, which is a favorable voice coil resistance. We shall assume the magnetic induction to be 20,000 gausses, which is a high value but a possible one at the present time. We then have for the motional impedance:

$$Z_M = \frac{B^2 L^2}{10^9 Z_m'} = \frac{10^{14} \times 10^{-9}}{9,450} \approx 10 \text{ ohms}$$

For the electric equivalent circuit we have the simple circuit shown in Fig. 5.102. This circuit has the very high efficiency of 71 per cent, which is quite surprising when we compare it with the low efficiencies obtained with direct-radiator speakers, but we should not attribute the result to the choice of constants which could not possibly be obtained in practice. Horn speakers have

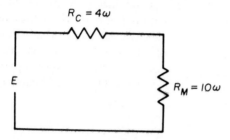

Fig. 5.102. Equivalent circuit for computing efficiency of horn speaker of Fig. 5.101. For the circuit, efficiency $= R_M/(R_M + R_C) = 10/14 = 71\%$.

been built with acoustic outputs of the order of 500 acoustic watts, and efficiencies of better than 60 per cent in the frequency range from 800 to 2,200 cycles.

In the preceding example, we have considered only the frequencies at which the mass reactance is small compared with the radiation resistance. As

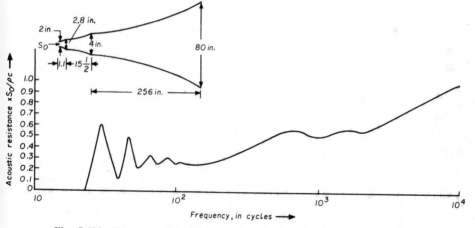

Fig. 5.103. Throat impedance characteristic of multiple-flare exponential horn. The cut-off frequencies calculated from the three sections are 25,100 and 1,400 cycles. Only the resistive component of the acoustic impedance is shown. [After Olsen and Massa, *Applied Acoustics*, Blakiston, Philadelphia, 1939, chap. 8]

the frequency rises, we are faced with the problem of a rising mass reactance and a stationary value of radiation resistance. This fact places stringent requirements on the design of the speaker, if a flat response over a wide frequency range is to be obtained. Excellent results can be obtained, however. Commercial "tweeter" horns are manufactured which have an essentially "flat" response from 1,000 to 12,000 cycles. The major problem here is the development of light diaphragm material of sufficient rigidity. In addition, a rising radiation resistance can be obtained by a compound horn consisting of two or three sections of different rates of flare. Since the cutoff frequency of a horn is a function of the flare, the over-all curve of radiation resistance shows quite distinctly the influence of three cutoff frequencies. Because of the complex nature of the structure, the curve is much smoother than those obtainable with three separate horns with corresponding cutoff frequencies. Such a curve is shown in Fig. 5.103.

5.11 Finite Horns

It is often impractical to build horns in which the dimensions render the reflection negligible. The throat acoustical resistance and reactance may then vary over wide limits as shown in Fig. 5.111. However, the acoustic power

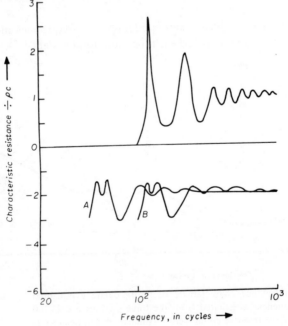

Theoretical variation of acoustic resistance of a finite horn speaker.

Power output of finite horn speaker (0 db arbitrary). Curve *A* is experimental output curve of speaker, for which all dimensions were 2.5 times those of theoretical horn. Curve *B* is curve *A* with frequency multiplied by 2.5.

Fig. 5.111.

output is comparatively little affected by these variations in acoustic impedance. The reason for this is that the motional impedance of the system is lowered by the increase in mechanical impedance, and since the motional impedance is in series with the voice coil resistance and the generator imped-ance (vacuum tube plus output transformer), a fortunate compensation takes place. Figure 5.111 also shows the power output for the same speaker, and it will be noted that though the acoustic resistance changes by a factor of 6:1, the power output is constant to within 2 db. For this reason we have not considered the theory of the finite horn.

As an example, let us assume a 4-ohm voice coil and a motional impedance that varies from 2 ohms to 8 ohms. Let us also assume that the voltage input to the speaker is constant, and the voice-coil resistance is 4 ohms. We have for the equation of power output,

$$P_R = \left(\frac{e}{R_e + R_M}\right)^2 R_M$$

where e is impressed voltage and R_e is electric resistance of coil. When $R_M = 2$ ohms, we have

$$P_R = \frac{e^2}{36} \times 2 = \frac{e^2}{18} \text{ watts}$$

When $R_M = 8$ ohms, we have

$$P_R = \frac{e^2}{144} \times 8 = \frac{e^2}{18} \text{ watts}$$

When $R_M = 4$,

$$P_R = \frac{e^2}{16}$$

and when $R_M = 5$,

$$P_R = \frac{5e^2}{81}$$

References

Harry F. Olson, *Elements of Acoustical Engineering*, 2nd ed., Van Nostrand, New York, 1947.

Leo L. Beranek, *Acoustics*, McGraw-Hill, New York, 1955.

The treatment followed in this chapter is based largely on Olson's text. However, the Beranek text contains a wealth of information on modern high-fidelity reproduction, and features an extremely thorough discussion of the design of the cabinet.

Problems

1. The diaphragm of an electrodynamic speaker has a mass of 1 g, a spring constant 10^7 dynes/cm, and a mechanical resistance of 400 mechanical ohms. Find the expression for the real and imaginary components of the motional

admittance and motional impedance if the coupling constant γ is 10^4. Plot the real and imaginary components of the motional impedance and the motional admittance as a function of frequency from 0 to 10,000 cycles.

2. Verify the impedance curves for the 1-in. and 16-in. speakers of Fig. 5.43 at frequencies of 100, 400, and 1,000 cycles from the mechanical constants given with the figure.

3. By referring to the curves of the piston resistance function, verify the values given in Fig. 5.41 for the peak amplitude in inches necessary to radiate 1 w of power by the 1-in., 4-in., and 16-in. pistons. Somewhat closer values may be obtained by using the tabulated values of the piston resistance function in Appendix 2. It will suffice to check the values at 100, 400, 1,000, 4,000, and 10,000 cycles.

4. Find the flare constant of an exponential horn if the radius of the throat is 1 cm, the radius of the mouth is 20 cm, and the length is 160 cm.

5. Plot the curves of acoustic resistance and acoustic reactance for the horn having a flare constant found in Problem 4 but of infinite length. Find the frequency above which these curves are a good approximation of the actual acoustic impedance of the horn of Problem 4. How does the performance depart from that of an infinite horn below this frequency?

6. Find the theoretical cutoff frequency of the horn of Problem 4.

7. It is desired to extend the valid region of the acoustic impedance curves of Problem 4 down to a frequency one-half that found in the problem without changing the length of the horn. Find the new mouth diameter and flare constant which must be used. Find the new cutoff frequency of the horn.

8. A loudspeaker field has a strength of 10^4 gausses. The drive-coil conductor has a length of 100 cm.

(a) Find the driving force for 100 ma of driving current.

(b) If the mass of the coil and cone is 10 g, the stiffness constant 5×10^6, and the mechanical resistance 1,000 ohms mechanical, and if the radius is 10 cm, find the total mechanical impedance at 100 cycles and at 1,000 cycles.

(c) What will be the motional voltage at each of these frequencies?

(d) Find the value of the coupling constant γ.

(e) Find the motional impedance at 100 and 1,000 cycles.

(f) Find the value of the motional admittance.

(g) Show the equivalent electric circuit if the voice coil resistance is 4 ohms and the inductance is negligible.

(h) Find the electric power dissipated, the total mechanical power, the acoustic power radiated, and the efficiency at 100 and 1,000 cycles.

Chapter 6

MICROPHONES

Bell's carbon-granule microphone which gave rise to the telephone industry was a long step forward in acoustics, but as a transducer it was far from ideal. The electric output resembled in some measure the sound input—closely enough so that when reconverted to sound, the sound was intelligible. However, the telephone was strictly a utilitarian device for conveying intelligence. One did not listen to music via telephone, since the reproduced sound was a highly distorted version of the original. In telephone engineering circles, this drawback was recognized and tolerated, because of the sensitivity obtainable with the carbon microphone. Indeed, distortion was deliberately increased by introducing resonances within the important speech range to obtain greater sensitivity, for sensitivity was the *sine qua non* of telephone communication, especially on long-distance lines.

In the period from 1910 to 1925, several apparently unrelated, but interesting developments were taking place. The Bell Telephone Company was experimenting with a mechanical amplifier for long-distance communication. This device would introduce even greater distortion, but it was hoped that it would make communication possible over somewhat greater distances. Millikan and Arnold were engaged in fundamental physical researches on the electron. DeForest had invented the triode, and though its operation was erratic and its life completely unpredictable, when it worked, its operation as an amplifier was spectacular, and it was evident, even in its unperfected state, that it would be a revolutionary device. DeForest and Arnold were brought together by the Bell System, and with the help of the engineering skill of the Western Electric Company, a stable electronic amplifier was finally produced. Although the amplification achieved was small by present standards, it was far above that produced by any former method, and equally important, the distortion was negligible, and the frequency range relatively unlimited. Cascading of amplifier stages could be employed to produce sound powers limited only by the power capacity of the triode itself; and even in early triodes, this was of the same order of magnitude as very loud sounds. Cross-country telephone systems were now possible. After conversion from sound to electric power, the waves would be greatly amplified before they were transmitted. When they had become attenuated with distance to a degree at which hearing would be difficult if they were retransduced to sound, a repeater station would be installed, and the electric wave amplified to its original strength. The electric wave at the output of the repeater was an almost perfect image of the electric wave at the output of the first transducer.

The stage was thus set for the development of high-fidelity transducers. Sensitivity was no longer any real concern. Great impetus was to come a little later, with the advent of radio broadcasting and sound motion pictures, but the first high-fidelity microphone was developed in connection with fundamental acoustic measurements. In 1917, E. C. Wente of the Bell Telephone Company, working with Fletcher in measurement of absolute intensities of complex tones, and seeking a method for the distortionless conversion of speech sounds into electric waves, was led to the utilization of the capacitor principle. Thus the capacitor microphone was born. The vacuum tube and the capacitor microphone revolutionized acoustics. Modern acoustics had begun.

The capacitor microphone opened up a new era in motion pictures. At last sound could be reproduced which had some semblance to natural sound. However, the first capacitor microphones and vacuum tubes, though responsible for spectacular advances, required great caution in use, especially in the motion picture industry. Both were guilty of disastrous noise bursts, the microphone because of the condensation of water vapor between its plates, the vacuum tube because of *microphonics*—erratic spurts of current from causes other than the signal supplied by the input voltage. The high impedance of the capacitor microphone required that the vacuum tube amplifier be located very close to the microphone. It would have been advantageous to locate the amplifier in a shock-mounted and sound-insulated cabinet remote from the sound stage, but the microphone impedance precluded the use of a cable. Accordingly the search began for microphones which would operate on other principles to give lower impedances and perhaps to have lower internal noise levels. As a result, the moving coil and the ribbon microphones were developed, the ribbon microphone having the additional property of directivity, which was very beneficial in the making of sound motion pictures. Wente also was in the forefront of the development of the moving-coil microphone, along with Thuras, while Olson and Massa were primarily responsible for the ribbon microphone in its commercial form.

The piezoelectric principle has also been applied successfully to microphones, the most important single step being the development of Bimorph elements by the Clevite-Brush Company. Piezoelectric, or "crystal" microphones are extremely light and simple in construction, and can be manufactured in small sizes for use in miniature apparatus, such as hearing aids. Their response characteristics compare favorably with other types of microphones, and because of their simplicity they are the least expensive of all microphones.

From the foregoing short history of microphones, it may be concluded that an ideal microphone would have high sensitivity, a low value of internal noise, should be free of distortion, and should have a directivity favorable to its particular use. It has become customary to distinguish between harmonic distortion and frequency distortion. The next article will consist of a detailed discussion of microphone characteristics under the following headings: directivity, sensitivity, noise, harmonic distortion, dynamic range, and fidelity.

This introduction has effected a classification of microphones from a historical point of view, emphasizing the qualities desired in microphones which resulted in the development of various types. Microphones may also be classed as pressure microphones or velocity microphones, since the sound wave is characterized by variations of acoustic pressure and particle velocity, and either of these variations may serve to stimulate the response of a microphone. There are other bases of classification, but they are of no interest in the present discussion.

Because certain electromechanical coupling factors are bilateral, i.e. capable of effecting the transduction of energy in either direction, the analysis of important microphones is closely related to that of sound generators (loudspeakers). With rare exceptions, bilateral transducers may be expected to obey the principle of *reciprocity*, which states that the response of the transducer as a microphone is related to its response as a sound generator by a simple equation. Since the property of reciprocity has its greatest importance in the *calibration* of microphones, we shall reserve the treatment for the chapter devoted to acoustic measurements.

6.1 Microphone Characteristics

1. *Directivity.* Since the speed of sound in air is about 340 m/sec, and the audible frequency range extends to at least 17,000 cycles, the wavelength at this high frequency is about 2 cm, or about 1 in. Although every attempt is made to keep the dimensions small, it is physically impractical, if not impossible, to build microphones of linear dimensions much smaller than an inch. Therefore the presence of a microphone in a sound field, particularly a high-frequency field, disturbs the field. The effect is sometimes called the high-frequency *diffraction* effect, though it is in a sense opposite in nature to the usage of the term in optics. Ordinarily, light appears to follow a straight-line course, as shown by the sharp shadows cast by opaque objects, but if small enough objects are used as obstacles, we become aware of the wave nature of light by the *bending* of the light around the obstacle, and we call this a diffraction effect. Conversely, in sound, at the low frequencies, the long wavelengths bend readily around obstacles of the size of the microphone, and the sound field is effectively the same before and after the presence of the microphone. On the other hand, as the sound wavelengths become smaller than the dimensions of the obstacle, effects are produced similar to those of geometric optics, such as acoustic shadow. The phenomenon of *pressure*

doubling takes place on surfaces perpendicular to the path of the sound, as would be expected in the plane-wave case (Art. 3.8). In general, the sound pressure field that exists prior to the placement of an obstacle is sensibly different at high frequencies from that which exists after the placement. Surfaces which are parallel to the particle velocity, however, may experience little or no change in pressure. Therefore a microphone whose diaphragm is perpendicular to the particle velocity experiences an enhancement of the high frequencies as opposed to the low, even though the microphone mechanism itself may not be frequency-sensitive.

A second type of directivity is a property of certain microphone movements, and is entirely independent of the length of the wave. This type of directivity is best explained by a description of the construction of the *velocity*, or *ribbon*, microphone (see Art. 6.5).

2. *Sensitivity.* The *sensitivity* or *response* of a microphone is defined as the open-circuit voltage developed per unit sound pressure at a given frequency. The figure is seldom given in volts per dyne per square centimeter, but instead, in decibels referred to 1 v per dyne per sq cm. A typical value for the sensitivity of a commercial microphone might be -60 db, or 1 mv/dyne/sq cm. Some manufacturers use the rating dbm (decibels compared to 1 mw in a sound field of 1 dyne per sq cm). Here, of course, the power will depend on the load impedance across which the voltage is generated.

Because of the diffraction effect at high frequencies, there is a certain ambiguity in specifying the response of a microphone, and this has led to the definition of *pressure response* and *free-field response*. If the pressure used in the response ratio is that which actually exists while the measurement is taken, the ratio is defined as the pressure response. If the pressure is that which existed in the field prior to the insertion of the microphone, the response is called the *free-field response*. The number of decibels by which the free-field response of a pressure microphone differs from its pressure response is called the *free-field correction*. In giving the free-field correction it is necessary to choose an axis for the microphone (the choice is usually quite obvious) and to specify the direction of the incident sound with respect to this axis.

It is now possible to define the directivity, independent of diffraction, as the variation of the *free-field response* with angle of incidence. Specifications of directivity are similar to those used for the piston radiator, such as polar curves, directivity factor, and directivity index.

As an example, the polar curve of Fig. 6.34 shows that the 640-AA capacitor microphone has a response at 8,000 cycles, which is 2 db less at an angle of 30° to the normal than for normal incidence. The difference is 4 db at 60° and 7 db at 90°.

The high-frequency diffraction effect may actually work to advantage if the major portion of the sound is incident normally upon the microphone. This is demonstrated by the response curves of Fig. 10.53(d) for a capacitor microphone. The pressure response begins to fall at about 1,000 cycles, and is down about 11 db at 10,000 cycles. However, because of the diffraction effect, the free-field response curve for 0° incidence is effectively flat out to 10,000 cycles, the response at 10,000 cycles being only 1 db less than the low-frequency response.

3. *Noise, Harmonic Distortion, and Dynamic Range.* Since microphones are basically vibratory systems, they will gradually depart from the linear law as the magnitude of the displacements increases. Departure from the linear law introduces harmonics of the driving frequency into the output, and the sound pressure which can be transduced is limited on the upper end by the permissible harmonic distortion. On the lower side, the output will probably be quite linear, but it is found that each microphone has an electric output even in a field of zero acoustic pressure. The totality of this electric output is called *self-noise* or *inherent* noise. There is a well-known formula for the noise produced in an electric resistor as a function of the resistance and the temperature because of the random motion of the electrons in the resistor. Thus noise is generated in the over-all electric resistance of the microphone. In addition, there is the noise associated with the random motion of the molecules in contact with the microphone diaphragm, which becomes significant if the microphone is sensitive enough. These two factors set the *dynamic range* of the microphone.

The dynamic range of a microphone is defined as the intensity range over which the output voltage is effectively proportional to the acoustic pressure (or particle velocity). This range is determined by the internal noise in a weak sound field and by the permissible harmonic distortion in a strong sound field.

4. *Fidelity.* Though operating within its dynamic range, thus being free from noise and harmonic distortion, a microphone may have a sensitivity which is a function of frequency. Older type microphones frequently had their mechanical resonances well within the range of important speech frequencies, and thus were marked by a high sensitivity at this frequency. A high-fidelity microphone will have an essentially *flat* frequency response within the frequency range for which it is intended. The *response curve* of a microphone is a plot of sensitivity versus frequency. Accompanied by the free-field correction curve, it becomes an adequate description of the performance of the microphone within its dynamic range.

While there are other general remarks that could be made on the subject of microphones, at this point it will better serve our purpose to describe the more important microphone mechanisms. We shall discuss in the following sections the moving coil microphone, the capacitor microphone, the crystal microphone, the ribbon microphone, and the carbon microphone; each has some point of major interest. Since the moving-coil microphone operates on principles similar to the dynamic loudspeaker, and in addition, is a beautiful example of the application of the acoustic fundamentals covered in the first four chapters, we shall begin the discussion with this microphone.

6.2 The Moving-Coil Microphone

The elementary moving coil microphone is similar in construction to the dynamic loudspeaker (Fig. 6.21). The voltage-generating element, in the form of a helical coil, is suspended in the air gap of a radial magnetic field by rigid attachment to a piston-like diaphragm, which is elastically retained at its

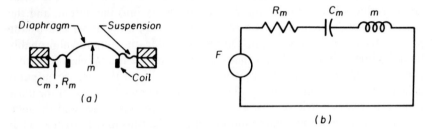

Fig. 6.21. Elementary moving-coil microphone.

circumference by a stiffness element which has also a small effective mechanical resistance R_m. Let us assume that the diaphragm acts as a piston of area S, and that an acoustic pressure P acts upon it. We therefore have, assuming an open-circuit coil, a resultant coil velocity

$$V = \frac{SP}{Z_m} \tag{6.21}$$

where Z_m is the mechanical impedance of the system, V is the coil velocity, and P is the acoustic pressure.

By the generator equation, the motion of the coil generates a voltage

$$E_M = BLV \times 10^{-8} \text{ volts} = DV \times 10^{-7} \tag{6.22}$$

This equation is a repetition of Eq. (5.23) for the dynamic loudspeaker; it is given again for the convenience of the reader. If we unite these two equations and introduce the motional impedance, we have, remembering that $Z_M = \gamma/Z_m = D^2/10^7 Z_m$,

$$E_M = \frac{DSP}{10^7 Z_m} = \frac{SP}{D} Z_M \tag{6.23}$$

The above equation shows that the quantity SP/D must have the dimensions of current, since Z_M is a true electric impedance. Furthermore, if the pressure is constant the current must be constant, since D and S are constants of the system. We have already developed the motional impedance in terms of the mechanical parameters and the electromagnetic coupling constant $\gamma = D^2/10^7$. We may therefore interpret the output voltage on open circuit as the voltage developed in the motional impedance by a current supplied by a constant-current generator of value $I = SP/D$. The mechanical and electric equivalent circuits of the elementary moving-coil microphone are shown in Fig. 6.22.

Since we are interested in the output voltage, we shall favor the electric circuit of Fig. 6.22 in our explanation, although it will be helpful at times to refer to the mechanical circuit. The variation of $|Z_M|$ (and consequently $|E_M|$)

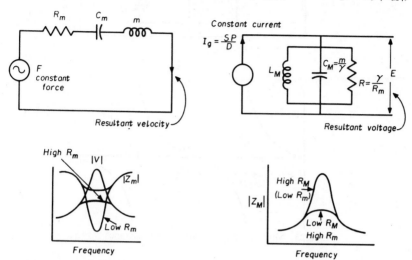

Fig. 6.22. Mechanical and electric equivalent circuits of the elementary moving-coil microphone.

is shown on the figure for high and low values of the mechanical resistance. By making the mechanical resistance large we can flatten out the resonance peak, but the response at high and low frequencies is not affected to any great degree. It occurred to Wente and Thuras that a multiply resonant circuit would widen the response. To illustrate multiple resonance we shall consider the electric network of pure reactances shown in Fig. 6.23.

To simplify analysis of this circuit, let us assume that $L_2 \ll L_1$ and $C_2 \ll C_1$. At frequencies below $f_2 = 1/(2\pi\sqrt{L_2 C_2})$, the $L_2 - C_2$ branch is capacitive, and at some frequency below f_2 there will be a parallel resonant frequency given by the expression $f_1 = 1/[2\pi\sqrt{L_1(C_1 + C_2')}]$, where C' is the effective capacitance of the $L_2 - C_2$ branch at this frequency. By our assumptions with regard to the relative size of the inductors and capacitors, this frequency is given approximately by

$$f_1 = \frac{1}{2\pi\sqrt{L_1(C_1 + C_2)}}$$

As the frequency rises, series resonance occurs at the frequency f_2; above this frequency the $L_2 - C_2$ branch is inductive, and a second parallel resonance occurs at the frequency $f_3 = 1/[2\pi\sqrt{C_1/(1/L_1 + 1/L_2')}]$, where L' is the

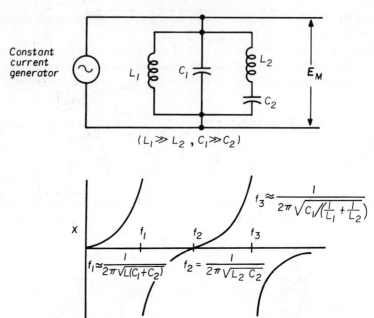

Fig. 6.23. Multiple resonant circuit and reactance curves.

effective inductance of the $L_2 - C_2$ branch at the frequency f_3. If f_3 is sufficiently above f_2, one can use the approximate expression,

$$f_3 = \frac{1}{2\pi\sqrt{C_1/(1/L_1 + 1/L_2)}}$$

Theoretically, the voltage E_M becomes infinite at the parallel resonant frequencies, and zero at the series resonant frequency, but the addition of resistances, as in Fig. 6.24, will modify the response, and curves of the type shown in Fig. 6.24(b) are obtained. By proportioning the resistance values properly, we can achieve the desired flatness between the maxima.

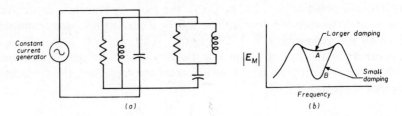

Fig. 6.24. Response curves of multiple resonant circuits with resistance.

The upper peaking frequency is introduced by the use of acoustical elements (Fig. 6.25). The space between the diaphragm and the magnet structure is closed off by a silk cloth which acts as an inertance in series with an acoustic resistance, shunted by the reactance of the cavity, C_{m2}. These acoustic impedances transform to mechanical impedances by the general relation $Z_m = S^2 Z_A$ (Art. 3.17), where S is the area of the diaphragm, and the total mechanical impedance of this circuit adds to the mechanical impedance

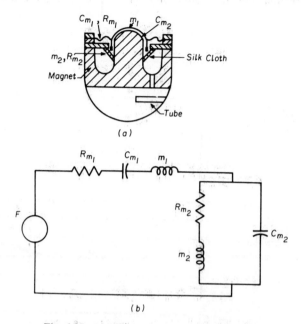

Fig. 6.25. Modified moving-coil microphone.

of the diaphragm and its suspension. The resulting mechanical circuit is shown in Fig. 6.25(b), and it requires only another application of the relation $Z_M = \gamma/Z_m$ to transform this circuit to the motional impedance circuit of Fig. 6.24(a).

The construction of a typical moving-coil microphone is shown in Fig. 6.25(a). The low-frequency response of this microphone is extended by further application of principles similar to those described for the high-frequency response. Since we have already described the moving coil microphone in some detail, further discussion will be reserved for Appendix 3.

Response curves of commercial moving-coil microphones are shown in Fig. 6.26.

6.3 Capacitor Microphone

In the capacitor microphone the moving element is an elastic metal diaphragm which responds to the variations of the sound field with flexure. The diaphragm is made one of the plates of a parallel-plate capacitor, the other plate being rigidly fixed (Fig. 6.31). Since the capacitance of a parallel-

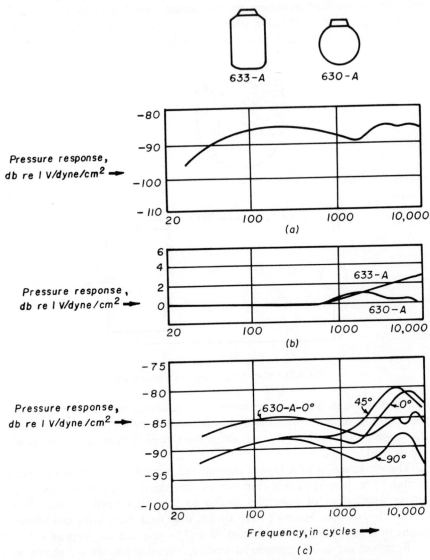

Fig. 6.26. (a) Typical pressure response of WE 630–A and WE 633–A moving-coil microphones. (b) Free-field correction for 633–A and 630–A microphones. (c) Variation of response with angle for 633–A microphone and comparison curve showing superiority of 630–A at perpendicular incidence.

These two microphones have similar internal structure, differing only in the geometry of the housing.

plate capacitor is inversely proportional to the distance between the plates, the capacitance can be made an essentially linear function of the displacement

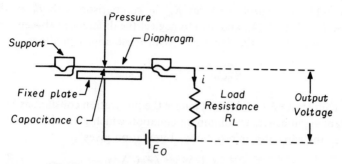

Fig. 6.31. Simplified drawing of capacitor microphone.

as long as the displacement is a small fraction of the average plate separation. If t is the instantaneous plate separation and δ is the average instantaneous displacement of the diaphragm,

$$\text{capacitance} = \text{Const}\left(\frac{1}{t}\right) = \text{Const}\left(\frac{1}{t_0 - \delta}\right)$$

$$= \frac{\text{Const}}{t_0}\left(1 + \frac{\delta}{t_0} + \frac{\delta^2}{t_0^2} + \ldots\right) \tag{6.31}$$

We shall hereafter write C_0 for Const/t_0.

Let us consider the current flow in the circuit shown in Fig. 6.32, in which the variation of capacitance is sinusoidal; that is,

$$C = C_0 + C'e^{j\omega t} \tag{6.32}$$

where C is the instantaneous capacitance, C_0 is the capacitance in the absence of pressure, C' is the peak value of the variation, ω is the angular frequency of the variation. In the resistance-capacitance circuit we have the relation,

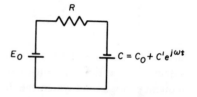

Fig. 6.32. Capacitor microphone circuit.

$$E_0 - iR_L = \frac{q}{C} \quad \text{or} \quad CE_0 - iCR_L = q \tag{6.33}$$

Differentiating,

$$E_0 \frac{dC}{dt} - R_L\left(i\frac{dC}{dt} + C\frac{di}{dt}\right) = i$$

Substituting the value of C from Eq. (6.32) and rearranging,

$$(E_0 - R_L i)C'je^{j\omega t}\omega - R_L C\frac{di}{dt} = i \tag{6.34}$$

Since the value of C' is always small compared with C_0, the voltage across the resistor is only a small fraction of the impressed voltage E_0. Therefore it is permissible to neglect the term $R_L i$ in comparison with E_0 in the first parenthesis of Eq. (6.34), and also to neglect the difference between C and C_0 in the second term of the equation. With these approximations,

$$R_L C_0 \frac{di}{dt} + i = E_0 C' j\omega e^{j\omega t} \tag{6.35}$$

If we integrate Eq. (6.35) and ignore the integration constant as having no important significance, we obtain an equation which gives the equivalent a-c circuit of the capacitor microphone. Integration gives

$$R_L i + \left(\frac{1}{C_0}\right) q = \left(\frac{E_0 C'}{C_0}\right) e^{j\omega t} \tag{6.36}$$

The equivalent circuit is shown in Fig. 6.33.

Although this equivalent circuit enables us to compute the output voltage in terms of the peak capacitance variation, the load resistance, the static value of capacitance, and the voltage E_0, we still have to derive the peak capacitance

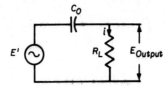

Fig. 6.33. Equivalent circuit of capacitor microphone.

$$E' = E_0 C'/C_0$$
$$E' e^{j\omega t} = E_0 C' e^{j\omega t}/C_0$$

variation in terms of the acoustic pressure and the mechanical constants of the system. In addition, we must determine from the mechanical constants the frequency range over which the displacement may be expected to be proportional to the incident pressure.

A membrane, like a string, is a multiply resonant system. Similar to the string, its resonant frequencies are given by an equation of the type

$$f_i = \left(\frac{K_i}{2\pi a}\right) \sqrt{\frac{T}{\sigma}} \tag{6.37}$$

In this case, a is the radius of the membrane, T is the tension per unit length of the boundary in dynes per centimeter, and σ is the surface density in grams per square centimeter. Unlike the case of the string, the constants giving the resonant frequencies are not integers. The first resonant frequency occurs when the constant K_1 has the value 2.4. The rise of amplitude at resonance can be controlled by damping, and if the damping is of the proper value, the displacement will be essentially constant with frequency up to the first resonance. Beyond this frequency, the membrane acts approximately like a mass-controlled harmonic vibrator, with the displacement inversely proportional to the square of the frequency (a drop in response of 12 db per octave). The response curves of capacitor microphones all show the flat early portion, a moderate rise, and an extremely steep drop.

We must now find the displacement per unit pressure up to the resonant frequency. Since theory shows the system to be effectively stiffness-controlled up to the frequency $f = (2.4/2\pi a)\sqrt{T/\sigma}$, and since the "stiffness" of the system is proportional to the tension (compare with Eq. 1.27), we may expect the displacement to be inversely proportional to the tension up to this frequency. Further, the displacement of points on the membrane decreases as we approach the periphery, following the curve J_0 of Fig. 4.92. It is therefore necessary to compute the *average displacement* over the membrane. It is found that this average displacement is

$$y \approx \left(\frac{PS}{8\pi T}\right)e^{j\omega t} \tag{6.38}$$

Theoretically, this approximation is permissible only to the frequency

$$f_0 = \frac{1}{2\pi a}\sqrt{\frac{T}{\sigma}} \tag{6.37a}$$

but since we are assuming that damping will preserve the flatness of the response to the resonant frequency, we shall use this formula for the displacement over the range of the microphone.

From Eq. (6.31) we have·for instantaneous capacitance, neglecting terms of second and higher order,

$$C = C_0 + C'e^{j\omega t} = C_0\left(1 + \frac{y}{d}\right) \tag{6.39}$$

where d is the separation between the plates with zero displacement. The equation for the variable capacitance caused by the displacement is

$$C'e^{j\omega t} = \left(\frac{C_0}{d}\right)y = \left(\frac{C_0 PS}{8\pi dT}\right)e^{j\omega t} \tag{6.310}$$

The alternating voltage developed from this displacement is

$$E'e^{j\omega t} = \left(\frac{E_0}{C_0}\right)C'e^{j\omega t} = \left(\frac{E_0 PS}{8\pi dT}\right)e^{j\omega t} \tag{6.311}$$

Hence we have for the sensitivity,

$$M = \frac{E_0 S}{8\pi dT} \tag{6.312}$$

In designing a capacitor microphone, the first consideration is fidelity, which means that the constants are first chosen with regard to Eq. (6.37). It is found that the effect of flattening the resonance peak by damping actually extends the essentially flat region of the response curve somewhat beyond the calculated value of the resonance frequency. Examining Eq. (6.37), we note first that the radius should be small, which is also beneficial for high-frequency operation from the point of view of diffraction. The permissible ratio of tension to density is about the same in steel and aluminium, but the smaller tension needed in aluminium for the same T/σ ratio makes it preferable to use aluminium for greater sensitivity (Eq. 6.312). As an example, a commercial capacitor microphone has an aluminium diaphragm with a radius of about 2 cm and a thickness of about 0.003 cm. If an attempt is made to place the resonant frequency *beyond* the working range of the microphone, it is found that unless one compromises with a very low sensitivity, one approaches the elastic limit of the diaphragm material. Small spacing between the diaphragm and the back plate is found to contribute acoustic stiffness and viscosity, both of which are beneficial, the stiffness permitting the use of a smaller mechanical tension for the same resonant frequency, and the viscosity helping to damp the rise at resonance. Since sensitivity is inversely proportional to the separation (Eq. 6.311), the separation is made about as small as possible, considering manufacturing tolerances. Grooving the back plate makes the stiffness of the trapped air independent of frequency, while at the same time effectively preserving the close spacing necessary for sensitivity and viscous damping.

Since the design of the microphone is complicated by the necessity of making several compromises, as should be fairly obvious from the preceding discussion, it is inadvisable to attempt the solution of a typical design problem. Instead, we shall assume a set of typical parameters used in the condenser microphone, and solve an illustrative problem based on these parameters.

Diameter of diaphragm..........	4 cm ($S = 4\pi$ sq. cm)
Working range (approximate)	0–10,000 cycles
Thickness of diaphragm	0.003 cm
Spacing between plates	0.003 cm
Polarizing voltage	300 v
Density of aluminium	2.7 g/cm³

A certain amount of compromise as well as trial and error is contained in the solution. Suppose we take $f_0 = 3,000$ cycles. This gives about 7,200 cycles for the fundamental resonant frequency. If we rely on damping to control, as well as the trapped air to raise the resonance frequency, we may expect that the smoothed out resonance rise will probably extend to about 10,000 cycles. The surface density, computed from the volume density of aluminium and the thickness of the diaphragm, is approximately 0.008 (i.e. 0.003×2.7). Solving Eq. (6.37a) for the tension,

$$T = 4\pi^2 a^2 f_0^2 \sigma = 4\pi^2 \times 4 \times 9 \times 10^6 \times 0.008 = 1.15 \times 10^7 \text{ dynes/cm}$$

This gives for the sensitivity,

$$M = \frac{E_0 S}{8\pi dT} = \frac{300 \times 4\pi}{8\pi \times 0.003 \times 1.15 \times 10^7}$$
$$= 0.0043 \text{ volts/dyne/cm}^2$$

Expressing the sensitivity in decibels,

$$M = 20 \log_{10}(0.0043) = -47 \text{ db}$$

It is probably coincidental that this sensitivity is very close to that of the Western Electric 640-AA capacitor microphone, one of the best-known microphones in the field. The response curves of Fig. 6.34 show the variation of

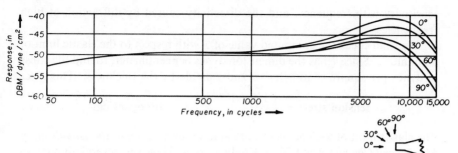

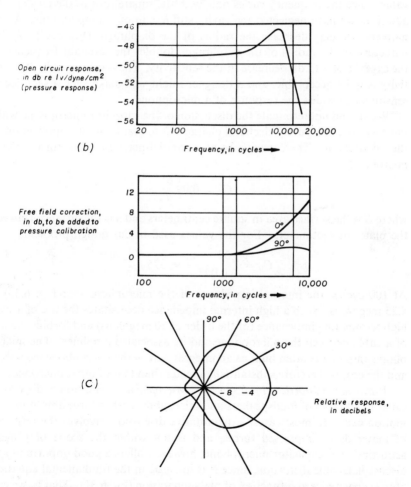

Fig. 6.34(a). Free-field response for 640-AA capacitor microphone. (DBM = decibels relative to a power level of 1 milliwatt in a resistive load corresponding to the nominal amplifier output impedance.)

Fig. 6.34 (b). Pressure response, free-field correction, of 640–AA microphone.
(c) Directivity pattern of 640–AA microphone at 8,000 cycles.

sensitivity with frequency, and the directivity caused by diffraction at high frequencies.

We shall check the computed value of T with respect to the elastic limit of aluminium. Since T has the dimension dynes per centimeter, to find the stress in dynes per square centimeter we must divide by the thickness. This gives

$$\text{tension stress} = \frac{1.15 \times 10^7}{0.003} = 3.8 \times 10^9 \text{ dynes/cm}^2$$

The elastic limit of 99.6 per cent pure aluminium is given in the *Handbook of Physics and Chemistry* as 1.35×10^9 dynes/cm^2. However, several aluminium alloys have higher elastic limits. Even if it were required to decrease the tension slightly, the resonant frequency would probably be close to the desired value, since the frequency varies only with the square root of the tension. In addition, we have neglected the cavity stiffness in our computations. Alternatively, we may decrease the radius of the diaphragm (Eq. 6.37). A 2:1 reduction in the radius of the diaphragm doubles the resonant frequency at the expense of a 12 db decrease in the sensitivity. The resulting -59 db sensitivity is quite acceptable, and a designer might well make such a sacrifice in sensitivity to widen the response of a microphone.

We should not terminate the discussion of the capacitor microphone without mentioning a purely electrical characteristic that limits the application of the microphone. The capacitance of a parallel-plate air capacitor in micro-microfarads is

$$C_0 = 0.09 \frac{S}{d}$$

where S is the surface area in square centimeters and d is the distance between the plates in centimeters. For the values used in our design problem,

$$C_0 = \frac{0.09 \times 4\pi}{0.003} = 375 \ \mu\mu\text{f}$$

At 100 cycles, the internal impedance of the microphone (see Fig. 6.33) is 4.25 megohms. Such a high internal impedance necessitates the use of a very high terminating impedance (of the order of 20 megohms) and forbids the use of a cable between the microphone and its associated amplifier. The microphone amplifier is often built as an integral part of the microphone assembly, and the cost is therefore substantially greater than that of other microphones.

Harmonic Distortion in Capacitor Microphones. Harmonic distortion exists in all types of loudspeakers and microphones when large amplitudes of motion exist. In most cases, a quantitative discussion involves the response of materials to impressed forces, and is not within the scope of general acoustics. The capacitor microphone, however, offers a good opportunity to discuss harmonic distortion, since it is intrinsic in the fundamental equation of the capacitance as a function of plate separation (Eq. 6.31). That is, we can still assume that the system is mechanically linear, so that a sinusoidal force produces a sinusoidal displacement, and thus follows the assumptions of classical acoustics and vibration theory. At the same time, we shall find harmonic components in the voltage output, since the capacitance variation is a nonlinear function of the displacement (which is itself sinusoidal) by Eq. (6.31). As a matter of fact, the displacement is always small with respect to the quiescent plate separation t_0, so that the second term δ^2/t_0^2 is quite small with respect to the linear term. Furthermore, the third term is smaller than the second in the same ratio. Thus, where we can with good approximation take only the linear term for moderate displacement amplitudes, we are justified in taking only the first and the second for moderate departures from the distortionless. We shall restrict the discussion to the output derived when the terms higher than the second power are neglected.

We shall discuss only the sinusoidal terms arising from the capacitance variation, since the previous article has developed the ultimate voltage output as a function of this capacitance variation. We now have for the instantaneous value of the capacitance variations,

$$C' = C_0 \left(\frac{\delta}{t_0} + \frac{\delta^2}{t_0^2} \right) \tag{6.313}$$

where δ is the instantaneous value of the displacement; i.e.

$$\delta = \delta_0 \cos \omega t \tag{6.314}$$

Substituting in Eq. (6.313),

$$C' = C_0 \left(\frac{\delta}{t_0} \cos \omega t + \frac{\delta^2}{t_0^2} \cos^2 \omega t \right) \tag{6.315}$$

If we employ the trigonometric identity $\cos^2 \theta = \frac{1}{2}(1 + \cos 2\theta)$, the expression for the instantaneous capacitance variation becomes

$$C' = C_0 \left(\frac{\delta}{t_0} \cos \omega t + \frac{\delta^2}{2t_0^2} \cos 2\omega t + \frac{\delta^2}{2t_0^2} \right) \tag{6.316}$$

The third term in the right-hand member of Eq. (6.316) is an addition to the direct voltage and may be ignored. We thus have in the voltage output a fundamental term whose rms value is proportional to the ratio of the displacement to the quiescent value of the separation, and a second-harmonic term proportional to the square of this ratio.

6.4 The Crystal Microphone

The crystal microphone operates by the principle of piezoelectricity. Piezoelectricity may be defined as electric polarization produced by mechanical strain in crystals belonging to certain classes, the polarization being proportional to the strain, and changing sign with the strain. For illustration, let us consider Fig. 6.41. If the orientation of the crystal cut is such that compression along the x axis causes the upper face to become positive with respect to the lower, the polarity of the charge will be reversed if the crystal is subjected to a tension force along the *x* axis. The effect is reversible. The effect whereby strain causes polarization is called the *direct* effect. By the *inverse* effect, a crystal will become strained by electric polarization. We shall be primarily concerned with the direct effect in the discussion of the crystal microphone, although the inverse effect is important for other acoustic applications.

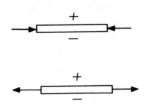

Fig. 6.41. Piezoelectric effect in Rochelle salt crystal.

Rochelle salt* has the strongest piezoelectric effect of all piezoelectric substances, and is employed in most commercial microphones. Although a microphone could be constructed with a single crystal as the voltage-generating element, two crystals are usually sandwiched together to form an assembly known as a *bimorph*. Either a series or a parallel connection may be made, the series connection giving a larger output voltage, the parallel connection giving a lower internal impedance. Each crystal is plated on both faces, for ease of electric connection. Besides enabling the designer to get a higher output voltage or a lower internal impedance, the bimorph has a lower distortion than a single crystal, the second-harmonic distortion from one crystal tending to cancel the second-harmonic distortion from the other.

In the crystal microphone, the bimorph element is subjected to bending by the acoustic pressure which impinges on the diaphragm. Figure 6.42 shows

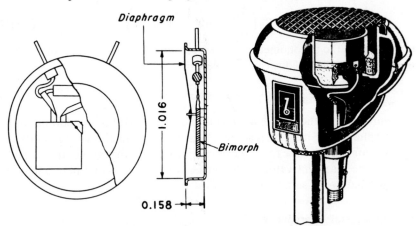

Fig. 6.42. At left is shown a sectional view of a Brush Model BB–160 hearing-aid microphone. At right, a cutaway view of a Brush Model BA–109 Public Address microphone showing microphone cartridge, foam rubber mounting, and electrical connections.

---

* Rochelle salt is permanently damaged if exposed to temperatures above 115°F, or to very low or very high humidity for protracted periods. Other piezoelectric substances are coming into use. A "ceramic" element is used in the Brush microphone shown at right in Fig. 6.42.

an indirectly actuated crystal microphone assembly with a drive pin connected from the center of the diaphragm to the bimorph, which is thus subjected to cantilever action, with consequent stretching of the upper crystal and compression of the lower crystal. In the arrangement shown in the figure, the bimorph is supported at three corners, and the force is applied at the fourth.

The mechanical, piezoelectric, and electrical properties of Rochelle salt which are important for microphone design are shown in the design curves of Fig. 6.43. The crystal microphone is designed as a stiffness-controlled system, and therefore the resonant frequency must be above the highest frequency of

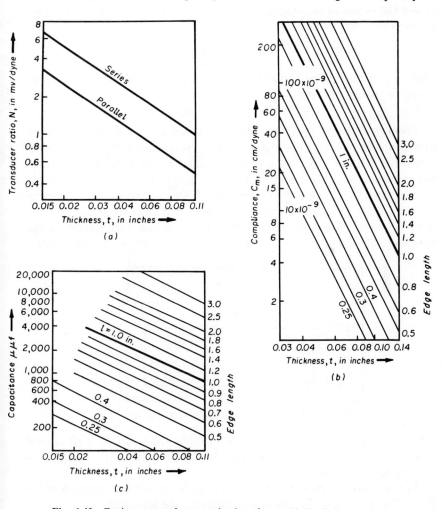

Fig. 6.43. Design curves for crystal microphone. (a) Rochelle salt square-torque bimorph, transducer ratio N. (b) Rochelle salt square-torque bimorphs, compliance C_m. (c) Rochelle salt square-torque bimorph, weak field capacitance C_e for series connection.

the response curve. Once the resonance frequency has been chosen, and the system mass established (it is made as low as possible, and is due chiefly to the diaphragm) the compliance of the bimorph element can be computed. A suitable bimorph element can then be chosen from chart (b) of Fig. 6.43. Then the sensitivity may be computed from chart (a) and the internal capacitance from chart (c). To illustrate, let us assume that a microphone is to be constructed with a spherical housing of radius 4 cm, and a diaphragm of radius 2 cm and mass 0.1 g, with an upper frequency limit of 4,000 cycles. The orientation of the crystal within the housing is such that its diagonal cannot exceed the radius of the sphere. We must first solve for the necessary compliance from the fundamental equation,

$$f_0 = \frac{1}{2\pi\sqrt{C_m m}}$$

where C_m = mechanical compliance, m = mass. With the values given, we obtain for the compliance,

$$C_m = 15 \times 10^{-9} \text{ cm per dyne}$$

From chart (b) this compliance may be obtained with a crystal of thickness 0.09 in. and length along the edge 1 in., which is small enough to be contained within the housing. For this crystal, we obtain a sensitivity of 0.6 mv dyne (for parallel connection) from chart (a). From chart (c) we find that the internal capacitance for a series connection is 900 $\mu\mu$f. However, the internal capacitance for a parallel connection will be four times as much, or 3,600 $\mu\mu$f. We have mentioned in the discussion of the capacitor microphone the disadvantage of having a small internal capacitance. The internal capacitance

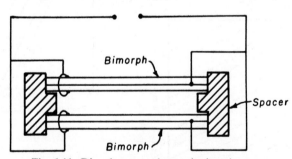

Fig. 6.44. Directly actuated crystal microphone.

obtained in parallel-connected crystal microphones is usually high enough that they may be safely connected by cable to an amplifier without undue loss of high-frequency response.

For an acoustic pressure of 1 dyne/cm² the force on the diaphragm will be $F = PS = 1 \times \pi r^2 = 4\pi$ dynes, and therefore the sensitivity is

$$M = \frac{E}{P} = 4\pi \times 6 \times 10^{-4} = 75 \times 10^{-4} \text{ } v \text{ cm}^2/\text{dyne}$$

$$M = -42.6 \text{ db re 1 dyne/cm}^2$$

Commercial crystal microphones have a sensitivity of about −50 db. We have neglected several sources of loss in the illustrative example.

A wider frequency response at the sacrifice of sensitivity can be obtained with a *directly actuated* crystal microphone. The construction is shown in Fig. 6.44. Typical response curves of crystal microphones are shown in Fig. 6.45.

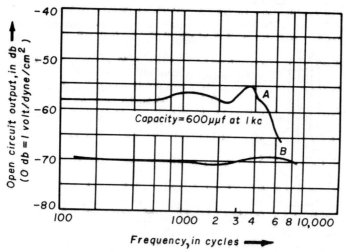

Fig. 6.45. Curve *A* is frequency response of an experimental Brush Public Address microphone cartridge using a ceramic bender bimorph element. Curve *B* is typical response of a directly actuated microphone.

6.5 The Ribbon Microphone

In all the microphones which we have discussed so far, only one face of the diaphragm is exposed to the sound field. As a result, the net driving force is a product of the acoustic *pressure* and the area of the diaphragm. In order to make the output voltage independent of frequency for constant acoustic pressure, the impedance characteristic is designed to complement the method of voltage generation. Thus the moving-coil microphone is essentially resistance-controlled because the output voltage is proportional to the velocity, and the capacitor and crystal microphones are stiffness-controlled because the voltage output is proportional to the displacement. The ribbon microphone is similar to the moving-coil microphone in that the voltage-generating element is a moving conductor in a magnetic field, and therefore the output voltage is proportional to the velocity of motion; but, unlike the moving-coil microphone, it is designed as a mass-controlled system. A thin metallic ribbon open to the sound field on both faces is suspended between the pole pieces of a magnet, as shown in Fig. 6.51. Practically speaking, the stiffness is negligible, so that the impedance is directly proportional to the frequency. Therefore, to develop a pressure response constant with frequency, a force proportional to frequency must be developed in a sound field in which the pressure is constant with frequency.

Figure 3.21 and the accompanying analysis show that the net force on a volume element in a sound field will be proportional to the *pressure gradient*, and the length of the element, in the direction of propagation of the sound. In the ribbon microphone, the *effective* distance between the front and back faces of the ribbon is equal to about half the total width of the magnetic structure. In a *plane* wave we have for the pressure,

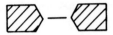

Section through pole piece

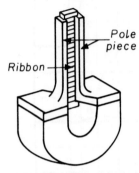

Fig. 6.51. Simplified diagram of the ribbon and magnetic structure for a velocity microphone.

$$p = p_0 e^{j(\omega t - kx)} \qquad (6.51)$$

so that the pressure gradient is given by

$$\frac{\partial p}{\partial x} = -jkp = -j\frac{\omega}{c}p \qquad (6.52)$$

If the direction of the incident sound is normal to the plane of the ribbon, we therefore have for the magnitude of the net force on the ribbon,

$$F = \frac{SPa\omega}{c}$$

where P = rms pressure, a = effective distance between front and back of ribbon, S = surface area of ribbon. The output voltage will be

$$E = \frac{SPa\omega}{c} \cdot \frac{D}{Z_m} = \frac{SPa\omega D}{c\omega m} = \frac{SPaD}{cm} \qquad (6.53)$$

where m is the mass of the ribbon, and D is the coupling constant, as in Art. 6.2. Thus the *pressure response* is independent of frequency.

If the pressure gradient is in the plane of the ribbon, there will be no pressure differential between the faces of the ribbon, and therefore no component of force transverse to the magnetic field. Generalizing, the output voltage is

$$E = \frac{SPaD}{cm} \cos \theta \qquad (6.54)$$

where θ is the angle between the normal to the ribbon and the direction of the incident sound. The microphone therefore has an intrinsic directivity which is independent of frequency.

At high frequencies, the response drops sharply. It is easily seen that the net force on the ribbon will be zero when the wavelength of the sound equals the effective distance between the front and rear faces of the ribbon. For best results the effective front-to-back distance should be less than $\frac{1}{2}$ wavelength at the highest frequency to be reproduced. Further, as the diffraction effect makes itself felt, the microphone tends to act as a pressure microphone, and as a mass-controlled system, should have a drop in response of 6 db per octave. At low frequencies, the pressure sensitivity increases as one approaches the source. The theory of spherical waves in Chapter 4 shows that the velocity becomes large with respect to the pressure when the distance from the source is small compared with the wavelength. Reference to the equation defining pressure and particle velocity in terms of the velocity potential (Eq. 4.211a) will show that the pressure gradient is the time derivative of the particle velocity (multiplied by the density), and therefore will have the same variation with distance from the source. Because of this relation between the pressure gradient and the particle velocity, the ribbon microphone is also known as the *velocity microphone*; indeed this is the common term.

The polar plot of Fig. 6.52 shows that the response of the velocity microphone is *bidirectional*. A *unidirectional* response may be achieved by the use of a velocity microphone in combination with a pressure microphone (which is essentially nondirective). If the microphone sensitivities are designed so

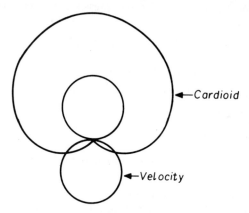

Fig. 6.52. Directivities of velocity and cardioid microphones.

that the output of the velocity microphone in the direction of incidence is equal in magnitude and in phase to that of the pressure microphone, the combined output will be given by the equation

$$E_\theta = E_0(1 + \cos \theta) \qquad (6.55)$$

where E_0 is the output of the pressure microphone, E_θ is the output of the combination at the angle θ. The curve which is obtained by a polar plot of this equation is shown in Fig. 6.52, and is called a *cardioid*. For this reason, the microphone is called the *cardioid microphone*. The ribbon microphone acts as a pressure microphone if the back face is shielded from the sound field, and it will act as a cardioid microphone if half of the back face is shielded, and the other half left exposed. In many respects, this microphone, consisting

of a single ribbon, and having very desirable frequency response and directivity, is a triumph of applied acoustics.

The applications of the ribbon microphone are numerous and fairly
obvious. In sound motion pictures, sets are thoroughly soundproofed to
reduce external noise, but the camera noise can never be eliminated. Since the
velocity microphone has a very sharp null in the plane of the ribbon, the
pickup will be negligible if the microphone is oriented so that the camera is in
the plane of the ribbon. The cardioid microphone is adapted to stage presen-
tations, since the speech or music from the stage will be greatly favored over
the noise of the audience. Though we have stressed the enhancement of *low*
frequencies at close distances, *gradient microphones*, in general, favor near
sources over distant sources, and therefore find application as *close-talking
microphones*, which are useful in noisy environments. Though it is not possible
to discuss them here, microphones can be constructed in which the output is
proportional to the second derivative of the pressure (second-order gradient
microphones). Such microphones give even greater discrimination against
distant sounds.

From Eq. (6.53), we have for the pressure response of the velocity
microphone,

$$M = \frac{SaD}{cm} \text{ v/dyne cm}^2 \qquad (6.56)$$

Example: Compute the theoretical sensitivity of the ribbon microphone
for the following typical parameters given by Olson:

Mass of ribbon: 0.001g
Width of ribbon: 0.2 in.
Length of ribbon: 2.2 in.
Flux density: 9,000 gausses
Effective front-to-back distance: less than $\frac{1}{2}$ wavelength at the highest frequency in
the range.

Solution: If we take 8,000 cycles as the upper frequency limit, the wavelength is about 4 cm. We shall therefore take the front-to-back distance to
be 1 cm, which is a quarter wavelength. The coupling coefficient

$$BL \times 10^{-8} = 9,000 \times 2.2 \times 2.5 \times 10^{-8} = 5 \times 10^{-4}$$

The ribbon area, $S = 2.2 \times 2.5 \times 0.2 \times 2.5 = 2.75 \text{ cm}^2$

Substituting in Eq. (6.56),

$$M = \frac{2.75 \times 1 \times 5 \times 10^{-4}}{34,000 \times 0.001} = 4 \times 10^{-5} \text{ v/dyne cm}^2 = -88 \text{ db re 1v/dyne cm}^2$$

The sensitivity of the RCA KB-2C velocity microphone is quoted as
-56 db re 1 mw/dyne cm^2 with a 250 ohm load. The power across the load in
watts is about 10^{-9}, which requires a voltage of about 5×10^{-4} volt, or -66 db
re 1 v/dyne cm^2. This is the voltage across the secondary of a step-up transformer whose primary is fed by the ribbon microphone. The voltage across
the primary may be anywhere from 20 to 30 db lower compared to 1 v.

6.6 The Carbon Microphone

The carbon microphone, not unlike the capacitor microphone in principle, consists of a variable impedance element supplied with a polarizing voltage and controlled by the acoustic pressure. The variable element is a cell of carbon grains. One of the faces of this cell or box is a flexible membrane, which is exposed to the sound field (Fig. 6.61). The alternating pressure of the sound wave causes variations in the total resistance of the order of 0.1 per

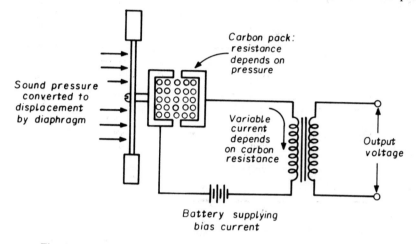

Fig. 6.61. Simplified diagram of the structure of a carbon microphone.

cent, the resistance being inversely proportional to the displacement of the diaphragm. For this reason, the output has a harmonic content, independent of any nonlinearity in the mechanical system.

The carbon element has a high self-noise. Although this has been reduced in later models, it is still the greatest drawback to the carbon microphone, and to a great extent, determines the design and application. The resonant frequency is determined by the diaphragm tension, as in the capacitor microphone. However, since the noise level disqualifies the microphone for high-fidelity application, the resonant frequency is often placed well within the normal speech range, thus sacrificing fidelity for sensitivity. The extent of the compromise between sensitivity and fidelity depends upon the application. The sensitivity is a function of the percentage change in resistance per unit pressure. There is no simple way to compute this change, and for this reason we shall not attempt to analyze the carbon microphone in as detailed a manner as we have done for other microphones.

The equivalent circuit can be most readily derived by considering the microphone with zero electric load impedance. The microphone can then be represented by the circuit of Fig. 6.62(a). We shall make the simplifying assumption that the resistance is a linear function of the diaphragm displacement, and that the microphone is working below its natural resonant frequency. In the circuit, R_0 represents the quiescent resistance of the microphone (of the order of 50 ohms), and R' represents the variation brought about by acoustic pressure. Because of our assumption of linear dependence, we may

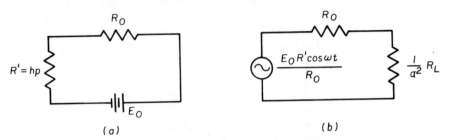

Fig. 6.62. (a) Shows circuit of a carbon microphone with zero-load impedance. (b) Shows equivalent a-c circuit with a load R_L, coupled through a transformer with a turns ratio of a:1.

write the equality $R' = hp$, where p is the instantaneous pressure, and h is a proportionality constant. Since a positive instantaneous pressure will cause an instantaneous decrease in resistance, we have for the total resistance R,

$$R = R_0 - hp \qquad (6.61)$$

For the current in the circuit we have

$$i = \frac{E_0}{R_0 - hp} \qquad (6.62)$$

Expanding this quotient as we did for Eq. (6.31) of the capacitor microphone,

$$i = \frac{E_0}{R_0}\left(1 + \frac{h}{R_0}p + \text{higher powers of }\frac{hp}{R_0}\right) \qquad (6.63)$$

The first term in the parenthesis gives a direct current which is unimportant. Consequently, the linear component of output current has the value

$$I_1 = \frac{E_0 hP}{R_0} \cdot \frac{1}{R_0} \qquad (6.64)$$

We now have rms values. This is the short-circuit current that would flow from a generator of emf $E_0 hp/R_0$ and internal impedance R_0 (Fig. 6.62(b)).

For maximum power output, the load should match the internal impedance of the generator. The load is always connected by means of a transformer, so that it will not appear in the d-c circuit and add to the effective internal impedance. Where the microphone drives a vacuum tube, a voltage and impedance step-up will be used. The power output of a carbon microphone is great enough to drive a small speaker without any amplification. In this case, an impedance step-down will be used to match the low impedance of the speaker coil.

Carbon microphones have voltage outputs in the range -25 to -45 db, since there is considerable variation of the design. In any event, they are the most sensitive of all microphones, particularly when their low internal impedance is considered.

References

Harry F. Olson, *Elements of Acoustical Engineering*, 2nd ed., Van Nostrand, New York, 1947.

Leo L. Beranek, *Acoustic Measurements*, Wiley, New York, 1949.

Problems

1. Show that the free-field correction may actually compensate for the falling off of the response curve if the rise in the free-field correction curve occurs at a frequency beyond that of the bend in the pressure response curve. Compare the capacitor and velocity microphones from the viewpoint of the reason for the fall in the response curve.

2. Show that the general expression for the force on the ribbon of a velocity microphone will be

$$F = PSe^{j\omega t}(1 - e^{-jkl\cos\theta})$$

From this expression show that the sensitivity in general is given by the expression,

$$M = \frac{2BlS}{10^8 \omega m} \sin\left(\frac{kl\cos\theta}{2}\right)$$

where l is the effective front-to-back distance.

3. A microphone suspension is essentially linear up to a pressure of 10 dynes/cm² rms. Its self-noise is 0.1 mv. Find the dynamic range. Express the self-noise in decibels re 1 v/dyne cm². Express the dynamic range in decibels. Find the acoustic pressure corresponding to the self-noise if the microphone has a sensitivity of -60 db. Find the particle displacement corresponding to this pressure at frequencies of 10, 100, and 1,000 cycles.

4. The contribution of the voice-coil impedance to the equivalent circuit of the electrodynamic speaker is shown in Fig. 5.32. Show that a loaded microphone has a branch consisting of voice-coil impedance and load impedance in parallel with the motional impedance circuit. Find the open-circuit voltage of a moving-coil microphone produced by an acoustic pressure of 1 dyne/cm² if the diaphragm area $S = 10$ cm², the electromagnetic coupling constant $D = 10^6$ dynes/amp, and the mechanical resistance $R_m = 10^4$ mechanical ohms, assuming that the system is driven at its resonant frequency. Find approximately the open-circuit voltage at 500 cycles if the stiffness is 10^7 dynes/cm and the total mass is 0.5 g. Find the voltage across the load at resonance if the voice-coil resistance is 10 ohms and its inductance negligible, assuming that the load will also be 10 ohms resistive. Find the power in the load.

5. A capacitor microphone has a plate separation of 0.001 in. Show that the maximum displacement of the diaphragm for which the output may be assumed linear to an accuracy of 0.5 per cent is $\delta_0 = 0.01t_0$. For a microphone having characteristics similar to those of the illustrative problem of Art. 6.3, what would be the acoustic pressure corresponding to this displacement at frequencies of 10, 100, and 1,000 cycles? What is the dynamic range of the microphone at each of these frequencies if the self-noise is 0.1 μv?

6. Construct polar curves for the cardioid microphone for the cases where the pressure microphone has a sensitivity one-half that of the velocity microphone; twice that of the velocity microphone.

Chapter 7

RECORDING

In 1807, when Young described a smoke-blackened drum by which the frequencies of sounding bodies could be measured, the only serious acoustic experiment that had been performed with any accuracy was the measurement of sound velocity. In Young's apparatus, a sharp scriber was held lightly against the surface of the drum while the drum rotated, and the motion of the sounding body was transmitted to the scriber in such a manner that the scriber moved in the direction of the drum axis. Young's principle was taken over by Scott and improved by the addition of a horn and a diaphragm. Scott called his instrument the "phonautograph." Koenig applied himself vigorously to the improvement of the phonautograph, and succeeded in obtaining a great number of excellent "phonautograms." It is interesting that all these men regarded recording as a fundamental tool of basic acoustic theory. It is easy to see why this is so. The rapidity of the variations of the sound wave make direct observation impossible. If the sound is made to produce a record, the character of the variations may be deduced from the recorded trace.

The phonograph of Edison, which is thought to have been suggested by the phonautograph, contained a feature that the phonautograph lacked—that of reversibility. The record that was produced by the sound could be used to *reproduce* the sound. Such systems should be thought of as recording-reproducing systems rather than simple recorders. In modern usage, however, the term "recorder" includes both types.

It is well known that the history of the recording-reproducing system from Edison's time down to the present has been chiefly one of commercial exploitation. It is also true, however, that acoustic principles played an important part in the perfecting of the phonograph; and that the phonograph, in turn, was an invaluable tool in the development of acoustic theory. The invention of the vacuum tube revolutionized the science of recording, as it revolutionized the development of the microphone and the loudspeaker; and today the objectives of the early experimenters have almost been reached. With the modern oscillograph, cathode ray oscilloscope or graphic level recorder, an almost perfect graphic record of the sound can be obtained. With modern disk, magnetic tape, or photographic film recording-reproducing systems, sound can be reproduced which is an almost perfect acoustical facsimile of the original.

221

Aside from its commercial aspects, recording is often an invaluable auxiliary in basic acoustic experiments. For this reason, it is pertinent to describe the essentials of the more important recorders in use at the present time. The performance factors are practically the same as those of microphones: sensitivity, fidelity, noise level, harmonic distortion, and dynamic range. In the following article, the principle of operation, essentials of construction, and the more important performance factors of the recorders mentioned above will be discussed.

7.1 The Oscillograph

The main components of the conventional oscillograph are an electric "movement," or galvanometer, a movable photographic film, and an optical system. The movement consists of a conducting coil supported in a magnetic field by a suspension which resists torsion. A current in the coil develops a torque which, within limits, is instantaneously proportional to the current. A very light mirror on the suspension turns with the coil. A light beam is focused on this mirror by an optical system, and is reflected onto the film. The motion of the film is uniform, and perpendicular to the plane of rotation of the mirror. An auxiliary electric system consisting of microphone and amplifier produces variations of the coil current proportional to the instantaneous variations of the sound pressure. In this way a permanent record of the pressure variations is produced on the photographic film.

Since the movement has torsional elasticity and mass, it has the characteristics of a vibrating system. It is the practice to make the resonant frequency

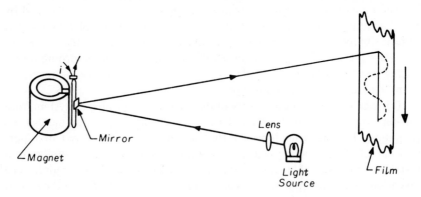

Fig. 7.11. Oscillograph, showing a permanent-magnet, moving coil, and optical system.

of this system higher than the highest frequency to be recorded, so that the displacement of the system is proportional to the torque. The resonant frequency may be raised either by increasing the stiffness of the suspension or by reducing the mass or both. Since increasing the stiffness reduces the displacement proportionally, the sensitivity is similarly reduced. Reduction of the mass of the coil eventually involves a reduction of the number of ampere turns, and this too reduces the sensitivity. Accordingly, oscillographs which have a large frequency range have a low sensitivity, and therefore demand that large currents be used to achieve sufficient deflection. Magnification of the deflection can be produced by providing a long optical path, but the instrument becomes awkwardly large if too great an optical path is attempted. Figure 7.11 illustrates the basic components of the oscillograph. Table 7.11 gives sensitivities and natural frequencies of representative galvanometers.

TABLE 7.11

Representative Galvanometer Constants
(General Electric)

	Sensitivity, in ma/mm d-c, with 20-in. Optical Lever	Frequency	
		Resonance	Usable without Correction
1	2.50	4,200	3,000
2	0.08	700	400
3	6.00	9,100	6,000
4	1.40	2,000	1,300

Constancy of film speed is an important design requirement in oscillographs, since an uneven speed results in distortion which it is impossible to compensate for. The specifications of oscillographs always include the limits of accuracy of the film speed along with their sensitivity and frequency range. Since the oscillograph is designed as a stiffness-controlled system, the response curve is similar to that of the capacitor microphone.

7.2 The Cathode Ray Oscilloscope

The cathode ray oscilloscope is an electronic instrument that is excellent for the graphic portrayal of all types of wave shapes. The oscilloscope consists of a cone-shaped evacuated tube with a fluorescent screen at the face end and an *electron gun* at the neck end (Fig. 7.21). The electron gun provides a finely focused beam of electrons which illuminates the point at which it strikes the fluorescent screen. Between the gun and the face, the electron beam passes through two pairs of plates by which the beam of electrons may be deflected electrostatically in horizontal and vertical directions, the deflections being proportional to the voltage difference existing across a pair of plates.

The most common use of the oscilloscope is for measurements in which the wave shape is repetitive. The horizontal *sweep* rate is made linear in one direction with an extremely rapid return in the opposite direction. The repetition rate of the sweep is set to some submultiple of the fundamental frequency of the wave to be examined. The sound wave is transduced to a corresponding electric variation, amplified, and impressed on the vertical deflecting plates of

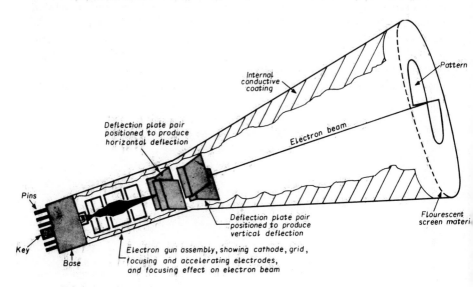

Fig. 7.21. Cutaway view of an electrostatic-deflection type of cathode ray tube, showing electron gun assembly, horizontal and vertical deflection plates, and screen.

the oscilloscope. If the repetition rate is set equal to the wave frequency, a single cycle is described over and over again, thus achieving a much greater brightness than if the fluorescence were to be excited only a single time by the electron beam.

For observation of transient waves, the horizontal sweep is quiescent until *triggered* and does not repeat itself. The phosphor used for fluorescence must be active enough that sufficient brightness is obtained in a single trace for observation or photography, and the *persistence* of the phosphor may be made relatively long. Often the sweep is triggered automatically by the wave-pulse to be observed. This is done by inserting a *disabling bias* into the horizontal sweep circuit and causing this bias to be overcome when the vertical deflecting voltage reaches some predetermined value. Since the triggering occurs in time after the beginning of the pulse to be observed, the vertical deflecting voltages are *delayed* in an auxiliary electric circuit before being applied to the vertical deflecting plates.

The fidelity of the cathode ray oscilloscope is almost unlimited when compared with other acoustic devices, the limiting quantities being the mass of the electron and the travel time through the deflecting plates. For acoustic applications, both are practically negligible. The oscilloscope is also capable of extremely high sensitivity, since only voltage amplification is necessary, and this may be accomplished to almost any degree with great fidelity by electronic amplifiers. The disadvantage is that the oscilloscope is not well adapted to the continuous observation of a wave of transient character. Although it can be used similarly to the mechanical oscillograph for continuous-motion recording by running the film in such a direction that it provides the time base, while only one set of the deflection plates is used, this quickly becomes economically unsatisfactory because of the tremendous film speeds required if the frequency response of the oscilloscope is fully utilized. A much more economical method is to use both pairs of deflecting plates, and to move the film past the varying pattern, obtaining a series of traces which are consecutive in time, but displaced vertically on the film, each representing an equal period in the history of the variation (Fig. 7.22).

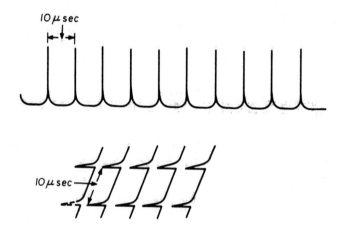

Fig. 7.22. Two methods of continuous-motion oscilloscope film recording. At top, the film motion is the time base (vertical deflection plates only were used). Below, oscilloscope sweep was used (both horizontal and vertical deflection were employed), but the film was also moved.

Summing up, in some applications one can obtain as much information on one still photograph with the cathode ray oscillograph as with the moving-film mechanical oscillograph. For observation of short transients, the oscilloscope is somewhat more economical and convenient than the oscillograph, since the transient can be used to trigger the sweep, thus limiting the observation to the important part of the event. (In the oscillograph, the film motor must be brought up to speed before faithful photographs can be taken.) It can be used in the same manner as the oscillograph for continuous recording, with the cathode ray beam serving the same function as the galvanometer, and as such, it has essentially no upper frequency limit, but the high film speed required for resolution of high frequencies restricts this employment to those researches which are sufficiently important to warrant the expense.

7.3 The Graphic Level Recorder

In both the oscillograph and the cathode ray oscilloscope, the deflection is linearly proportional to the deflecting voltage or current. The driving amplifiers are also linear, and thus the displacement of the trace is linearly proportional to the sound pressure (assuming a pressure-type transducer). Because of the great variations of sound pressures commonly encountered (the ear is sensitive to pressures over a range of over 10^7:1), it is often preferable to make the deflection proportional to the logarithm of the sound intensity. This can be accomplished by making the response of the driving amplifier logarithmic.

It is not too difficult to construct such a circuit with good stability and accuracy over a range of about 20 db. Fair results may be obtained over a somewhat wider range, but when the range approaches 60 db, which is desirable in measurements of reverberation time in architectural acoustics, either the circuit becomes unreliable, or elaborate devices are necessary. The problem is solved in the graphic level recorder by the use of a null method and a logarithmic potentiometer.

Aside from its logarithmic properties and the null circuit which drives the recording device, a graphic level recorder is similar in most respects to the oscillograph. A strip of paper is drawn along horizontally while a writing pen or stylus moves vertically across the paper with a displacement proportional to the logarithm of the input voltage. The Brüel and Kjaer graphic level recorder shown schematically in Fig. 7.31 will be described to illustrate the process in its main essentials.

The voltage input from the microphone or other source is impressed across the logarithmic potentiometer, and the voltage between the movable arm and the ground end of the potentiometer is delivered to an amplifier which provides the driving current to the writing mechanism (at points A, B, and C, Fig. 7.31). The stylus or pen is rigidly attached to the driving coil, which is given an axial motion in the radial magnetic field by the driving current. Since the movable potentiometer contact is also rigidly attached to the drive coil, the motion of the coil alters the driving current, and the circuit may be arranged so that the alteration will always oppose the change in driving current. The input voltage is applied across a potentiometer. A *bias* voltage (control P_1 in the figure) is used so that the circuit is in equilibrium (zero current in the drive coil) for a particular voltage across the potentiometer and a particular position of the movable arm on the potentiometer. If the voltage across the potentiometer changes after the bias has been set, the mechanism will move the arm until it regains its new equilibrium voltage, an increasing voltage moving it to the right, a decreasing voltage to the left. Since the potentiometer is wound so that the voltage delivered to the amplifier is a

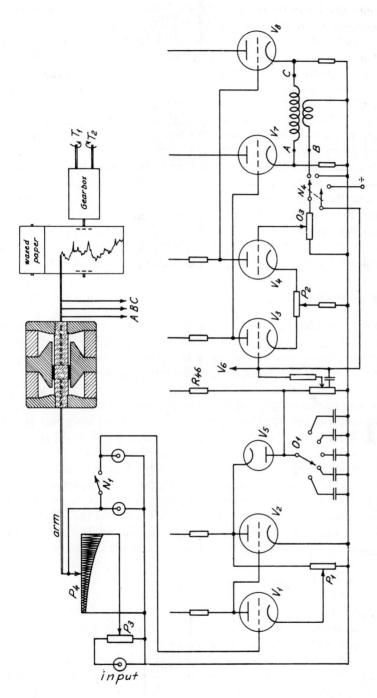

Fig. 7.31. Schematic diagram of Brüel and Kjaer graphic level recorder.

logarithmic function of the position of the moving constant, the *displacement of the recording stylus will be a logarithmic function of the input voltage.*

The circuit is designed to produce a strong restoring force for even the slightest unbalance, the maximum error being determined by the distance between two potentiometer contracts. The Brüel and Kjaer recorder is capable of a writing speed of 75 cm/sec. Thus if a 60 db potentiometer is used (such may be the case if a reverberation time measurement were made) and the width of the paper is 5 cm, a reverberation time of only $\frac{1}{15}$ second may be accurately measured. The horizontal axis may be spread out or compressed, as desired, by the adjustment of the paper speed.

An important performance characteristic of the graphic level recorder is its *overshoot*. On sharp impulses, the inertia of the movement tends to carry it slightly past the proper peak value, and the error in the recorded peak is called overshoot. Some graphic level recording manufacturers rate the maximum overshoot as 1 db, and this is approximately the value to be expected in recorders of other manufacturers, although the Brüel and Kjaer recorders contain circuit features which should assure practically negligible overshoot.

7.4 Film Recording

Although the mechanical oscillograph is a type of film recorder, the record obtained with the elementary oscillograph is not adapted to reproduction. With the rapid improvement of high-quality sound reproduction systems and the advent of sound motion pictures, it became highly desirable to develop some method of sound on film which lent itself to playback, because of the ease of synchronizing picture and sound by recording both on the same film. The obvious method of reproduction is to run the recorded trace back past a photocell, thereby producing current changes proportional to the recorded sound pressure. Two methods susceptible to playback with a photocell have been developed, namely, variable-area and variable-density recording.

In either, a galvanometer is given an angular displacement proportional to the sound pressure, exactly as in the oscillograph. For variable-area recording, modifications in the optical system are effected so that the width of the exposed area varies in accordance with the angular displacement of the galvanometer; for variable-density recording, the entire available width of the sound track is always exposed, but the exposure is made proportional to the galvanometer displacement (Figs. 7.41 and 7.42).

A typical light-modulating system for variable-area recording is shown diagrammatically in Fig. 7.41. The galvanometer in this system is usually a moving-iron-armature device carrying a mirror about $\frac{1}{8}$ in. square. When an electric signal is applied, this mirror swings about a central axis in such a way that the triangular image which falls on the slit is moved at right angles to the slit, the light intensity remaining at a constant value. The image of the slit is always focused on the film, but the portion of the slit which is illuminated is governed by the relative optical positions of the slit and the triangular aperture, and therefore the width of the exposed portion is proportional to the deflection of the galvanometer.

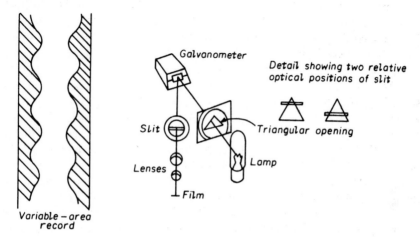

Fig. 7.41. Variable-area recording system.

The lenses form a reduced image of the slit on the moving film. This line image is usually about 0.00025 in. wide in 16-mm film recording. The maximum illuminated length of line is 0.076 in. in standard 35-mm recording, and 0.060 in. in 16-mm recording.

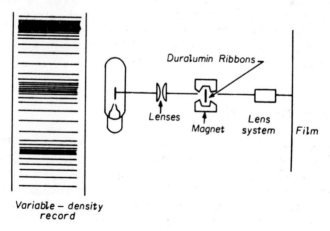

Fig. 7.42. Variable-density recording system.

The corresponding light modulator and optical system for variable density recording are shown in Fig. 7.42. The "light valve" generally used for this type of recording consists of a pair of tiny stretched duralumin ribbons in a strong magnetic field. These ribbons are arranged in the same plane, with their edges about 0.001 in. apart, forming a slit about 0.200 in. long. This slit is illuminated by the lens system, while a second pair of lenses form a system that images the slit on the film at a reduction of about 4:1 in the direction of its width and 2:1 in the direction of its length. Thus the final image, in 35-mm recording, measures about 0.00025 by 0.100 in. The audio signal currents are passed through the ribbons, which move in such a way as to vary the intensity of the light which reaches the film.

The standard linear speed of the film in 35-mm recording is 18 in. per second; in 16-mm recording, 7.2 in. per second. Thus at 7,200 cycles, which is near the upper limit of the frequency range normally reproduced by theater equipment, the wavelength on 16-mm film is 0.001 in. The latter value is commonly believed to be near the upper limit of the resolving power of the film (which is determined by the grain of the film), although microscopic examination of sound records on modern fine-grained films show that much finer detail than this can be reproduced.

As in the oscillograph, the upper limit of the frequency range in sound film recording is usually fixed in practice by the natural frequency of the galvanometer. Low-pass filters cutting off at frequencies slightly lower than the resonant frequencies of the light-modulating devices are included in the audio inputs of most film recording systems. Recently, film recorders have been constructed which have a flat response up to 30,000 cycles.

It is obvious that in order to obtain clean records at high frequencies the width of the recording light beam must be considerably less than the wavelength (on the film) of the highest frequency to be recorded. In variable-area recording, too wide a recording image introduces both harmonic distortion (see Art. 6.1) and attenuation of high frequencies. A ratio of 1 : 5 between image width and wavelength is about the minimum for good results. In most of the equipment now used the ratio is about 1 : 8 at a frequency of 9,000 cycles.

7.5 Magnetic Tape Recording

As a new high-fidelity medium for the recording of sound, magnetic tape has had significant influence on acoustic techniques. In magnetic recording the magnetic induction of a ferromagnetic tape is varied in a manner corresponding to the acoustic intensity of the sound to be recorded. One of the features of magnetic recording is that erasure of the record may be readily accomplished, and the same tape used over and over again. In addition, since no intermediate process intervenes between recording and playback, as in disk and photographic film recording, trial runs may be made before the permanent recording takes place. The recording may be readily edited by cutting out unwanted material and rejoining the tape with a simple splice; conversely, sections of the recording which are particularly interesting for one reason or another may be easily separated from the over-all record and joined into a continuous loop. This is done, for example, where it is desired to subject a small sample of the record to detailed frequency analysis.

In magnetic recording, the tape is unwound from one reel and wound onto another by a motor of very uniform speed. The tape is first subjected to a strong ultrasonic *erase* field, and then to the recording field (Fig. 7.51). That part of the tape passing the recording head at any instant will be subjected to a *magnetizing force* proportional to the current in the recording head at that

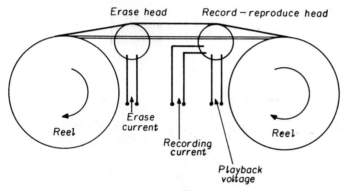

Fig. 7.51. Magnetic tape recording-reproducing system.

instant, and will have a magnetic flux density induced which is governed by the strength of the magnetizing force. In the mechanism shown, the flux lines are longitudinal in the tape; although other methods can be used.

It is known that the flux density which is induced in a ferromagnetic material by a magnetizing force is not linearly proportional to the magnetizing force. An explanation of this point would require a rather elaborate digression into the theory of permanent magnetism, and is not within the scope of this text. However, the ratio between the instantaneous magnetizing force (or recording current) and the magnetic induction which remains on the tape after the magnetizing force is removed can be found by a study of the magnetic properties of the material, and is known as *remanence*. If the remanence is plotted against the magnetizing force, a curve is obtained which is called the *transfer characteristic* of the tape. Such a characteristic is shown in Fig. 7.52. It will be noted that this transfer characteristic is not linear, and therefore some additional means must be taken to achieve the desired linear reproduction.

This process is called *biasing*, and can be accomplished by mixing a strong ultrasonic bias field with the sound signal field, so that the *peaks* of the combined field vary over a straight-line portion of the transfer characteristic. Thus if the sound field varies sinusoidally, the *average* value of the magnetic induction will also be sinusoidal. The bias frequency oscillations are unimportant practically since they are subjected to smoothing action in the reproduction process, and at any rate they are inaudible.

The tape leaves the recording head with a remanent induction which, from point to point on the tape, is proportional to the instantaneous value of the

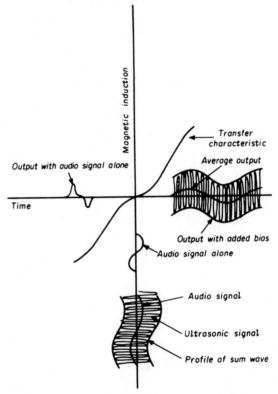

Fig. 7.52. Linearization of output by ultrasonic bias.

audio signal impressed upon it. The flux lines threading the tape establish return paths through the air which are maintained until the tape is brought into the neighborhood of some permeable material, or until the tape flux is altered by erasure. Figure 7.53 shows the approximate paths of flux in and near a tape on which a sine wave has been recorded. The second half of the figure shows the redistribution of flux lines when the tape is brought into contact with the playback head. A voltage will be developed in the playback head proportional to the time rate of the change of flux threading the coil, which in turn is proportional to the rate of change of induction in the tape under the gap.

The foregoing discussion has been based on the assumption that the recording process takes place on a tape that is magnetically neutral. The purpose of *erasure* is to remove any magnetization, whatever its source, from the tape before it enters the recording head. It has been known for a long time that a ferromagnetic material may be reduced to a neutral state if a series of decreasing fields alternating in sign are applied to the material. In erasing, the original (highest) value of the erase flux must be at least equal to the highest

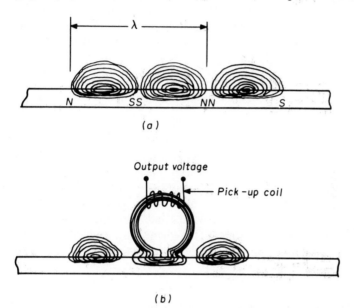

Fig. 7.53. Flux lines on magnetic tape in air and in the vicinity of a reproducing head. (*a*) Flux lines in air (flux lines not shown below tape). (*b*) Rearrangement of flux lines effected by reproducing head.

value used in recording. If several cycles of the erase field have a value high enough to saturate the tape, removal of overloaded passages can be guaranteed. The tape is subjected to 6 or 8 cycles of the erase field while within the erase-head gap, which is much wider than the recording-head gap. As it leaves the gap, the strength of field to which it is subjected gradually decreases as it recedes from the "leakage" field, and the necessary demagnetizing action takes place.

7.6 Response of Magnetic Recording-Reproducing Systems

We have explained in a previous article that every attempt is made to make the remanent induction proportional to the acoustic pressure. However, the distance between two adjacent positive poles on the tape (the tape wavelength) will be inversely proportional to the recorded frequency. Since the tape moves with a uniform speed, the rate of change of the flux which enters the playback head will be directly proportional to the frequency for a constant amplitude of recorded flux. In the ideal case, there would be a consequent 6 db rise in response per octave. Such a characteristic is called the *ideal response charac-teristic*.

However, the finite gap width of the playback head limits in a very critical manner the highest frequency which can be reproduced. When the wavelength of magnetic induction on the tape becomes equal to this small gap width, there is essentially zero magnetic force across the magnetic circuit of the play-back ring, and therefore zero induced voltage in the playback coil. For a gap width of 0.00025 in. and a recording speed of $7\frac{1}{2}$ in. per second, the critical frequency is 30,000 cycles. The general formula for the critical frequency is

$$f_0 = \frac{\text{recording speed}}{\text{gap width}}$$

At some frequency below the critical frequency, the response characteristic begins to fall away from the ideal recording characteristic, and becomes con-cave downward. The point at which the curve begins to fall with increase in frequency is called the "turnover" point. It occurs at a frequency about half that of the frequency of zero response in the optimum case, and is often a smaller fraction. Thus small gap widths and high tape speeds are essential for very high-frequency recording. The engineering problem for recording by magnetic tape in the megacycle region is truly a formidable one, but recording

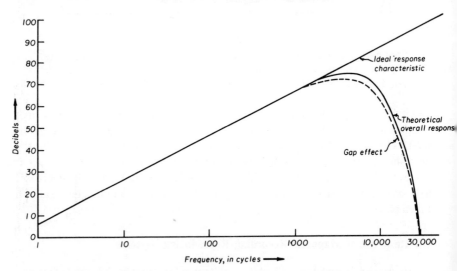

Fig. 7.61(a). Theoretical response characteristic of magnetic recording-reproducing system with tape speed of $7\frac{1}{2}$ m sec^{-1} and 0.00025-in. gap.

of television pictures has actually been accomplished. The theoretical over-all response curve is shown in Fig. 7.61(a), and it should be compared with the actual response curve of the Brush BK-1090 recording-reproducing head, which is given in Fig. 7.61(b). The departure from a flat response is of minor importance, as it can easily be compensated by equalizing circuits in the associated amplifier. There is no way to compensate for the drop to zero at the critical frequency, so that it constitutes an intrinsic limitation of the system.

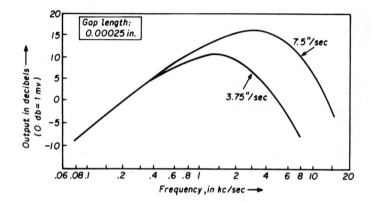

Fig. 7.61(b). Output vs. frequency for a BK–1090 record-reproduce head with red oxide, coated plastic base tape.

The intrinsic limitation with regard to frequency is not peculiar to magnetic recording. It has its parallel in photographic film recording in finite grain size on the film, and finite width of the exploring light beam; and in disk recording, in the finite size of the cutting stylus. The ideal solution, in each case, is well known; namely, reducing magnitudes of critical components and increasing the speed of the medium, whether it be the longitudinal speed of the film or tape, or the rotational speed of the disk. This increase in speed increases the wavelength recorded on the medium, and accordingly reduces the amount of resolution needed in the playback process.

7.7 Disk Recording

In disk recording, the recording medium is a waxed disk, and the recording element a sharp stylus. If the stylus is allowed to rest on the disk near the circumference and given a slow radial motion while the disk is rotated at a comparatively rapid rate, the stylus will cut a spiral groove in the disk. The stylus is supported in a massive holder called the cutterhead. If the sound signal causes forces to be generated between the stylus and the cutterhead, these forces cause in turn an additional cutting action, since the inertia of the cutterhead is great enough that its impedance is effectively infinite at sonic frequencies. The motion of the stylus in response to these forces may be either vertical or transverse (radial). Vertical cutting is called *hill and dale* recording. The cutterhead employed for electrodynamic hill and dale recording closely resembles the electrodynamic loudspeaker (Fig. 7.71), the stylus corresponding in function to the speaker diaphragm. An auxiliary pickup coil feeds back to the driving amplifier a voltage proportional to the driving voltage. The amplifier employs this voltage to compensate for the rise in response of the mechanical system at its resonant frequency, which occurs well within the working range of the recorder.

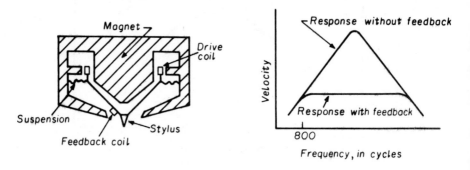

Fig. 7.71. Electrodynamic recording head, and response curve.

In lateral recording, it is evident that the lateral motion of the point of the stylus may never exceed half the distance between grooves. Increasing the distance between grooves cuts down on the amount of recorded material that may be placed on a disk of any given size. Therefore much thought has been given to the most efficient response characteristic. Research has shown that a system which is stiffness-controlled to 800 cycles and resistance-controlled above has the best over-all characteristics, although other response characteristics are used. Since the response of the reproducing head, as well as of the associated amplifiers can be designed to compensate for the response characteristic, a fair amount of flexibility is permitted in the choice of the characteristic. For example, it has been found that an accentuation of high frequencies is useful because of the *record noise* (scratch) which is always present in disk recording, and which is composed predominantly of higher frequency components.

Pickups resemble microphones in many respects. Several principles are used, among the more common being the electrodynamic and the piezoelectric, which correspond, respectively, to the moving-coil and the crystal microphone. The pickup rests lightly on the record. It is not driven radially, as is the cutterhead, but follows the groove as the record rotates. The inertia of the head is such that the more massive part (such as the magnet of an electrodynamic pickup) will follow the path of the cutterhead, while the stylus and coil follow the minute variations of the cutterhead stylus. In this way a voltage is generated in the pickup which is proportional to the driving current in the cutterhead stylus. The inverse responses of a cutterhead and pickup are shown in Fig. 7.72.

In production manufacture of records, a metal master disk is made from the original wax record by electroplating. From this master disk a number of secondary metal disks are made. The production records are shellac or plastic disks, which are made from the secondary metal disks by a stamping process.

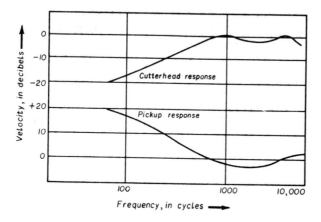

Fig. 7.72. Response curves of Fairchild cutterhead and pickup.

There are several sources of distortion in disk recording, although some of these have been reduced to a negligible amount by improved design and others can be overcome by replacement of elements which become worn in the continued repetition of the process. The tangential speed of the stylus in the groove is not uniform because of the geometry of the system, causing a "tracking error" to occur. The theory of tracking error is rather involved, but it may be shown that the distortion can be reduced to 4 per cent with a straight tone arm, and 0.5 per cent with an angular offset in the arm. The latter distortion is negligible compared with other sources of distortion. Distortion also arises from the fact that the curve traced by the center of a needle sliding in a sinusoidal groove is not sinusoidal. Such distortion may be reduced by reducing the size of the tip of the needle. As the stylus becomes worn, its shape tends to change from spherical to wedge-shaped, and both nonlinear distortion and a loss in high-frequency response are the result. This is true of practically all stylus materials except the diamond, which has remarkable wearing properties. Finally, nonuniformity of turntable speed causes a type of distortion known as "flutter," and one of the major design elements in disk recording is constancy of turntable speed. "Wow" is another variety of distortion associated with disk recording. It occurs if the hole is not centered with respect to the stamped record.

References

Harry F. Olson, *Elements of Acoustical Engineering*, 2nd ed., Van Nostrand, New York, 1947.

Michael Rettinger, *Practical Electroacoustics*, Chemical Publishing, New York, 1955.

Rettinger's treatment is devoted entirely to magnetic tape recording. Disk and film recording are well described in Olson's text. The best references for the oscillograph, the oscilloscope, and the graphic level recorder are catalogue material obtainable from General Electric, Dumont, RCA, and Brüel and Kjaer.

Chapter 8

SPEECH, HEARING, NOISE, AND
INTELLIGIBILITY

So far in this text we have considered in a fundamental way the production, transmission, and reception of sound waves. Speech, music, and noise are the three categories into which fall practically all natural sounds. Hearing is the natural method for the reception of such sounds, and indeed is the ultimate termination of most acoustic systems which involve artificial sound apparatus. The artificial sources and receivers (loudspeakers and microphones) have been considered first because they can be treated on a purely physical basis, whereas the natural elements require an entrance into the realms of anatomy and psychology, and, in general, demand the use of methods which are partially subjective.

Fortunately, the subjects of this chapter can be treated almost entirely from the operational point of view.* As an example, Fletcher, in 1925, in attempting to define *loudness*, found that it was possible to get listeners to agree with surprising accuracy on the relative loudness of two sounds of different pitch, and as a result he drew up conversion curves from physical intensity and frequency to psychological loudness. Later, he explained the quantitative judgment of loudness on a physiological basis. This later knowledge, however, was not essential for a utilitarian view of the loudness-intensity relation, and indeed resulted in no essential change in the original conversion curve. Thus the operational method can give worth-while results with little or no knowledge of the mechanism which gives rise to these results. This is not to disparage the work of Fletcher,[1] Bekesy,[2] Galambos and Davis,[3] and others, whose precise measurements of the response of the internal ear to various types of stimuli have been of far-reaching importance in an understanding of the process of hearing. Rather, it is almost impossible to do justice to such work within the confines of a single short chapter. Besides, the large-scale subjective experiments described in this chapter have undoubtedly guided these and later investigators in their fundamental researches in the anatomy of hearing.

---

* All references in this chapter have been grouped on p. 278, and noted by corresponding numbers in the text.

One of the most fascinating aspects of hearing is the aesthetic response of the human mind to the varying tone combinations that are known as music. Physics and mathematics can contribute significantly to an understanding of the characteristics that endow tone combinations with the richness demanded of great musical compositions. The study of the physical, physiological, and psychological aspects of music is definitely an important branch of acoustics. The various types of scales, consonance and dissonance, counterpoint, cadence, temperament, and intonation, all are scientific aspects of musical art. Yet it is felt that the discussion of music, as such, is outside the province of a text of this type, and the decision must be made, though reluctantly, to omit such discussions.

As significant as music has been in human affairs, the aspect of hearing in relation to human communication is vastly more important. Therefore this chapter is based on those aspects of psychoacoustics that are in some way related to intelligibility. The main considerations are three in number: speech characteristics, hearing acuity, and the influence of the ambient or background sounds (noise).

Speech, the most important of all sounds, has five aspects: the interpretative aspect, by which one recognizes speech sounds; the loudness aspect, by which the mind orders the incoming sound on a scale running from soft to loud; the pitch aspect, by which the mind orders the sound on a scale running from low to high; the quality aspect, by which the mind classifies a sound as harsh or pleasing, rich or drab, mellow or discordant; last, the tempo aspect, by which the mind decides whether the words are spoken excitedly or deliberately. Music has all these aspects, except perhaps the first, and noise has all but the first and last.

This chapter will therefore be concerned with the meanings of loudness, pitch, and quality; with the acuity of the ear; with the masking of one sound by another; with certain characteristics of speech and noise; and finally, with the perception of speech as determined by the power emitted by the speaker, the masking effect of the noise in the environment, and the hearing acuity of the listener. Consideration will also be given to the generation of subjective harmonics caused by the nonlinearity of the hearing mechanism, to localization of the source by binaural listening, and to the effects of high-intensity noise, apart from those having to do with intelligibility.

8.1 The Ear and Hearing

The organ of hearing, both structurally and functionally, is divided into three main parts, called the outer ear, middle ear, and inner ear (Fig. 8.11). The outer ear consists of the external ear (the pinna) and the external ear canal, a narrow tube about 2.5 cm long which is terminated by a membrane called the eardrum. From elementary considerations, the resonant frequency of a 2.5 cm tube is about 4,000 cycles, which correlates with the fact that the ear is most sensitive at this frequency, although it is not the only reason for this effect. The middle ear consists principally of three small bones (ossicles) which connect the drum to another membrane, the oval window, which serves as a boundary between the middle and inner ears. The inner ear consists of a

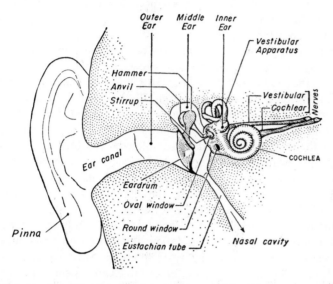

Fig. 8.11. Simplified drawing of the human ear. [After Shortley and Williams, *Elements of Physics*, 2nd ed., Prentice-Hall, Inc., 1955.]

coiled, tapering tube called the cochlea.* The cochlea is divided along its length by a narrow membrane called the basilar membrane, and contains a liquid, the cochlear fluid, on both sides of the membrane. The basilar membrane is covered with microscopic hairs, and the nerve endings which transmit to the brain sound-generated stimuli are distributed along the membrane in these hairs. The present theory of hearing is approximately as follows: the eardrum is set into vibration by the sound; the vibration is carried through the ossicles to the oval window, which in turn sets the cochlear fluid into vibration; the hairs along the basilar membrane are stimulated by the vibration of the cochlear fluid, and carry nerve energy to the brain. The combination of eardrum, ossicles, and oval window acts as an impedance-transforming mechanism between the low acoustic impedance of the air and the higher acoustic impedance of the cochlear fluid, much as a plate of the proper thickness can serve as an impedance matching device between two fluids of different characteristic impedance. In the case of the ear, a more elaborate device is necessary,

---

* Only those parts of the inner ear which enter the hearing process will be discussed. The vestibular portion of the ear, including the three semicircular canals, is concerned with motion sensing, equilibration, etc.

since a simple plate would tend to be frequency discriminatory. As an indication of how the matching is achieved: (1) the ossicles act as a machine with a mechanical advantage, and (2) the oval window is of much smaller area than the ear drum. Both of these characteristics are beneficial in matching a smaller to a larger characteristic impedance. The outer and middle ears together might be considered a band-pass filter with a pass band from about 20 to 15,000 cycles.

The brain judges pitch by the portion of the basilar membrane which is stimulated by the sound, and this seems to be determined primarily by the frequency of the sound. It is thought that the vibration which is communicated to the oval window by the ossicles sets the cochlear fluid into a kind of resonant vibration, much as standing waves are generated in a closed tube. The position of the standing-wave antinode would then determine which portion of the membrane would be stimulated. The brain judges loudness primarily by the amount of nerve energy entering the brain, and this is determined primarily by the intensity of the sound, although, as we shall see, some frequencies are more effective in stimulating the membrane than others. Experiments by Stevens and Volkman[4] on subjective pitch and by Bekesey on the stimulation of the basilar membrane by tones of different frequency are primarily responsible for the explanation of pitch on an anatomical basis, while those of Davis and Galambos on the number of nerve discharges caused by sounds of different loudness represent the clearest demonstration of the anatomical aspect of loudness.

8.2 Typical Sounds and their Characteristics

In preceding chapters, the treatment of sound has been based almost entirely on the assumption of sinusoidal vibration. Psychologically, a sinusoidal variation within the audible frequency range produces what is called a pure tone. But the ear is rarely subjected to pure tones, and it is pertinent at this point to consider what classification can be made that will help to explain the reaction of the ear to sound in general. For this purpose, audible sound will be divided into four categories: pure tones, music, speech, and noise. The pure tone has already been defined. By a musical tone is meant a steady-state complex tone in which the frequencies are simply related. We shall consider a musical tone to consist in general of a fundamental tone and its harmonics, i.e. a series of *integrally related* frequencies. The subsequent article on subjective tones will show that this is a permissible simplification. The test of a musical tone is whether or not the tone complex can be simply expressed as a Fourier series.

Speech has a more complex frequency characteristic than the musical tone, yet most of the phonetic sounds have a fairly well-defined frequency spectrum. Noise, on the other hand, is sound which, practically speaking, has lost all frequency characteristics.* The worth of this division can be perceived from an examination of the four spectrograms of Fig. 8.21, which illustrate the tone of an ocarina, the tone of an oboe, a portion of speech, and a noise sample. These spectrograms are interpreted as follows: the horizontal axis represents

Pure tone: Solo played on an ocarina, an instrument of very pure tone.

Musical tone: Solo played on an oboe, an instrument rich in harmonies. Notice equal vertical spacing.

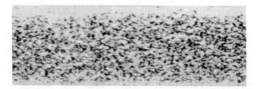

Voice: The words "Bell Telephone Laboratories." Notice the definite, though complicated, character of this spectrogram.

Noise: Random movement on a floor, showing lack of easily recognizable frequency characteristics.

Fig. 8.21. Spectrograms of music, speech, and noise. [Courtesy of Bell Telephone Laboratories.]

time, the vertical axis, frequency, and the blackness of the trace, amplitude. It will be seen that the vowel *ee* shows definite frequency bands, and that the noise spectrogram shows noise to be a confused mass of heterogeneous sound. By comparison, the musical tone has a very simple structure.

---

* Knudsen has pointed out that this omits power-line and motor hum, important sources of noise considered as unwanted sound. However, as we shall see, it is unpitched noise that causes difficulty from a theoretical point of view.

Although noise lacks distinct frequency characteristics, it does have a certain gross distribution over the range of audible frequencies. This is shown in Fig. 8.22, which is another type of record of machine noise. This record is obtained by examining different octaves of the noise with an octave-band filter. It will be seen that certain frequencies predominate, and that there is a definite falling off toward the high frequencies. However, the characterization of a noise spectrum is a more difficult task than that of any of the other spectra,

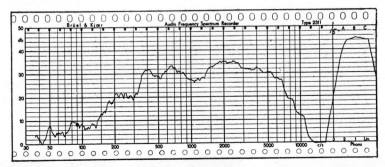

Fig. 8.22. Frequency spectrum of noise from a small lathe. [Courtesy of Clevite-Brush.]

and special means have been devised to characterize it, employing the concept of *spectrum level*. A spectrum level of noise will be shown in Art. 8.7 and the means of obtaining it will be described.

8.3 Loudness

Loudness is a judgment of the brain by which it orders sounds on a scale running from *soft* to *loud*. This current standard definition of loudness fails by classical standards of what a definition should be, in that it contains as part of the definition the very word to be defined. It does, however, have the virtue of eliminating preconceptions as to what is meant by the term loudness. For instance, loudness is *not* equivalent to intensity; it is purely psychological. Intensity, on the other hand, has already been defined on a purely physical basis. However, loudness is closely connected with intensity, and the loudness-intensity relation is the subject of the present article.

Human sensations are often difficult to quantify, yet easy to order. Thus, if a person is asked which of two sounds is the louder, he can usually make a distinct judgment. However, if he is asked *how much* louder, he is not so sure —but more of this later. Because of the difficulty which attends quantification of loudness judgments, the original investigators of the loudness-intensity relation decided to sidestep such questions at the beginning. Listeners were presented with two sounds, usually pure tones of different frequency, and asked to state which was the louder. The louder was then softened, and the softer intensified, until the subject was hard put to decide which was the louder. He had then made a judgment of *equality* of *loudness*. This is the primary judgment needed for quantification. The fact that two tones judged to be equally loud may have different intensities immediately sets loudness apart from intensity.

In a series of tests with pure tones, Fletcher and Munson[1] established the contours of equal loudness shown in Fig. 8.31.[5] In these tests, which took place in a noisefree chamber, a great number of listeners matched tones of various frequencies with a standard 1,000 cycle tone on the basis of equal loudness. The zero level of the 1,000 cycle tone was such that it gave a free-field pressure of 0.0002 dyne/cm[2] at the point where the ear was located.

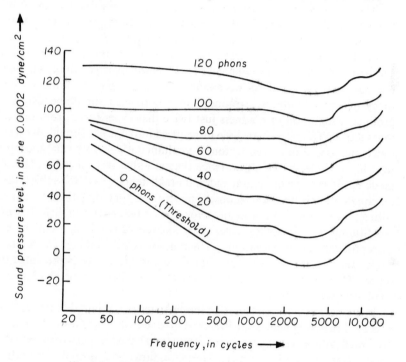

Fig. 8.31. Contours of equal loudness of pure tones.

As a result of these tests, it was decided to establish a unit which would express the fact that the loudness of two tones might be equal despite a difference in their intensities. The investigators were very cautious here. Since they had as yet no *loudness scale*, but only a means of establishing equality of loudness, they decided to use the term *loudness level*. The "*phon*" was the term assigned to the unit of loudness level. The 0 db 1,000 cycle tone was assigned a loudness level of zero phons, the 10 db 1,000 cycle tone a loudness level of 10 phons, etc. (see Fig. 8.31). Thus the contours of equal loudness level are zero phons, 10 phons, etc., as shown in the figure. Other important conclusions that followed from such measurements are the following:

1. The zero phons contour is the approximate noisefree threshold of audibility for young acute ears. It is *not* the average threshold of hearing. It has been accepted as an arbitrary threshold, however, by the American Standards Association.

2. The 120 phons contour is the threshold of feeling. About 20 db above this contour the subject begins to experience a sensation of pain rather than hearing[6] (see Art. 8.11).

3. The area included between the approximately flat 120 phon contour and the extrapolated threshold contour is called the *auditory sensation area*.

The last step in the process of quantification was the development of a loudness scale. Fletcher and others were to correlate loudness with the amount of nerve energy entering the brain, as stated in Art. 8.1, but the initial point of view was purely operational. Two different methods were followed. The first was a further development of the method by which the equal loudness contours were obtained. If it is assumed that the two ears act independently, tones of equal loudness introduced into both ears simultaneously should produce a sensation of loudness just twice that experienced from one of the tones alone. Then if a single tone introduced into one ear should give a sensation equal to that of two equal tones simultaneously in both ears, the stronger tone has a subjective loudness twice that of either weaker tone. The test is made by alternating monaural and binaural listening, until the subject decides on equality of the two sensations. The stronger tone may then be combined with a tone of equal loudness, and a loudness ratio of 4:1 established. Further repetition gives a loudness scale. This method of combining equal tones is susceptible of several variations. The tones may be combined in an auxiliary device and presented to one ear while the comparison tone is presented to the other. There is no limit to the number of tones that may be combined if an auxiliary device is used.

A second method of subjective loudness testing required that the listeners make a direct judgment on the relative loudness of two tones. Listeners were presented with a standard reference tone, and asked to vary the strength of a comparison tone until it seemed to be twice, thrice, etc. as loud as the reference tone. The scatter was rather great, but when the results were examined statistically, they bore out the results obtained with the method of combining tones. It is interesting that inexperienced listeners show a much wider scatter than those who are familiar with methods of sound measurement, a fact which has led some investigators to suggest that experienced listeners have learned to judge a 3 db drop or rise in a tone, and to estimate a 2:1 ratio accordingly. Such judgments, of course, would invalidate the entire purpose of the test; but despite occasional criticisms, the over-all findings have been accepted by most acousticians. Indeed, Firestone and Geiger,[7] Churcher-King-Davies,[8] Ham and Parkinson,[9] and others later succeeded in checking Fletcher's results up to ratios of 10:1. As a result of his early tests, Fletcher announced a scale of true loudness. He took as his unit the loudness of a tone having a loudness level of 40 phons; this unit is now called the *sone*. A sound judged to be twice this loud would have a loudness of two sones, whatever its loudness level in phons. Proceeding on this basis, it is possible to draw up a curve of loudness against loudness level. The presently accepted loudness vs. loudness level curve is shown in Fig. 8.32.

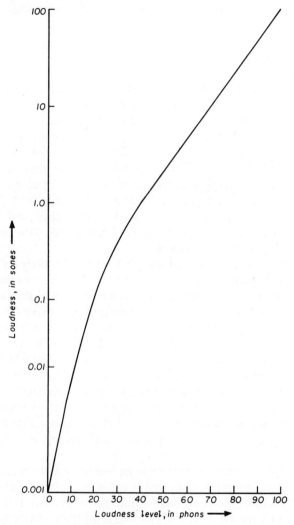

Fig. 8.32. Loudness vs. loudness curve.

The *sensation level* of a tone is the number of db by which it exceeds its threshold. The sensation level of a 40 db tone is 40 db at 1,000 cycles, but it is only about 20 db at 300 cycles, and is about 2 db at 100 cycles (see Fig. 8.31). This is for persons with maximum acuity of hearing. For the average person, the sensation levels are 5 to 10 db less, and for deafened persons considerably less. In fact, the shift in the sensation level is a measure of hearing loss. However, the arbitrary threshold of Fig. 8.31 will be taken as a working threshold in subsequent discussions of sensation level. The figures given above are for the noisefree sensation level. Noise has the effect of changing the individual's threshold, and therefore the effective sensation level, for a particular tone.

8.4 Pitch and Timbre

Pitch is a judgment of the brain by which it orders sounds on a scale running from low to high. If only sinusoidal tones were to be considered, pitch and loudness would completely characterize a tone. The problem becomes more difficult when tones with several harmonics are considered, but such tones can be completely characterized by the trio of characteristics: loudness, pitch, and timbre. When tones more complex than musical tones are considered, the concepts of pitch and timbre tend to become difficult to apply. We shall therefore begin the discussion of pitch with the pure tone. Pitch investigations begin with the realization that pitch and frequency, though closely related, are not synonymous. The progress of the investigation is broadly similar to that of loudness.

At one time, Fletcher[1] proposed that pitch be based entirely on frequency, with the numerical value of the pitch equal to the logarithm to the base 2 of the frequency. Subsequent investigation, however, showed that loudness as well as frequency influenced pitch, and it was decided to make the pitch scale purely subjective. As an example, if two notes of rather low intensity having a 2:1 frequency ratio are presented to the average person, he will judge them to be octaves of each other. But if either tone is raised greatly in intensity, it will begin to sound flat, even though its frequency is maintained constant. This phenomenon led investigators into a series of experiments which were closely analogous to the establishment of equal loudness contours. The last phase was an attempt to make quantitative pitch judgments, together with the construction of a scale of pitch independent of frequency, and the choice of a unit.

As an example of the distinction between frequency and pitch, an 80 phon tone of 210 cycles will often be judged equal in pitch to a 40 phon tone of 200 cycles. (This differs considerably for different observers.) If it is assumed that the pitch of a tone *is* what it *appears* to be, if the majority of observers agree, pitch must depend on loudness as well as frequency. Figure 8.41 shows the frequency shift necessary to preserve the pitch of a tone as the loudness is increased. In each case, one of the tones had a loudness level of 40 phons, and the frequencies of the two tones were equal. The curves show the common pitch, the loudness of the comparison tone, and the shift in pitch brought about by raising the loudness level. It will be noted that the louder tone always has a lower pitch in the region included on the curves, and that the effect is greatest between 70 and 300 cycles, and relatively insignificant above 1,000 cycles.

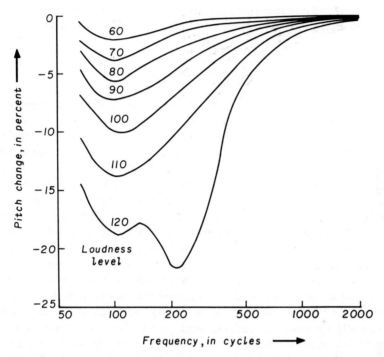

Fig. 8.41. Pitch as a function of loudness. Curves show the amount by which the pitch of a pure tone of any frequency is shifted as the tone is raised in loudness level from 40 to the level of contour.

Lastly, observers are asked to adjust the frequencies of two pure tones of the same loudness level, until one appears to have twice the pitch of the other. The tones are not given to the observer simultaneously, but in sequence, so that he cannot make use of the beat method in matching them. Such experiments as have been performed up to the present appear to show that the relation between pitch and frequency is not linear, and have resulted in the establishment of the pitch-frequency scale similar to the loudness-level scale. A 1,000 cycle, 40 phon tone is then defined as having a pitch of 1,000 subjective pitch units, which are called *mels*. A tone having an apparent pitch twice as high has a pitch of 2,000 mels, and so forth, regardless of its frequency.

Several investigators have felt that pitch discrimination[10] is fundamental to the recognition of speech sounds, and an intelligibility theory has been proposed which is based on minimum recognizable pitch increments.[11] However, such theory is still in somewhat of a formative state, and we shall follow French and Steinberg[12] in an approach to intelligibility which is based on sensation level. In this theory, the importance of pitch is secondary to loudness. For this reason, other recent findings with respect to pitch, which might be pertinent in a different approach, will be omitted. A good review of pitch can be found in Fletcher's *Speech and Hearing in Communications*.

8.5 Masking

Masking is an important consideration in psychoacoustics, because the listener is seldom in a noisefree environment. The establishment of the noise-free threshold, which was done by Sivian and White[5] in 1922 as the preliminary to the tests which resulted in the contours of equal loudness, is of great value in setting the limit of the acuity of the human ear, thereby separating audible from inaudible sounds. But it is also important to discover what sound levels are necessary for hearing in an average environment. The Bell Telephone Laboratories, at about the same time, decided to institute a study of the masking of one sound by another. Interest in this subject existed because so many phone booths were in noisy locations. As an instance, there are several thousand phone booths in the New York City subways.

It is well known from experience that one can perceive a soft tone in the presence of a louder tone, and yet soft tones will inevitably be lost in a very noisy environment. If, while sound A is being impressed on the ear, sound B is gradually increased in loudness until sound A can no longer be heard, sound A is said to be *masked* by sound B. Quantitatively, masking is defined as the number of decibels by which the listener's actual threshold of audibility is raised by another sound. If either or both sounds are complex, it is difficult to express the value of the masking in a general manner. Therefore it was decided to begin the investigation of masking with a study of the masking of pure tones by pure tones.

A typical test showed that if a 1,200 cycle tone of intensity level 60 db re 0.002 dyne/cm^2 was used as the masking tone, a tone of 1,250 cycles had to be raised to 46 db above its threshold level before it could be perceived in the presence of the masking tone, while a tone of 3,000 cycles could be perceived when it was only 8 units above its threshold. Further experimentation shows that if the level of the masking tone is raised to 100 db, the 3,000 cycle tone must be raised to 75 db above its threshold level, while those frequencies below 300 cycles can be heard when their intensity is only slightly above their threshold value. The results of the masking by the 1,200 cycle tone at different intensities are shown in Fig. 8.51. Similar results are obtained for other masking frequencies. The following conclusions may be drawn:

1.   Masking is most effective for tones of frequency in the neighborhood

of the masking tone. The beat phenomenon accounts for the drop at the frequency of the masking tone.

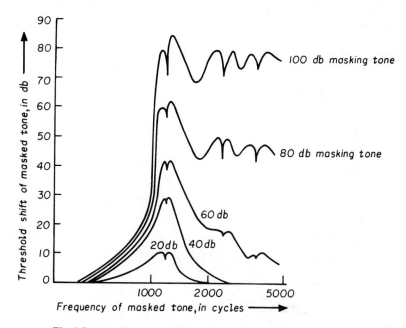

Fig. 8.51. Masking by a 1,200 cycle tone at different intensities.

2.   Dips in the masking curve at harmonics of the masking frequency are due to the generation of subjective tones, because of the nonlinearity of the hearing mechanism.

3.   For high-intensity masking tones, masking is effective for all frequencies above that of the masking frequency, while relatively ineffective for frequencies below, if they are not in the immediate neighborhood of the masking tone. A study of the generation of subjective tones (Art. 8.6) will show that this is not independent of the first conclusion.

One is usually most interested in masking caused by *noise*. A transition from the simplest theoretical case of masking by pure tones to the important practical case of masking by noise can be made by studying the masking effect of complex tones of known composition. Let us consider a complex tone of three components: a 300 cycle tone with a sensation level of 10 db, a 400 cycle tone with an intensity level of 50 db re 0.0002 dyne/cm², and a 2,000 cycle tone with a sensation level of 10 db.

Referring to Fig. 8.52, which exhibits masking in a more convenient manner for this problem, we find that the threshold of a 300 cycle tone is shifted by more than 10 db by a 50 db 400 cycle tone, and that therefore the 300 cycle component will be inaudible. The threshold shift of the 2,000 cycle tone is less than 10 db and it will be heard. Suppose, now, that this complex tone is amplified linearly, which often happens in sound systems, and that the intensity level of each tone is increased by 30 db, so that the 300 cycle tone is 40 db above its threshold, the 2,000 cycle tone is 40 db above its threshold, and the 400 cycle tone has an intensity level of 80 db re 0.0002 dyne/cm². Figure 8.52 shows that the 300 cycle tone is now audible, and the 2,000 cycle

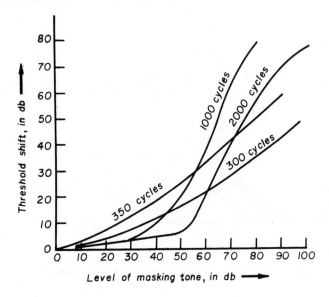

Fig. 8.52. Masking by 400 cycle tone, shown by threshold shift of frequencies from 300 to 2,000 cycles.

tone inaudible. The ultimate result in this example is a change in the quality of a complex tone, although this result is purely incidental for our purpose, which is to further clarify the concept of masking.

Referring again to Fig. 8.51, we find that the threshold of audibility for a 1,600 cycle tone is shifted by 25 db by a 1,200 cycle tone having a pressure level of 60 db. Since the threshold is slightly under zero db at 1,600 cycles (Fig. 8.31), the new threshold becomes slightly under 25 db. Sometimes curves such as 8.51 are called masking "spectra" of pure tones, since they give the magnitude of masking as a function of the frequency of the masked tone. The masking spectra of narrow bands of noise resemble the masking spectra of lower intensity pure tones, in that the masking is effective only in the vicinity of the noise band.

The sensation level has been defined in Art. 8.3 for a noisefree environment. The sensation level in a noisy environment is equal to the sensation level in a noisefree environment minus the masking. If we take H as the noisefree sensation level, M as the masking, and E as the effective sensation level

(level in a noisy environment), we have

$$E = H - M \qquad (8.51)$$

Masking by noise will be discussed in greater detail in Art. 8.7.

8.6 Subjective Tones—Nonlinear Response

The dips in the curves of Fig. 8.51 at harmonics of the masking frequency proved very interesting to the investigators conducting the experiments on masking of pure tones by pure tones. It was first suspected that there were harmonics present in the masking tone. Investigation showed, however, that these dips were still present when the masking tone was made purely sinusoidal to a very high degree. It was therefore concluded that the harmonics are generated within the ear itself. For this to be possible, some part of the ear must contain a mechanism which is nonlinear.

In the first chapter, the production of beats was interpreted as a swelling and fading of the amplitude of a sound wave caused by the alternate reinforcement and cancellation of two component tones. It is now necessary to state that a new tone is not necessarily produced at this beat frequency, since an *alternation* of pressure at a certain frequency is required to produce a component tone of the same frequency. If the two tones are mixed in a nonlinear device, however, the output will contain, in addition to the two input frequencies, a *tone* at a frequency equal to their difference. Furthermore, if a single tone is introduced into such a nonlinear device, various harmonics of this tone will be produced. All of classical acoustics is based on the assumption of linearity between stress and strain. Thus a sinusoidal force always produces sinusoidal velocity at the frequency of this driving force and we can write the familiar relation

$$v = Yf \qquad (8.61)$$

where v = velocity, Y = admittance, f = force.

It may happen, however, that this relationship is not observed. The simplest departure is one in which the velocity, written as a function of the force, contains both a linear and a quadratic term. That is

$$v = Y_1 f + Y_2 f^2 \qquad (8.62)$$

For the above relation, let us investigate the instantaneous velocity in the case of a sinusoidal force.

$$\begin{aligned}
v &= Y_1 A \sin \omega t + Y_2 A^2 \sin^2 \omega t \\
&= Y_1 A \sin \omega t + \tfrac{1}{2} Y_2 A^2 (1 - \cos 2\omega t) \\
&= Y_1 A \sin \omega t - \tfrac{1}{2} Y_2 A^2 \cos 2\omega t + \tfrac{1}{2} Y_2 A^2 \qquad (8.63)
\end{aligned}$$

The effect of the second-power term is thus to produce a second-harmonic output and a "d-c" term which is of minor importance. In many acoustic devices the coefficient Y_2, while not zero, is much smaller than Y_1. As a result, the output is approximately proportional to the input as long as a certain input level is not exceeded. For higher input levels, however, the non-linearity of the device may become significant. From an examination of Fig. 8.51 we would be led to the conclusion that this transition point for the human ear is somewhere between 40 and 60 db for a 1,200 cycle tone.

It is now pertinent to study the output of a nonlinear device arising from the second-power term when a pair of frequencies are impressed on the input. The output will then be represented by a function of the form,

$$v = (\cos \omega_1 t + \cos \omega_2 t)^2$$
$$= \cos^2 \omega_1 t + 2 \cos \omega_1 t \cos \omega_2 t + \cos^2 \omega_2 t \qquad (8.64)$$

This can be readily changed by the use of trigonometric identities to the equivalent form:

$$(\tfrac{1}{2} + \tfrac{1}{2} \cos 2\omega_1 t) + (\tfrac{1}{2} + \tfrac{1}{2} \cos 2\omega_2 t)$$
$$+ \cos (\omega_1 + \omega_2)t + \cos (\omega_1 - \omega_2)t \qquad (8.65)$$

which shows that the following frequencies are present in the output:

1. Second harmonics of each of the component tones.
2. A tone having a frequency equal to the difference of the components.
3. A tone having a frequency equal to the sum of the components.

The two component frequencies will also be present in the output, and in general higher harmonics will be present, because of the presence of higher power terms in the output-input relation.

In the case of a single tone, the intensity of the various harmonics may be estimated in the following manner. In the presence of a strong, fixed-frequency master tone, say an 80 db, 1,200 cycle tone, an exploring tone is changed in frequency until beats are obtained, and then in intensity until the beats are most prominent. Since it is known that beats are best recognized when the intensities of the component tones are equal, the intensity of the exploring tone for greatest beat intensity may be taken as the intensity of the harmonic. Figure 8.61 shows the intensity levels at which harmonics first appear, while Fig. 8.62 shows the sensation levels of the harmonics of a 50 cycle tone for four different values of the fundamental (first harmonic). The surprising thing about the latter figure is that in several cases the *sensation level* of a harmonic is actually *greater* than that of the fundamental. This fact has led some hearing experts to suspect that low-frequency tones may not actually be heard as such, but that they are recognized by the harmonics that they produce in the ear.

In somewhat the same manner, the sensation levels of sum and difference tones are measured when a pair of tones is impressed upon the ear. The results are much more complex, for the sum and difference tones first produced can combine with the original tones and one another to produce secondary and tertiary terms, and terms of higher order.

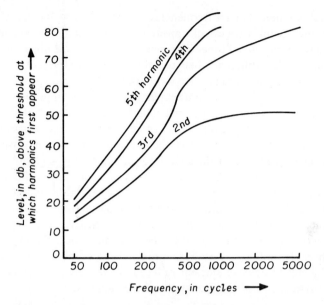

Fig. 8.61. The level above threshold at which subjective harmonics are generated in the ear, as a function of frequency.

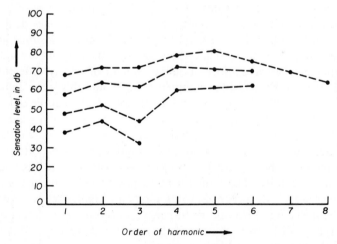

Fig. 8.62. Sensation levels of subjective harmonics of a 50 cycle tone. [After Fletcher.]

The above findings help to explain an interesting phenomenon which has been known for some time and which has practical importance in the design of low-priced reproduction systems, such as those used in small household radio and television sets. This is the phenomenon in which the ear supplies the fundamental if a series of harmonics is presented to the ear with the fundamental missing. Thus if frequencies of 300, 400, and 700 are presented to the ear, the complex tone will appear to have a pitch of 100 cycles. In general, if a series of related tones is presented to the ear, the apparent pitch is equal to the smallest difference between the various components. This fact may be used to good advantage when we recall that hum frequencies of 60 and 120 cycles, which are present to some extent in practically all present-day electrical apparatus, may cause serious masking throughout most of the important audible spectrum. Since filtering of these power line frequencies requires heavy and fairly expensive apparatus, the audio systems of inexpensive radio receivers are designed so that the sound power radiated is negligible below a frequency of about 150 cycles. Because nearly all tones having fundamental frequencies below this figure are accompanied by several harmonics, the ear supplies the fundamental for most of the bass notes, and the quality of music is acceptable. If, on the other hand, all the frequencies below 150 cycles were missing subjectively as well as in the reproduction device, the music would have a noticeable tinniness. Aside from the filtering problem, it would in any event be difficult to achieve efficient radiation of low frequencies because of the small physical size of the speakers and the cabinets.

8.7 Noise

Noise, in a sense, is the totality of all sounds within the range of hearing to which the attention is not directed. Thus noise is sometimes defined as undesired sound. While this is a good functional definition, it omits an important characteristic of noise. That is, since noise is made up of the combined sound output of a great number of sound sources of widely different frequencies, it can also be defined as unpitched sound, and this is the definition which will be more useful in the present discussion. Noise can be objectionable in several ways. Its very presence may be a source of annoyance, and thus indirectly cause a loss of intelligibility in conversation because of lack of attention. Second, it may cause *masking* of desired sounds (most often speech sounds) in the sense that the listener, try as he will, cannot detect the desired sound through the noise. Third, intense noise may cause hearing damage and possibly other organic disturbances, while noise only slightly below the danger level may be the cause of nervous disturbance. In certain hazardous occupations, this type of disturbance may easily be a source of greater peril than the direct organic damage caused by the noise.

Except for the loss of intelligibility due to masking, the above effects will be treated in a subsequent article in this text by the inclusion of tables of tolerable noise levels which have been published by more or less authoritative institutions. Justification of these levels is hardly within the realm of a physics text. However, masking by noise can be handled on a fundamentally physical level. Much thought and research have been devoted to this subject and a variety of useful knowledge has emerged. An important problem is to formulate a criterion for the over-all loudness of an unpitched sound. Perhaps even more basic is the problem of defining the meaning of intensity for an unpitched sound. It must be remembered that our definitions of intensity have always assumed the existence of a sinusoidal vibration. Since the problem of assigning intensity and loudness values to noise is at the seat of the understanding of noise theory, we shall devote a fairly detailed treatment to the problem.

We define the intensity of a pair of tones as the sum of the intensities of the tones individually.* The over-all intensity level of a pair of tones of equal intensity will exceed by 3 db the intensity of the individual component tones, and it is readily shown that the intensity level of N equal component tones, each of equal intensity level n db will be

$$I = 10 \log_{10} N + n \qquad (8.71)$$

Thus if each of the notes of the diatonic scale has an intensity level of 60 db, the over-all level will be 69 db (Fig. 8.71a). Let us now suppose that the octave which runs from 128 to 256 cycles is broken up into 128 separate tones, each separated by 1 cycle, and each having a level of 60 db. From Eq. (8.71) the over-all level of the 128 tones will be 81 db. On the same basis the over-all level of a half octave (64 tones each of 60 db intensity level) would be 78 db. It is thus seen that the intensity measurement of a noise involves not only the strengths of the individual tones which go to make up the noise, but also the *band width* of the noise which is measured. In the example of the 128 equal tones the band width is, in a sense, a property of the "noise" itself. Band width may also be a property of the system which transmits or receives the noise. Regardless of its origin, the entrance of the band width into the problem necessitates the introduction of another concept, that of *spectrum level.*

Suppose each of the tone combinations of the previous problem were to be shown by a plot. Inasmuch as each consists of a definite number of pure tones (that is, tones of a precise frequency) the plots would be a type called *line spectra*, consisting of a series of vertical lines [Figs. 8.71(a) and (b)], the length of these lines being plotted to a decibel scale. In (b), which consists of tones only 1 cycle apart, it would take an instrument of very great resolution to respond perfectly to a tone while shutting out completely tones 1 cycle above and below. It is useful, however, to make the assumption that such an instrument, a filter of a 1-cycle band width, exists. Further, if one of the tones, say the 180 cycle tone, actually consists of two tones of frequencies 179.9 and 180.1 cycles, each of intensity 57 db, the 1-cycle filter will give the same reading (60 db) as if a pure tone of 180 cycles were present.† This is exactly the performance desired for the definition of spectrum level. Instead of drawing a

---

* This definition of over-all intensity is usually made only for two random noises. It is permissible at this point on a tentative basis.

† In other words, one can predict the readings of the band filter from the line spectrum but not the line spectrum from the band filter readings.

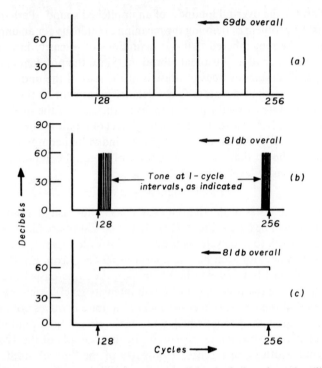

Fig. 8.71. (*a*) Line spectrum and over-all level of diatonic scale; (*b*) line spectrum and over-all level of single tones at each integral frequency is from 128 to 256 cycles; (*c*) "white nose" spectrum having same over-all level as (*b*).

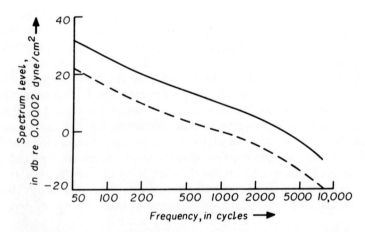

Fig. 8.72. Spectrum level of average room noise, with over-all level of 43 db. re 0.0002 dyne/cm². Dashed curve shows room noise for quieter location, with over-all level of 33 db. [After D. F. Hoth, *J. Acoust. Soc. Am.*, **12**, 499 (1951).]

line spectrum for the series of 128 tones, which necessitates the assumption of a knowledge that they *are* pure tones, we shall draw a horizontal line of unit length with an ordinate of 60 db for each 1-cycle interval, which shows only that a 1-cycle filter centered at each integral frequency over the octave gives a reading of 60 db. Such a hypothesis bridges the gap between discrete and continuous sounds. Actually, a noise will consist microscopically of discrete spectra, but the individual tones will be so numerous that it is better to consider the spectrum as continuous. This results in a curve of the type of Fig. 8.71(c). In general, the spectrum level curve will not be a flat over a band. Figure 8.72 is the spectrum level curve of average "room noise," where the over-all level is 43 db. In the general case, if B_n represents the ordinate in decibels at the frequency f, the over-all level of intensity over the band between f_1 and f_2 is

$$B_N = 10 \log_{10} \int_{f_1}^{f_2} 10^{B_n/10} df \qquad (8.72)$$

The integral simply represents the area under the spectrum level curve between the limiting frequencies. It is somewhat more complicated than it would otherwise be, because the ordinates are in decibels, while the intensities must be added arithmetically. The justification of Eq. (8.72) is left as an exercise for the reader.

In the case of "white noise" (amplitude flat with frequency) the following form holds:

$$B_N = B_n + 10 \log_{10}(f_2 - f_1) \qquad (8.73)$$

which is quite similar to Eq. (8.71).

Noise spectra are commonly obtained in intervals of an octave, or some

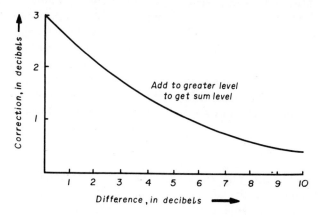

Fig. 8.73. Curve for combining two sound levels to get total sound level.

fraction thereof. Recently, there has been an attempt made to standardize on $\frac{1}{3}$ octave bands. For such a filter, a noise spectrum will consist of a series of approximately horizontal segments, each $\frac{1}{3}$ octave wide. The band level in each band can then be found by the Eq. (8.73), where B_n is the spectrum level at the center frequency of the band. The over-all intensities in the various bands can then be added according to Fig. 8.73. Judicious grouping before addition will simplify the process.

A comparison of masking by pure tones and masking by narrow bands of noise is shown in Fig. 8.74, which should be compared with Fig. 8.51. Figure 8.74 shows the masking caused by a band of noise extending from 1,050 to 1,250 cycles, and having over-all levels as shown on the masking curves.[1, 13] The important conclusion to be drawn from these curves is that narrow bands of noise are effective only in the immediate vicinity of the band. Unlike high-intensity pure tones, noise bands do not cause masking at frequencies far removed from the band. The reason for this is that none of the single frequency components of the noise has intensity great enough to generate subjective tones.* The fact that the masking effect of the noise is concentrated about the noise band is of great importance in intelligibility theory, for masking of speech in most important cases is a result of noise. It will be noted that the masking effect of the noise is approximately equal to its band level. The masking is not constant over the band, because the band filters used in the test are not ideal. Nevertheless these curves have led to the conclusion that the masking effect of the noise within certain critical bands is equal to its band level. The only exceptions are for very high- and very low-intensity noise.

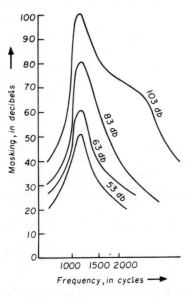

Fig. 8.74. Masking by band of noise extending from 1,050 to 1,250 cycles and having over-all levels shown on curves.

8.8 Speech

Considered in its physical aspect, speech is a complex of fundamental sounds produced by the vocal cords, oral and nasal chambers, tongue, lips, and teeth. It is the object of this article to describe the more important characteristics of speech sounds, to correlate them with the facts of hearing

---

* This assumes that the noise is *random*. The definition of random noise is rather involved, but effectively it means that the noise contains no strong single-frequency components.

acuity that have already been established, and to estimate the percentage of phonetic sounds that will be perceptible in terms of speech level, hearing acuity, and environment. If 100 per cent of the phonetic sounds can be perceived under given conditions, the *intelligibility* is said to be perfect. Certain arbitrary tests have been established by which the intelligibility may be given a quantitative rating under less favorable conditions. Out of such arbitrary tests, and statistical evaluation, has evolved a fairly exact science. The qualification is used because the subjective element, which the physicist likes to eliminate from his data, is at the very base of speech science.

A certain amount of purely physical data can be obtained. For instance, portions of speech can be recorded and examined by the oscillograph and the speech analyzer, and wave forms and frequency spectra of the fundamental speech sounds obtained (Fig. 8.81). Instantaneous and average pressure levels of speech passages can be recorded at standard distances from the speaker. The relative strength of phonetic sounds can be computed. Where the pressure level of instantaneous speech is above the threshold in a particular environment, the sound will be heard; otherwise, the sound will be missed. If the environment is noisefree and hearing is acute, this threshold will be the zero phons contour. In a noisy environment, the threshold will be shifted because of the masking effect of the noise. In either case, a predicted intelligibility can be obtained once the power in the phonetic sounds is known. Because so much depends on an understanding of what is meant by speech power, the following half dozen types of speech power will be defined:[1]

The *long average speech power* is the total energy radiated while the person is talking, divided by the time interval during which he talks.

The *instantaneous speech power* is the rate at which sound energy is being radiated at any instant. It frequently rises to 100 times the average speech power.

The *mean speech power* is the average speech power over a period of short duration. It is useful in showing the variations of speech power without showing the microscopic periodic fluctuations of the wave. It is also useful in eliminating silent periods from consideration, thereby giving a truer indication of the strength of the speech sounds as such. Fletcher has standardized the interval at $\frac{1}{100}$ sec, but $\frac{1}{8}$ sec intervals are also useful, because they represent the average duration of a syllable.

The *peak power* is the maximum value of the instantaneous power during the interval considered.

The *syllabic speech power* is the maximum value of the mean speech power which is reached when a syllable is spoken.

The *phonetic speech power* is the maximum value of the mean speech power for the vowel or consonant being spoken. *It is useful for comparing the relative amounts of power in the various speech sounds.* The phonetic power of the vowel in a syllable is usually closely equal to the syllabic power, because vowels far exceed the consonants in power.

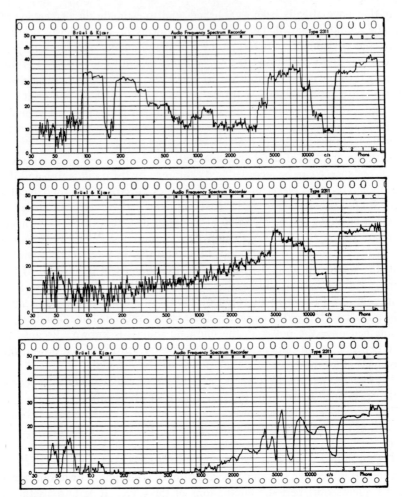

Fig. 8.81. Frequency spectra of speech sounds. [Courtesy of Clevite-Brush.]

The above line-up of definitions may appear to indicate that a detailed exposition of phonetics is to be undertaken in this treatment. Such is not the case. But a careful reading of the above definitions will give the reader a clear picture of the problems which are encountered in speech research. As an example, the mean speech power concept was developed as a way of by-passing the useless detail of the curve of instantaneous speech power. Further, the curves of equal loudness, which are the frame of reference, so to speak, for treatments of threshold and sensation level, are based upon the perception of pure tones, in which the element of duration is not involved, a pure tone having an essentially limitless duration. In speech, where the sounds are transient, the peak power does not seem to be the sole element in recognition.

It is rather a combination of power and duration, and here again the mean speech power concept is useful.

The development of apparatus by the Bell Telephone Laboratories which would give responses proportional to peak, mean, and long average speech powers helped immeasurably in speech research. In 1930, H. K. Dunn[14] announced a new analyzer for speech and music, and Sivian, Dunn and White[15] collaborated on an instrument which would measure long average speech power and mean speech powers of short intervals.

Intensive study of speech by the speech analyzer enabled the investigators to draw important conclusions regarding the phonetic powers of speech. According to Fletcher, "In the course of conversation, the fundamental vowel and consonant sounds are produced with varying degrees of power depending on their position in the sentence and the emphasis desired. In spite of this variation, some of the speech sounds are always more powerful than others, and it is interesting to know typical values used in conversation."[1] Sacia and Beck[16] obtained power values for the phonetic sounds from a study of speech spectra. Another method measures the power in a phonetic sound by attenuating it to a level at which it can no longer be heard. The number of decibels that each sound must be attenuated to make it inaudible is a measure of its phonetic power.

The following is a brief summary of some of the more important findings of such speech tests:

1.   For conversational speech, the average speech power is 32 μw, and the average pressure level at a distance of 1 m from the speaker is 65 db. The range from 57 to 73 db covers most talkers. If silent intervals are excluded, these levels will be raised by about 3 db. When one talks as loudly as possible, the long average pressure level can be raised to 86 db.

2.   The peak value of conversational speech is frequently over 100 times the long average power. It is 12 db above the average power about 17 per cent of the time. The mean speech power in $\frac{1}{8}$ sec intervals is 12 db above the long average power about 1 per cent of the time.

3.   The phonetic powers of the various speech sounds range from a maximum of about 120 μw down to less than 1 μw. The peak powers in the phonetic sounds range from about 1,800 μw down to about 1 μw.

4.   All things considered, the most powerful phonetic sound appears to be the vowel sound in *awl*, and the faintest, the *th* in *thin*, the ratio in these powers being 680. Quoting from Fletcher, "The difference in level expressed in decibels corresponding to this figure (680:1) is 28. From the data available the indications are that in an average room in the city the noise is such as to raise the threshold of hearing approximately 30 db. Also the sound is attenuated more than 40 db if the speaker is about 10 ft away from the listener. Consequently, under such circumstances, the sound *th* is barely audible."[1]

5.   "A round figure of about 0.01 microwatt represents the faintest sound,

and of about 5,000 microwatts the peak value of the loudest sound that will be encountered in conversation."

Dunn and White[17] made two extremely important contributions to speech science. First, they succeeded in obtaining the long average speech spectrum for conversational speech at a distance of 1 m from the speaker. French and Steinberg repeated their tests in 1949, obtaining a curve which closely corroborated that of Dunn and White. French and Steinberg, however, slightly idealized the spectrum curve (Fig. 8.82). This curve is a graph of the intensity

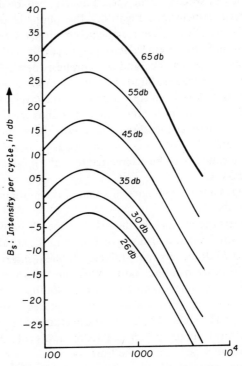

Fig. 8.82. Long average speech spectrum curve of conversational speech. Integrated level = 65 db at 1 m from talker (idealized long average). Spectrum curves also shown for long average levels of 55, 45, 35, and 30 db.

per cycle* in decibels against frequency, and has an integrated value of 65 db. On the same diagram are shown curves of conversational speech for other long average pressure levels.

Equally important was the analysis by Dunn and White of the relative occurrence of periods of stronger and weaker output in speech. They measured the percentage of $\frac{1}{8}$ sec intervals in which the mean speech power exceeded (or was less than) the long average power, and found that approxi-

---

* By intensity per cycle is meant the integrated intensity in a band of width one cycle.

mately 20 per cent of the intervals have a mean speech power greater than the long average. They then increased the scope of the investigation to find the percentage of $\frac{1}{8}$ sec intervals that exceeded other levels (e.g. a level of 10 db less than the long average power). Further, they discovered the extremely important fact that the relation was relatively independent of the frequency band. That is, approximately 20 per cent of the power intervals within the 955–1,135 cycle band exceeded the long average power in this band, as was true for over-all speech, and the same was true of each band. From these findings a curve could be plotted showing the cumulative level distribution of mean speech intensity (Fig. 8.83). It is called the *speech distribution curve*. Note that the abscissa of this curve is the ratio of the intensity to the long average intensity. As an example, using the curve for over-all speech which has an intensity level of 65 db at a distance of 1 m from the speaker for conversational speech, it would be concluded that about 50 per cent of the speech

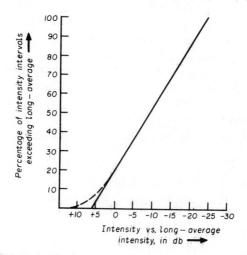

Fig. 8.83. Speech distribution curve. Cumulative level distribution of average intensity of speech in $\frac{1}{8}$ second intervals. Idealized curve typical of all speech bands and of over-all speech.

intervals have a mean intensity exceeding 55 db. A further conclusion is that if one is at a distance from the source at which the long average intensity is equal to his threshold, he would hear 20 per cent of the speech sounds.

The dashed portion of this curve gives experimental results at low values. From this curve one finds that 1 per cent of the mean intensity levels exceed the long average intensity by 12 db. However, when studying intelligibility as a function of speech level, it is useful to assume that the curve remains a straight line down to the axis of abscissas. This can be interpreted as giving a sensation level 6 db higher than the long average intensity (rather than 12). That is, we shall assume in the theory of intelligibility to be investigated in the next article, that speech is just detectable when the long average is 6 db below the individual threshold, even though the true sensation level is 12 db higher than the threshold.

8.9 Intelligibility and Articulation

An articulation test is an empirical procedure by which a quantitative measure of the intelligibility of speech is obtained. Intelligibility is defined as the percentage of arbitrary units of conversation correctly identified by the listener. These units may be sentences, words, or syllables, the intelligibility value decreasing as the duration of the unit decreases. Thus, of the three mentioned, sentence intelligibility will be the highest for any given conditions. Methods of scoring the results of the tests are quite complex[1, 18, 19] in many instances, and it is not necessary to go into detail on this point for an understanding of the principles. We shall center attention on syllable articulation, and define percentage articulation as the percentage of disconnected syllables correctly identified. As a general rule, syllables of the type CVC (consonant-vowel-consonant) are used for this test. A caller pronounces a group of such syllables, and a team of listeners records the syllables, comparing their record at the end of the test with the list of the caller. Experienced teams of callers and listeners have achieved a high degree of repeatability in articulation testing, and criteria have been set up for intelligibility based on the results of such tests, as we shall see in certain articles in the chapter on Architectural Acoustics.

Although syllable articulation has given a great amount of useful information on the factors which influence intelligibility, such as speech level, noise, and the acoustics of the enclosure, it has certain limitations, in common with all other known subjective measures of intelligibility, which impair its usefulness as a basic index of intelligibility. The value obtained from the typical articulation test is not independent of the skill and experience of the testers. Moreover, syllable articulation is not an additive measure of the importance of contributions made by the speech sounds in the different frequency regions. As an example, with an optimum value of speech level (such that approximately 100 per cent syllable articulation is obtained when all the speech frequencies reach the ear of the listener), 68 per cent syllable articulation is obtained when all the speech frequencies below 1,950 cycles are suppressed, and the same percentage articulation is obtained when all the frequencies above 1,950 cycles are suppressed (see Fig. 8.91). "Thus, the syllable articulation observed with a given frequency band of speech is not equal to the sum of the (syllable) articulations observed when the given band is subdivided into narrower bands which are then individually tested. For the purpose of establishing relations between the intelligence-carrying capacity of the components of speech and their frequency and intensity, a more fundamental index free of the above defect is needed. Such an index, called the *articulation index*, can be derived from articulation tests. The magnitude of this index is taken to vary from zero to unity, the former applying when the speech is completely unintelligible, the latter to the condition of best intelligibility."[12]

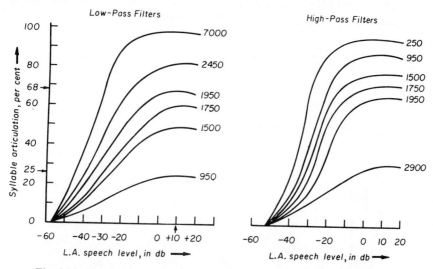

Fig. 8.91. Influence of speech level and band pass on syllable articulation.

The work of N. R. French and J. C. Steinberg in formulating this index will be summarized in the following treatment. It is strongly suggested that the reader consult the original paper if he is interested in intelligibility theory. It is also only proper to mention that many others have been instrumental in laying the groundwork of articulation theory, and among them are Fletcher, Munson, Knudsen, Egan, and Beranek.

Speech studies have shown that both level and band width are important in speech transmission. The curves of Fig. 8.91 show the combined effect of speech level and band width on syllable articulation. The zero level of the abscissa is such that the over-all speech level is 65 db at the point of audition. The (a) set of curves shows results obtained with low-pass filters, the (b) set the results obtained with high-pass filters. Thus the 7,000 cycle curve of Fig. 8.91(a) shows that practically perfect articulation exists if all the speech bands are passed and the speech level is 75 db at the ear of the listener. The 10 db (re 65 db) level is taken as the optimum level as a result of these tests.

By graphing the points of intersection of the curves of Fig. 8.91 with the vertical through the 10 db abscissa, French and Steinberg obtained the two "optimum level" curves of Fig. 8.92, exhibiting syllable articulation as a function of cutoff frequency. The point of intersection of the optimum level curves occurs at a frequency of 1,950 cycles and a syllable articulation of 68 per cent. The entire band (0–7,000 cycles) gives perfect intelligibility at the

10 db level. The intersection of the curves at 1,950 cycles shows that the 0–1,950 and 1,950–7,000 cycle bands contribute equally to intelligibility. Therefore each of these bands, at the 10 db level, has half the intelligence content needed for perfect intelligibility. French and Steinberg accordingly assigned each an articulation index (A.I.) of 0.5.

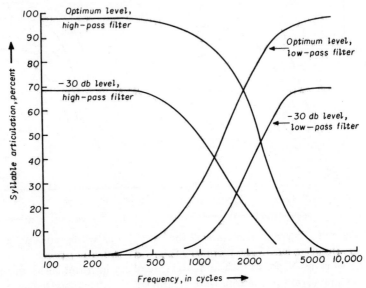

Fig. 8.92. Syllable articulation as a function of level and band width.

Having assigned an articulation index of 0.5 to each of two bands with the speech level at optimum for intelligibility, the investigators sought a method of assigning other values of articulation index (A.I.) in terms of level and band width. Since it appears that an A.I. of 0.5 results in a S.A. of 68 per cent, they referred to the curves of Fig. 8.91 to find the level at which the full band (7,000 cycle curve) has a syllable articulation (S.A.) of 68 per cent, which has already been associated with an A.I. of 0.5. This level is about 30 db below the zero level (or 35 db re 0.0002 dyne/cm²). The procedure by which the optimum level pair of curves were obtained may now be repeated for the vertical through the −30 db abscissa, the intersection of the −30 db level curves occurring at a S.A. of 25 per cent. Since a full speech band gives an A.I. of 0.5 at this level, and since the bands above and below contribute equally to intelligibility, a S.A. of 25 per cent is correlated with an A.I. of 0.25 in the same way that a S.A. of 68 per cent was correlated with an A.I. of 0.5. (It is a coincidence that 25 per cent corresponds to an A.I. of 0.25.)

The two correlations obtained suggest plotting a curve of S.A. vs. A.I. Since a correlation has been obtained for an A.I. of 0.25, it should be possible, on the assumption that A.I. is additive, to obtain a correlation for an A.I. of

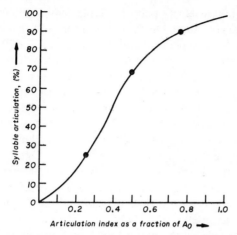

Fig. 8.93. Syllable articulation vs. articulation index.

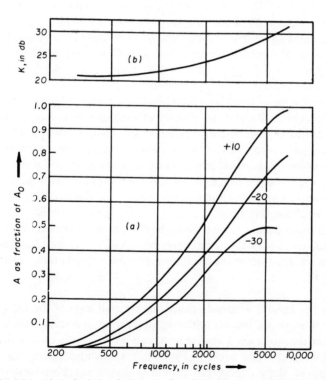

Fig. 8.94. (*a*) Articulation index as a function of level and cumulative band width (obtained from low-pass filter curves of Fig. 8.92) and conversion curve of Fig. 8.93. Band I: 250–375 cps; II: 375–505; III: 505–645; XVI: 3,255–3,680. Part (*b*) Band-width factor K for bands of equal contribution to articulation index $K = \log_{10}(f_2 - f_1)$.

0.75. At the optimum level any pair of complementary filters must together carry all the intelligence. It may be found from Fig. 8.91 that a 950 cycle low-pass filter gives a S.A. of 25 per cent and therefore an A.I. of 0.25 at optimum level. Therefore a 950 cycle high-pass filter has an A.I. of 0.75. The high-pass filter curves show that the 950-cycle filter gives a S.A. of 90 per cent. By a continuation of this process the S.A. vs. A.I. curve of Fig. 8.93 is obtained. From this curve and the low-pass filter curves of Fig. 8.91, curves of A.I. vs. cutoff frequency can now be drawn (the curves of Fig. 8.94). From the optimum level curve one can get an indication of the relative contribution of different frequency regions of speech to intelligibility. One very obvious conclusion is that the frequencies below 230 cycles do not contribute at all to intelligibility. This, however, is a minor point. The great importance of the optimum curve of Fig. 8.94(a) is that one can find the frequency bands that contribute equally to intelligibility (when the speech level is optimum) by choosing equal intervals on the vertical axis, and projecting horizontally to the curve. The points of intersection of these horizontals with the optimum curve set the limits of the bands of equal contribution to intelligibility. French and Steinberg arbitrarily chose 20 bands. That is, they chose increments of articulation index equal to 0.05. The first, second, third, and sixteenth bands are tabulated on the figure. The extent of these bands can best be shown by the plot of K in Fig. 8.94(b) where $K = 10 \log_{10} (f_2 - f_1)$, where f_2 and f_1 are the limits of the bands.

The curve for the -20 db level is obtained in a manner similar to the 10 db and -30 db curves. By plotting a series of such curves, one can obtain the fraction of the total possible contribution in any band (0.05) as a function of level by noting the rise of each of the level curves in this band. As an example, let us examine the third critical band. The curves are enlarged for this band in Fig. 8.95(a) and it will be seen that whereas the rise in the 10 db curve is 0.05, the -20 db curve rises by 0.038 and the -30 db curve rises by 0.024. The curve of ΔA vs. level for this band is shown in Fig. 8.95(b). Similar curves are obtained for other bands. If we let ΔA_m be the maximum contribution to A.I. by any band, and ΔA be the actual contribution at lower levels, then we may define W as the fraction of the maximum possible contribution. That is,

$$\Delta A = W \cdot \Delta A_m \qquad (8.91)$$

If W in any band is graphed against the over-all level of the speech, it is found that W increases linearly with speech level up to a value of 0.7, with a rise of 10 per cent for each 3 db rise in speech level. This is exactly the slope of the speech distribution curve of Fig. 8.83! French and Steinberg, noting this equality of slopes, made an extremely important observation: "The similarity of the slopes of the articulation index curve and the speech distribution curve suggests that the *percentage of maximum articulation in a band is equal to the fraction of speech intervals that can be heard.*" This is a fundamental attack on the problem of intelligibility as a function of the characteristics of speech and the acuity of the ear. Further, because the masking effects of noise have been rather well established, it lends itself to an ultimate expression of intelligibility as a function of hearing acuity and the levels of speech and *noise* at the ear of the listener. We shall see in the next chapter

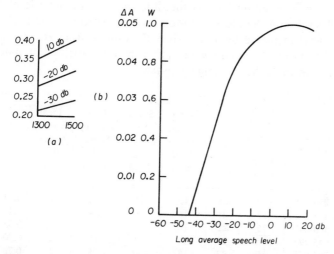

Fig. 8.95. Contribution to total articulation index in band VIII as a function of speech level. (*a*) Derivation of curve of variation of ΔA with long average speech level in eighth critical band. (*b*) 0 db = 65 db. re 0·0002 dyne/cm².

that Knudsen attacked the problem of intelligibility in auditoriums in a manner quite similar. He isolated the factors upon which intelligibility in auditoriums depends, and succeeded in obtaining a concise formula for intelligibility based on these factors.

The means by which French and Steinberg were able to derive quantitative relations for articulation index in terms of speech characteristics will be briefly described. To obtain the total A.I. under any conditions, one obtains the ΔA in each of the 20 bands, and adds. It is somewhat more convenient to discuss the W for a band than the ΔA. The slopes of the W curve and the speech distribution curve are each equal to $\frac{1}{30}$, if the percentage in Fig. 8.83 is considered as a decimal ratio. Further, the percentage of audible intervals is zero when the ideal sensation level is zero, and increases linearly with the ideal sensation level (Fig. 8.83). Therefore it can readily be shown that *the numerical value of W in any band is* $\frac{1}{30}$ *of the ideal sensation level in that band*. It should be remembered that the ideal sensation level H' is 6 db above the long average speech level in a band. The following problem illustrates the use of several of the concepts discussed in this and previous articles.

Problem: Compute the articulation index in a noisefree environment when the over-all speech level is 26 db re 0.0002 dyne/cm².

Solution: The long average spectrum level in each speech band is obtained from the spectrum level curve of Fig. 8.82. By the K-factors shown on Fig. 8.94, each of these is converted to a band level. The threshold at the center frequency of each band is obtained from the Fletcher-Munson curve. The "long average" sensation level is the difference of the band level and the threshold level, and the ideal sensation level for speech is the long average sensation level increased by 6 db. Then W is found from H', the ΔA's are computed from the W's and added to find the total articulation index. The results are shown in the accompanying table.

Band	Frequency Limits	Long Average Speech Spectrum Level	K	Long Average Speech Band Level	Single Frequency Threshold	Long Average Sensation Level	Ideal Speech Sensation Level	W	ΔA
1	250-375	-2	21	19	15	4	10	0.33	0.0165
2	375-505	$-3 \cdot$	21	18	10	8	14	0.47	0.0235
3	505-645	-5	21	16	3	13	19	0.63	0.0315
4	645-795	-6	22	16	1	15	21	0.70	0.0350
5	795-955	-7	22	15	0	15	21	0.70	0.0350
6	955-1130	-9	23	14	0	14	20	0.67	0.0335
7	1130-1315	-12	23	11	0	11	17	0.57	0.0285
8	1315-1515	-14	23	9	0	9	15	0.50	0.0250
9	1515-1720	-15	23	8	-2	10	16	0.53	0.0265
10	1720-1930	-17	23	6	-4	10	16	0.53	0.0265
11	1930-2140	-19	24	5	-6	11	17	0.57	0.0285
12	2140-2355	-21	24	3	-6	9	15	0.50	0.0250
13	2355-2600	-23	24	1	-7	8	14	0.47	0.0235
14	2600-2900	-25	25	0	-7	7	13	0.43	0.0215
15	2900-3255	-26	26	0	-7	7	13	0.43	0.0215
16	3255-3680	-28	27	-1	-6	5	11	0.37	0.0185
17	3680-4200	-30	28	-2	-6	4	10	0.33	0.0165
18	4200-4860	-32	29	-3	-4	1	7	0.23	0.0115
19	4860-5720	-34	30	-4	-3	-1	5	0.17	0.0085
20	5720-7000	-35	31	-4	0	-4	2	0.07	0.0035

The sum of the twenty ΔA values in the last column gives an articulation index of 0.46.

The ideal effective sensation level in the presence of noise is given by the relation,

$$E' = H' - M \tag{8.92}$$

From the definition of the ideal noisefree sensation level,

$$H' = B_S + 6 - b \tag{8.93}$$

where B_S is the band speech level, and b is the threshold level at the center frequency of the band.

The masking is equal to the sensation level of the noise within a critical band. The critical bands for noise in which this relation holds true are slightly narrower than the 20 bands of equal contribution to intelligibility, but we may assume with small error that the masking effect of the noise in each of the 20 bands equals its band level, i.e. $M = B_N - b$, where $B_N = B_n + K$, and where B_n is the noise spectrum level at the center frequency of one of the 20 bands, and B_N is the band level of the noise. Therefore

$$E' = B_S + 6 - b - B_N + b = B_S + 6 - B_N \qquad (8.94)$$

Since the band levels of both speech and noise exceed the spectrum levels by

Band	Frequency Interval	B_n Noise Spectrum Level, Over-all Level 43 db	B_s Speech Spectrum Level, Over-all Speech Level 55 db	W $\dfrac{B_s+b-B_n}{30}$	ΔA	B_s Speech Spectrum Level, Over-all Speech Level 59 db	W	ΔA
1	250-375	17	27	0.53	0.0265	31	0.67	0.0335
2	374-505	15	26	0.57	0.0285	30	0.70	0.0350
3	505-645	13	24	0.57	0.0285	28	0.70	0.0350
4	645-795	12	23	0.57	0.0285	27	0.70	0.0350
5	795-955	11	22	0.57	0.0285	26	0.70	0.0350
6	955-1130	10	20	0.53	0.0265	24	0.67	0.0335
7	1130-1315	9	17	0.47	0.0235	21	0.60	0.0300
8	1315-1515	9	15	0.40	0.0200	19	0.53	0.0265
9	1515-1720	8	14	0.40	0.0200	18	0.53	0.0265
10	1720-1930	8	12	0.33	0.0165	16	0.47	0.0235
11	1930-2140	7	10	0.30	0.0150	14	0.43	0.0215
12	2140-2355	6	8	0.27	0.0135	12	0.40	0.0200
13	2355-2600	5	6	0.23	0.0115	10	0.37	0.0185
14	2600-2900	4	4	0.20	0.0100	8	0.33	0.0165
15	2900-3255	2	3	0.23	0.0115	7	0.37	0.0185
16	3255-3680	0	1	0.23	0.0115	5	0.37	0.0185
17	3680-4200	−2	−1	0.23	0.0115	3	0.37	0.0185
18	4200-4860	−3	−3	0.20	0.0100	1	0.33	0.0165
19	4860-5720	−5	−5	0.20	0.0100	−1	0.33	0.0165
20	5720-7000	−7	−6	0.23	0.0115	−2	0.37	0.0185
					0.363			0.497

An Articulation Index of 0.363 gives a Syllable Articulation of 37 per cent, whereas an A.I. of 0.497 gives a S.A. of 68 per cent. The former is unsatisfactory, the latter is just acceptable (see Art. 9.8). The example demonstrates the benefit to be derived from speech amplification in overcoming noise.

the same factor K, this may also be written

$$E' = B_s + 6 - B_n \tag{8.95}$$

Finally,
$$W = \tfrac{1}{30}(B_s + 6 - B_n) \tag{8.96}$$

The use of this equation will be illustrated by the solution for A.I. in the case where the room noise over-all level is 43 db, and follows the typical room noise curve, and the long average speech level is 55 db. The problem is also solved when the speech level is increased 4 db by amplification.

An interesting application of Eq. (8.96) is the case in which the signal-to-noise ratio is unity, band for band, with both speech and noise well above the threshold. The equation gives $W = 0.20$, and a resulting articulation index of 0.20. The syllable articulation will therefore be 20 per cent. It is interesting that the corresponding sentence articulation is 70 per cent. The perception of intelligence, or "signal" through noise is a problem that extends beyond speech and hearing and has important military applications. For example, in underwater listening with hydrophones, there is a certain ambient noise level produced by the turbulence of the sea. Experience has shown that it is possible to detect a signal several db below this ambient noise level. The theory of critical band widths also shows that the signal may be detectable in a certain band even if the over-all strength of the signal is too weak to be detected through the over-all noise. For this reason underwater listening systems are provided with band-pass filters, so that the operator may reject any portion of the spectrum not contributing to the signal to be recognized.

8.10 Binaural Hearing Effects

The most important result of hearing with both ears is the judgment of the direction of the sound source and the distance to the source. While in some cases there have been large discrepancies in results obtained with different observers, fairly accurate observations have been made in controlled experiments on the localization of pure tones. Two main effects[21,22] are reported, and both are thought to be a result of comparisons within the brain of the effect of different acoustic pressures impinging on the separate ears.

If an apparatus is arranged to feed one of the ears with a tone of fixed phase, and the phase of the tone fed into the other ear is varied, the source appears to be directly in front of the listener when the phase difference is zero. As the phase difference is increased, the source appears to rotate along the arc of a circle toward the ear in which the phase is leading. When the image appears to be approximately opposite one ear, it suddenly jumps to the side opposite the other ear, and upon further phase increase, returns to the median plane. Several methods of phase variation have been used, and in each case it was found that the apparent angular displacement was proportional to the difference in phase between the two ears, the constant of proportionality varying somewhat with frequency. The following formula represents the average results of the experiments:

$$\frac{\phi}{\theta} = 0.0034f + 0.8$$

where ϕ is the phase difference at the two ears, θ is the angular displacement from the median plane, and f is the frequency of the sound. For example, the phase difference of a 500 cycle tone is always about 2.6 times the angular displacement of the apparent source. When the phase difference reaches 180°, the image has been displaced about 70°. As the phase difference increases past 180°, the source apparently jumps to −70° and returns toward the median plane, reaching it when the phase difference reaches 360°.

If the difference in the phases of the tones presented is kept constant, and the intensity of one is varied, an angular displacement of the apparent source is also produced. However, the results are much less definite, and variations from one individual to another are very great. In general, for any individual, the angular displacement of the apparent source is found to be proportional to the difference of the intensity level at the two ears. As the frequency of the exciting source approaches 1,000 cycles, the uncertainty in localization increases, and many individuals show no ability to localize a source if the frequency is above 1,000 cycles.

The localization of complex sounds is a fairly difficult phenomenon to explain, but results seem to show that as in the case of pure tones, the phase difference is the controlling factor. Localization of complex sound has been accomplished with fair success in military applications, such as the tracking of enemy submarines and airplanes. It was found that a considerable departure from the ideal may be tolerated, and yet a fairly good sense of localization may be obtained. Since phase is the controlling factor, binaural transmission systems include phase compensators to enable the listener to bring the apparent position of the source directly in front of the observer. The amount of compensation necessary to do this is an indication of the position of the source. Because of the fact that these compensators do not compensate all frequencies by the same amount, localization in such a system is somewhat indefinite, and may well produce apparent images in several directions.

While the above paragraphs describe certain facts in connection with binaural hearing, they by no means answer all questions. For instance, the location of a complex sound can, under ordinary conditions, be quite definite, and may even be made by a person who is totally deaf in one ear. Most acousticians rate our hearing education and experience as being the important intangible that enables us to localize sounds from a great variety of impressions, such as the position of reflecting surfaces, a knowledge of approximate intensities connected with various types of sound, and many other details almost inconsequential individually. It is interesting that location of the source is poor in jungles. Eyring[23] has observed an average error of about 20° in the location of gunshots by a selected group of observers. This may be partially because of the unfamiliarity of acoustic impressions, since Eyring, after only a relatively short experience with jungle acoustics, was able to suggest methods by which the listener could reduce his error.

The localization of actors by the listeners in stage performances adds materially to the illusion necessary for good theater. This localization may be lost when sound amplification is used. With a single-channel amplification system, the position of the speaker appears aurally to be fixed as he moves about the stage. Multiple-channel systems, called stereophonic systems,[19] have been devised in which three separate microphones feed three separate speakers, one at each side of the stage, and one at the center. While care must be taken lest the voice seems to "jump" from one loudspeaker to another, well-designed stereophonic systems preserve the naturalness of the performance while providing the volume necessary for good intelligibility.

8.11 Psychoacoustic Aspects of Noise

In Arts. 8.7 and 8.9, noise was discussed primarily in connection with intelligibility. Very high-intensity noises must also be considered with regard to hearing damage. Such noises may cause permanent damage to hearing even if they are of very short duration. Lower noise levels can cause gradual deterioration of hearing if the exposure is protracted. Table 8.111, due primarily to Beranek,[6] summarizes the current consensus on adverse effects of

TABLE 8.111
Thresholds of Tolerance and Typical Recommended Noise Levels

	Pure Tones	
Threshold of tolerance	*Naive ears*	*Exposed ears*
Discomfort	110	120
Tickle	132	140
Pain	140	
Immediate damage (not accurately known)	150 to 160	

Recommended noise levels	
Broadcast studios	15-20
Concert halls	20-25
Legitimate theaters, schoolrooms, sleeping quarters	25
Assembly halls with amplification	25-30
Hospitals, churches, courtrooms, libraries...........................	30
Restaurants...	45
Factories	40-65

high-intensity noise. Tables 8.112 and 8.113, which also were compiled by Beranek, give typical sound levels and typical power outputs of sound sources. Like all such tables, they are not intended to be taken too literally, serving more as a rough basis of comparison.

The above paragraph is concerned with noises of very high intensity. There is another aspect to the situation, however, which is troublesome in application. This is the sheer psychological annoyance of relatively low-intensity impulse noises several decibels above the ambient background. The table of characteristic sound levels shows that 50 db is a moderately low level, and one would not expect it to be especially irritating. Yet if a person in an ambient background of 25 db were to be subjected to random noise peaks of 50 db, he would be sharply aware of them. Experience shows that an increase

TABLE 8.112

Overall Sound Levels in Decibels re 10^{-16} watt/cm^2

Near Noise Source		*Environmental*
	140	
50-hp victory siren		
F-84 at take-off		
Hydraulic press	130	
Large pneumatic riveter		Boiler shop
Pneumatic chipper	120	
		Engine room of submarine
Trumpet auto horn		Jet engine control room
Automatic punch press	110	
Chipping hammer		Woodworking shop
		Inside DC-6 airliner
Annealing furnace	100	
Automatic lathe		Can manufacturing plant
		Inside Chicago subway car
Heavy truck	90	Inside motor bus
10-hp outboard		
	80	Inside sedan in city traffic
Light trucks in city		Office with tabulating machines
Autos		Heavy traffic
	70	
		Average traffic
		Accounting office
Conversational speech	60	Chicago industrial areas
	50	Private business office
		Light traffic
		Average residence
	40	
		Minimum in Chicago residential areas at night
	30	Broadcasting studio (speech)
		Broadcasting studio (music)
Whisper	20	Studio for sound pictures
Ultimate threshold of hearing, 1,000 cycles	0	

of 1 db is barely perceptible, 3 db is significant, 6 db is easily noticeable, and 20 db is intrusive. Yet 45 db is within the recommended ambient noise level region for homes and apartments, while 25 db is possible on a side street at night. Thus noises which would go unnoticed during the day might readily interfere with sleep at night.

TABLE 8.113
Acoustic Power of Typical Sources in Watts

	100,000
Ram jet	
Turbo-jet engine with afterburner	
Turbo-jet engine, 7,000-lb thrust	10,000
	1,000
4-Propeller airliner	
	100
75-Piece orchestra	
Pipe organ	10
Small aircraft engine	
	1
Large chipping hammer	
Piano	
Blaring radio	0.10
Centrifugal ventilating fan	0.010
4-Ft loom	
Auto on highway	0.001
Van axial ventilating fan (1,500 rpm)	
Voice shouting (average long time rms)	
Voice, conversational level	0.00001
Voice, very soft whisper	0.000,000,001

References

1. Fletcher, *Speech and Hearing in Communication*, Van Nostrand, New York, 1953.
2. Bekesy, *J. Acoust. Soc. Am.*, **24**, 399-410 (1952).
3. Davis and Galambos, *J. Neurophysiol.*, **6**, 39-58 (1943).
4. Stevens and Volkman, *Am. J. Psychol.*, **53**, 329-353 (1940).
5. Sivian and White, *J. Acoust. Soc. Am.*, April, 1933.
6. Beranek, *Acoustics*, McGraw-Hill, New York, 1954.
7. Firestone and Geiger, *J. Acoust. Soc. Am.*, **11**, 308 (1940).
8. Churcher, King, and Davies, *J. Inst. Elec. Engrs.* (London), **81**, 57 (1937).
9. Ham and Parkinson, *Am. J. Phys.*, **9**, 213-216 (1941).
10. Knudsen, *Phys. Rev.*, **22**, 84-102 (1923).
11. Galt, Unpublished memorandum to Munson, *J. Acoust. Soc. Am.*, 103A (1943).
12. French and Steinberg, *J. Acoust. Soc. Am.*, **19**, 90 (1947).
13. Egan and Hake, *J. Acoust. Soc. Am.*, **22**, 622-630 (1950).
14. Dunn, *Bell Lab. Record*, November, 1930.
15. Sivian, Dunn, and White, *J. Acoust. Soc. Am.*, January, 1931.
16. Sacia and Beck, *Bell Telephone System J.*, 1922.
17. Dunn and White, *J. Acoust. Soc. Am.*, **11**, 278 (1940).
18. Beranek, *Acoustic Measurements*, Wiley, New York, 1950.
19. Knudsen and Harris, *Acoustical Design in Architecture*, Wiley, New York, 1950.

20. Knudsen, *J. Acoust. Soc. Am.*, **1**, 56 (1929).
21. Stewart, *Phys. Rev.*, May, 1920, p. 433.
22. Hartley and Fry, *Phys. Rev.*, December, 1921, p. 431.
23. Eyring, *J. Acoust. Soc. Am.*, **18**, 257-270 (1946).
24. Shortley and Williams, *Elements of Physics*, Prentice-Hall, Inc., 1955.

Problems

1. Find the intensities of the following tones in watts per square centi-meter; 100 cycles, 20 phons; 200 cycles, 40 phons; 500 cycles, 50 phons; 1,000 cycles, 40 phons; 1,000 cycles, 70 phons. Find the corresponding acoustic pressures in dynes per square centimeter, in decibels re 0.0002 dyne/cm², and in decibels re 1 dyne/cm².

2. Tones of equal loudness, 1 sone, are sounded at the following fre-quencies: 100 cycles, 200 cycles, 500 cycles, 1,000 cycles, 3,000 cycles. Find (a) the decibel increase in intensity necessary to double the loudness at these frequencies; (b) to triple the loudness at these frequencies. Tabulate the intensities in watts per square centimeter.

3. The following pure tones are combined, the intensity level of each being given re 0.0002 dyne/cm²:

200 cycles 80 db	500 cycles 60 db	2,000 cycles 30 db
300 cycles 50 db	700 cycles 40 db	3,000 cycles 20 db
400 cycles 50 db	1,000 cycles 40 db	5,000 cycles 20 db

Find the over-all loudness and the over-all intensity, assuming that the intensities can be added as if the tones were random noises.

4. (a) Find the arbitrary sensation level of a 60 db tone at each multiple of 100 cycles from 100 to 1,000 cycles.

(b) Find the effective sensation level if a person's threshold is 10 db above the arbitrary threshold.

(c) Find the effective sensation level if masking by noise is equivalent to 20 phons at each frequency.

5. From Figs. 8.52 and 8.31, what must be the intensity level of a 350 cycle tone if it is to be heard in the presence of a 400 cycle tone that has an intensity level of 80 db re 0.0002 dyne/cm²?

6. What must be the intensity level (re 0.0002 dyne/cm²) of a 50 cycle tone if it is to generate a fifth harmonic in the ear?

7. From Figs. 8.62 and 8.31, find the effective intensity levels of the subjective harmonics of a 68 db 50 cycle tone.

8. Find the band level of room noise in the 1,000–1,500 cycle band if the over-all level of the room noise is 43 db.

9. Find the S.A. for high-pass and low-pass 1,500 cycle filters at the optimum speech level. What are the corresponding values of articulation index? What is the sum of the A.I.'s?

10. From Fig. 8.94, find the limits of the bands of equal contribution to intelligibility.

11. Find the articulation index and syllable articulation if the over-all level of room noise is 43 db and the over-all speech level is 60 db at the point of audition.

Note: Since the simplified theory restricts W to a value of 0.70, take W to be 0.75 in all bands where the computed value of W exceeds 0.70.

Chapter 9

ARCHITECTURAL ACOUSTICS

The goal of architectural acoustics is the design of structures contributing to the intelligibility of speech, the richness of music, and freedom from external noise. The primary problems are the selection of site, noise insulation, the design of the size and shape of enclosures, and reverberation control. The acoustical designer usually does not have full sway in any of these particulars. The bishop who favors the soaring grace of Gothic architecture for his cathedral may be mildly influenced by the fact that a moderately low ceiling is best from the acoustic viewpoint, but he will very likely ask the acoustician to take the Gothic and make the best of it. The architect who has based his design on the clean symmetry of a hemisphere set atop a cylinder may consider it unfortunate that these lines result in almost insuperable focusing problems, but too often he will leave it to the acoustical engineer to correct as best he can whatever acoustic faults the plan may have. In some cases, such as studio design, acoustics is the prime consideration, and the acoustic designer can make full use of the fundamental principles of his art.

The approach to acoustical design in architecture depends, to a degree, upon whether one takes the point of view of the engineer or the physicist. The engineer is satisfied with a few broad principles, based on approximate theories, which, if applied with common sense and understanding, will result in auditoriums meeting certain established criteria of excellence. The physicist, on the other hand, demands a more scientific and general treatment, based on the study of wave motion in an enclosure as determined by the three-dimensional wave equation and the boundary conditions of the enclosure. A complete general treatment is beyond the scope of this text, although an attempt will be made to illustrate the foundations of physical acoustics. The engineering approach is based primarily on geometrical acoustics; the physical approach, on wave acoustics.

Probably the foremost advances in architectural acoustics resulted from the researches of Wallace Sabine, whose studies were directed primarily at the influence of reverberation on the acoustics of chambers. Reverberation is the persistence of sound in an enclosure after emission by the source has ceased. It now appears, however, that reverberation is not the sole consideration in acoustical design. Morse and Bolt,[1]* summing up in a

---

* Numbered references in this chapter will be found on pp. 313-314.

review of room acoustics, have quoted the following as the important design requirements:

1. The mean square pressure should be as nearly uniform as possible throughout the seating area, and should be sufficiently great for intelligibility, comfort, and pleasure. Sabine took this uniformity as an assumption in his reverberation theory.

2. A certain percentage of the sound should reach the listener directly from the speaker, and less than a certain percentage should reach him indirectly, after reflection from any single surface. These requirements are involved in the concept of "liveness."

3. The decay rate of sound in the room should be nearly constant for the first 30 or 40 db, except for small superposed fluctuations which appear to make the decay more pleasing to the ear. This precludes the presence of *echo*, which is characterized by sharp discrete peaks on the decay curve, and which is very disturbing to audition. There is an optimum value for the decay rate which depends on the employment of the auditorium. This is an improvement on Sabine's criterion, which was based primarily on the time during which the level of the reverberant sound decreased 60 db.

The success with which a room meets these requirements may be accurately judged with regard to speech by articulation testing. For music, one must rely on the opinion of competent listeners. As far as physical design goes, the two most important elements are the choice of shape and size of room, and the treatment given walls, floor, and ceiling. The former aims at diffusion of the sound, the second at the proper *reverberation time*.

9.1 Shape and Size of Room

Geometrical acoustics demonstrates rather clearly that floor plans having circular or elliptical shapes should be avoided because of their focusing properties, and the consequent violation of the requirement that the sound pressure level be uniform throughout the room. Focusing may take place in all three dimensions, and thus may lead to very high concentrations at some points and exceptionally low levels at others. When such regular geometrical shapes are used in combination with room sizes in which the path difference between a direct and reflected ray of sound is as great as 65 ft, the results are extremely bad, since sound takes about $\frac{1}{17}$ sec to travel 65 ft, and two sounds separated by such an interval can be distinguished by the human ear. Echoes[2, 3] are one of the most annoying of all acoustical faults. If focusing is significant, the echo may be very strong at focal points. A circular floor plan is also prone to produce the phenomenon of "creeping," as in the famous "whispering galleries," in which a whisper directed tangentially to the wall will travel around the circumference of the room. Focusing and creeping effects can be overcome by treatment of the walls with convex surfaces. If this is not desired, and in general it is not a good room shape, treatment of the walls, floor, and ceilings with absorptive materials will lessen the harmful effects, though such treatment will not remove them entirely.

A rectangular floor plan is to be preferred to those mentioned in the preceding paragraph, although if opposite walls are smooth and parallel, and the floor is parallel to the ceiling, serious low-frequency resonances and "flutter echoes" will be present. Because of the directivity of high-frequency sound, the length usually should be greater than the width. According to Knudsen,[2] ratios of length to width from 2:1 to 1.2:1 have been found satisfactory, although in a small room the sound level is sufficiently high for good hearing for a larger variation in length to width ratios, for the sound diffuses quickly throughout the room by multiple reflection from the walls.

With respect to size, the optimum volume per seat usually is the lowest value consistent with requirements of visibility, comfort, and aesthetics. If the volume is small, it is easier to provide sufficient pressure level, the reverberation problem is less severe (as will be seen from the reverberation theory to be studied in a subsequent article), and the echo problem is less likely to arise.

We have already mentioned that barrelled and domed ceilings are to be avoided because of their focusing properties. Conversely, well-designed ceiling splays may be used to direct the sound (by reflection and as a "wave guide") into those parts of the auditorium that are likely to have lower pressure levels, chiefly the seats in the rear.[2,3] An example of such ceiling design is shown in Fig. 9.11. The same principle may be used in wall design, splays being used both to break up the parallelism responsible for flutter echo, and to direct the sound beneficially.

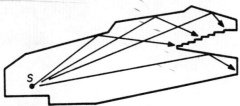

Fig. 9.11. Showing beneficial reflection from a well-designed theatre ceiling. [After Knudsen.]

9.2 Standing Waves in a Room

Like resonant strings and fluid columns, rooms have normal modes of vibration and natural resonant frequencies. If a string is disturbed, any of the normal modes may be excited, the strength of the various modes depending on just how the string is disturbed (in the example of the plucked string of Art. 2.11, the amplitudes of the various harmonics were inversely proportional to the square of the order of the harmonic). If the disturbance is sinusoidal in character, the string will be "driven" at the frequency of the disturbance, and the amplitude of motion will be inversely proportional to the impedance of the string at the driving frequency. The string in resonant vibration has been compared to a collection of simple harmonic oscillators, each with the same resonant frequency. Since the impedance of a vibrator, aside from that due to mechanical resistance, is low at a resonant frequency, the amplitude of motion will be high if driven at, or close, to, a normal frequency. A steady-state vibration, of course, will take place at the frequency of the driver, regardless of the normal frequencies of the driven system∫ But if the driver has a complex and varying frequency characteristic, as a symphony orchestra, then transient vibrations at the normal frequencies of the symphony hall will be excited as the orchestra roams over its gamut of frequencies. These will of course die out rather quickly. But if the orchestra were to come to a sudden stop, the sound in the room would be composed at that instant of the normal modes which had been excited just prior to the sudden cessation of the driver. This is strikingly illustrated by photographs of the decay of sound in a room obtained by Knudsen, showing oscillographs of the decay of sound in a small room with hard walls (Fig. 9.21). It may be seen from the decay curves that normal modes at both 92.9 and 99.7 cycles are excited by a driving frequency of 96.7 cycles, which is approximately halfway between.

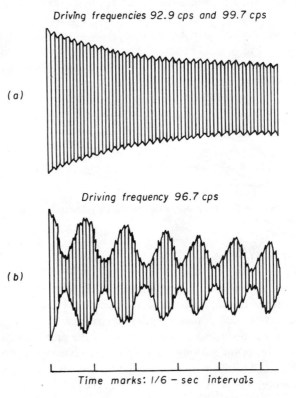

Fig. 9.21. Oscillographs of sound decay in a small room with hard walls.

The decay rate of the normal vibrations is of course a function of the damping. At these low frequencies, the damping is due almost entirely to absorption by the boundaries of the room. At frequencies above about 500 cycles the absorption in the air must be taken into account in the accurate computation of decay. Thus, Knudsen[2, 3] has shown that at 4,096 cycles the air absorption and the energy loss to the walls, even in a small room, are of the same order of magnitude. It will be possible to simplify the discussion considerably while still preserving the main framework of the theory if we neglect air absorption, and therefore we shall in this article ascribe the decay entirely to a loss of energy to the walls.

Figure 9.21 demonstrates that a pure tone will excite resonant modes in its vicinity. A musical tone will excite several groups. A noise source will excite the various normal modes to a degree approximately proportional to its spectrum level curve. The speaking voice, or, *a fortiori*, the sound from an entire symphony, will excite a great number of vibrations. Whatever the source of excitation, the room is in a state of damped free vibration when the source becomes silent. The persistence of these resonant vibrations is termed *reverberation*.

For an investigation of reverberation in a room, it will be necessary to find a solution of the three-dimensional wave equation in Cartesian coordinates (Eq. 4.210). It will be remembered that no attempt was made to solve this equation in the fourth chapter, since the spherical form of the equation was more useful at that point. For a room with rectangular symmetry, however, Eq. (4.210) is obviously well suited. We shall solve this equation as we have so many other equations; that is, by assuming a form of solution by comparison with similar differential equations, and checking the assumed solution by substitution in the differential equation. We rewrite the three-dimensional wave equation in the form

$$\frac{\partial^2 \phi}{\partial x^2} + \frac{\partial^2 \phi}{\partial y^2} + \frac{\partial^2 \phi}{\partial z^2} = \frac{1}{c^2} \frac{\partial^2 \phi}{\partial t^2} \tag{9.21}$$

and compare it with the equation of the vibrating string,

$$\frac{\partial^2 \xi}{\partial x^2} \neq \frac{1}{c^2} \frac{\partial^2 \xi}{\partial t^2} \tag{9.22}$$

For the standing wave case Eq. (9.22) has the solution

$$\xi = A(\sin kx)e^{j\omega t} \tag{9.23}$$

where $k = n\pi/L$.

It is to be noted that the solution of Eq. (9.22) consists of a real sinusoid in the space factor and a complex exponential in the time factor. It is plausible to expect that the solution of Eq. (9.21) has a solution in which the space factor is the product of three factors, one in x, one in y, and one in z, that is, a solution of the form

$$\phi = \phi_0 e^{j\omega t} \cos k_1 x \cos k_2 y \cos k_3 z \tag{9.24}$$

If this solution is substituted back into the differential equation, there results the equality,

$$k_1^2 + k_2^2 + k_3^2 = \frac{1}{c^2}\omega^2 \qquad (9.25)$$

which is the condition that must be met if the form (9.24) is to be the solution to Eq. (9.21).

The form (9.24) can also be made to satisfy boundary conditions within a rectangular enclosure if the walls are rigid. The x component of particle velocity will be a sine form in x, and similarly for the y and z components. If the origin of coordinates is taken at one of the corners of the room, the boundary conditions will by this fact be met at the walls $x = 0, y = 0, z = 0$. Let L, W, and H represent the length, width, and height of the room. Then to fulfill the boundary conditions at the walls $x = L, y = W, z = H$, a second set of conditions must be fulfilled, namely,

$$\sin k_1 L = 0, \qquad \sin k_2 W = 0, \qquad \sin k_3 H = 0$$

Therefore we have for k_1, k_2 and k_3,

$$k_1 = \frac{n_1\pi}{L}, \quad k_2 = \frac{n_2\pi}{W}, \quad k_3 = \frac{n_3\pi}{H} \qquad (9.26)$$

where the n's are any integers. By Eq. (9.25), this gives for ω/c,

$$\frac{\omega}{c} = \pi\sqrt{\left(\frac{n_1}{L}\right)^2 + \left(\frac{n_2}{W}\right)^2 + \left(\frac{n_3}{H}\right)^2} \qquad (9.27)$$

and for the normal frequencies,

$$f = \frac{\omega}{2\pi} = \frac{c}{2}\sqrt{\left(\frac{n_1}{L}\right)^2 + \left(\frac{n_2}{W}\right)^2 + \left(\frac{n_3}{H}\right)^2} \qquad (9.28)$$

For each normal frequency, there is a corresponding normal mode; that is, a corresponding geometric configuration of vibration in the room. In some of these configurations (axial modes), the direction of propagation of the waves will be normal to two of the walls (tangential to four walls); in another set, the direction of propagation will be tangential to two of the walls, and normal to none (tangential modes); in a third set, the direction of propagation is tangential to none of the walls (oblique modes). Mathematically, the axial modes are defined by the vanishing of two of the three k's, the tangential modes by one of the three, and the axial modes by none of the three. The simplest modes are the axial modes in which the nonzero k equals unity; these modes represent, in a sense, the three fundamental modes of the room. The mathematical function which describes a particular normal mode is called an eigenfunction, a term borrowed from quantum mechanics. The eigenfunction for the (1, 0, 0) mode is

$$\phi_{(1,0,0)} = \Phi_0\left(\cos\frac{\pi x}{L}\right)e^{jc\pi t/L} \qquad (9.29)$$

where the constant Φ_0 is determined by initial conditions.

It is a relatively easy matter to find the normal frequencies if the dimensions of a rectangular room are known, since Eq. (9.28) gives a normal frequency for any combination of integers which may be substituted for n_1, n_2, and n_3. Tabulated results of a few of the lower frequencies are shown in Table 9.21. If two or more different modes (i.e. different combination of k-values) have the same resonant frequency they are called degenerate modes. The most important result of degeneracy is a piling up of energy at a particular frequency. For example, in a room that is perfectly cubical in shape the particle velocity at the center of the room will be a superposition of particle velocities of the x, y, and z axial modes at the common fundamental frequency $f = c/2L$. Therefore the room will vibrate very strongly to this frequency. This is an undesirable result, for this frequency will linger unduly long, and in other ways it will be favoured at the expense of other frequencies. Those who have followed the fascinating development of radio from the days when the

Table 9.21.

| $C = 1{,}130 \text{ ft sec}^{-1}$ | $W = 5 \text{ ft}$ |
| $L = 20 \text{ ft}$ | $H = 10 \text{ ft}$ |
Normal Mode	Normal Frequency (cycles)
1, 0, 0	28
0, 1, 0	38
0, 0, 1	56
1, 1, 0	48
1, 0, 1	62
0, 1, 1	68
1, 1, 1	73
2, 0, 0	56

Note the case of degeneracy at 56 cycles.

first horn speakers rattled and groaned at their resonant frequencies will realize immediately how disastrous such resonance is to good acoustics. An important factor regarding the normal modes of a room is that they cluster together at the higher frequencies, but are relatively far apart at the lower frequencies. One of the more important problems of wave acoustics is the computation of the number of normal modes in any frequency range as a function of the dimensions of the room. We shall forego the development of this equation, since it is fairly lengthy, and only a complete treatment by wave acoustics would justify its derivation. Its most important characteristic is that it predicts a very rapid increase in the number of modes per cycle as the frequency increases. As we shall see, geometrical acoustics is based on the assumption that the sound is completely diffuse throughout the enclosure. As a result, wave acoustics and geometrical acoustics approach each other at high frequencies (though this statement must be qualified), but give very different results at low frequencies.

In the last article of the third chapter, the decay of standing waves in pipes was analyzed, and it was found that the decay rate at the end walls is twice that at the side walls. If the cross section of the pipe is assumed to be rectangular, it could be said that the standing wave in the pipe is normal to two walls, and tangential to four walls. The room modes that have been called tangential are tangential to only two walls, and have both tangential and normal components on four walls. One might suppose that the tangential and normal components would average out on these four walls, but analysis shows that the existence of normal components on four walls gives the tangential modes a greater decay rate than the axial modes. Since the oblique modes have normal components on all six walls, they have the greatest decay rate. Analysis beyond the scope of this text gives approximately the following proportion between the decay rates in the special case* where the walls are homogeneous and of approximately the same area:

$$a_0 : a_T : a_A \simeq 9 : \tfrac{25}{4} : 4$$

The theoretical decay curve therefore, plotted to a decibel scale, is of the form shown in Fig. 9.22. The initial segment of this decay curve should represent a drop of 30 db for satisfactory acoustics.

It is interesting that the decay rate obtained for the side walls of a pipe is exactly that obtained by Sabine in his earliest analysis of reverberation in rooms. Unfortunately, the explanation of this relation would require a lengthy analysis of the absorption of standing waves in an enclosure. The same may be said of the derivation of the working formulas of architectural acoustics by wave acoustics. On the other hand, Sabine's method, though approximate in its assumptions, is at least a self-contained theory. Since the application of the working formulas of architectural acoustics is of greater import in a text of this character because of its relation to other branches of acoustics, we shall in the next article start from the beginning with Sabine's theory. In concluding, however, it should be stated that wave acoustics has explained the influence of room shape on good acoustics in a rather complete manner. It has shown that axial waves are most persistent and oblique waves decay most quickly, and therefore room shapes that discourage axial waves and encourage oblique waves are beneficial. Wall irregularities have a similar effect. In the first article, the discussion of room shape was confined to the focusing effect. Wave acoustics shows that room shape also enters into reverberation theory. A deeper analysis demonstrates that although wave acoustics has posed problems that are almost impossible of solution in the general case, it gives designers a far greater insight into what is happening to the sound in a room than Sabine's assumption that the energy density is homogeneous. It has already been remarked that the assumption of diffuse sound has been fairly well confirmed by wave acoustics, though not without qualifications, at the higher frequencies. But at the lower frequencies, especially in small rooms,[2, 3] where strong standing wave modes are relatively isolated, wave acoustics has made a distinct contribution.

We turn now to the traditional treatment of reverberation, employing Sabine's assumption of homogeneous energy density.

---

* It should be emphasized that these values were obtained with very restrictive assumptions. They are given only as an indication of typical values to be expected.

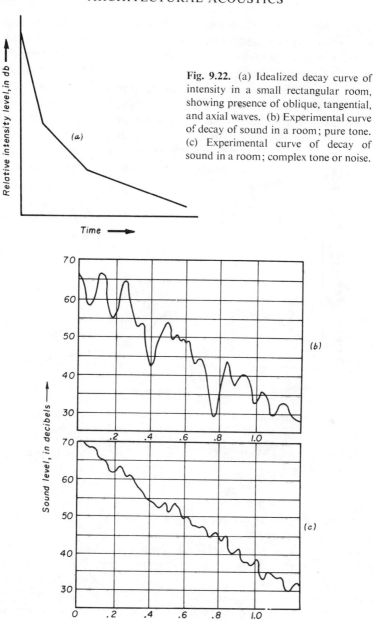

Fig. 9.22. (a) Idealized decay curve of intensity in a small rectangular room, showing presence of oblique, tangential, and axial waves. (b) Experimental curve of decay of sound in a room; pure tone. (c) Experimental curve of decay of sound in a room; complex tone or noise.

9.3 Sabine's Reverberation Theory

Suppose a source of sound energy in a closed room with perfectly reflecting walls. Since energy is being emitted continuously by the source, and none is leaving the room, the total energy content of the room will increase linearly with time, and the ultimate energy density and pressure level will approach infinity. On the other hand, if there is an opening in the room, the acoustic energy will increase until it reaches a value at which the power flow through the opening equals the power flow from the source, and thereafter the total energy content will remain constant. If the energy source now ceases to radiate, the total energy will gradually decay as the energy leaves through the opening. For the simplest approach to reverberation theory it is assumed that the energy density is uniform throughout the room, and on the basis of this assumption Fig. 9.31 shows the theoretical graph of total energy against time for a room with an opening where the emission from the source begins at $t = t_0$ and ceases at $t = t_1$.

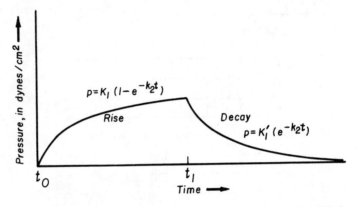

Fig. 9.31. Theoretical curves of rise and decay in a room with perfect diffusion.

The researches of Wallace C. Sabine on acoustic materials showed that most porous materials act in a manner similar to imperfect openings. When a sound wave reaches the surface of a porous material, some of the sound energy will be reflected, but a certain amount will enter the interstices of the material. As a result, a portion of the incident sound energy is converted into random heat energy. For practical purposes, the result is as if this energy had escaped through an opening, since it no longer appears as sound energy. Sabine was able to compare the effect of areas of absorptive material with that obtained by open windows, and to define an *absorption coefficient* for each acoustic material with which he worked. A large body of experimentation had been performed on the absorptive properties of acoustic materials, and several different types of absorption coefficients have been defined, the types depending on the method of measurement. However, to introduce the fundamental concepts of the theory, we shall define the absorption coefficient simply as the ratio of the sound energy absorbed by the surface of an acoustic material to the energy incident upon it. The absorption coefficient is definitely a function of the frequency of the incident sound. One commercial acoustic material has the rated absorption coefficient of 0.99 at 512 cycles (but much lower coefficients at other frequencies). It will be seen that in a chamber completely lined with this material, conditions would be very close to those prevailing in the open air for a 512 cycle tone. In particular, as one receded from a small source of sound, the intensity would decrease approximately as the inverse square law.

We shall now develop Sabine's theory of growth and decay of sound energy in a room, basing the theory on the assumptions of completely diffuse sound in the room (homogeneous energy density), and continuous, uniform absorption of sound by the boundaries. We begin with a verbal statement of the energy conditions within the room:

The rate of increase of energy within a room is equal to the rate of emission by the source minus the rate of absorption by the walls.

If we let P_E = rate of emission of the source, that is, the power of the source, W = energy density in the room, V = volume of the room, A = rate of absorption by the walls, we have the differential equation

$$V\frac{dW}{dt} = P_E - A \tag{9.31}$$

It can be shown that

$$A = \frac{c\alpha S W}{4} \tag{9.32}$$

where c = velocity of sound in the medium, α = absorption coefficient of the surface material, S = surface area of the room. Though we shall prove this important relation in the next article, for the present we shall assume it to be true and write the differential equation of energy density within the room:

$$V\frac{dW}{dt} + \frac{c\alpha S}{4} W = P_E \tag{9.33}$$

where P_E is assumed to be constant. This is a differential equation of the type

$$\frac{dW}{dt} + A'W = P_E' \tag{9.34}$$

where $A' = c\alpha S/4V$ and $P_E' = P_E/V$. It has the general solution

$$W = \frac{P_E'}{A'} + \text{Const } e^{-A't} \tag{9.35}$$

We can use this general solution to solve for either the build-up or decay of the energy density. To solve for build-up, we assume that the source is "turned on" at $t = 0$, and therefore that W is zero at the initial instant. We can then solve for the arbitrary constant, and obtain for it the value Const $= -P_E'/A' = -4P_E/c\alpha S$. We then have the solution for *growth of sound in a room*:

$$W = \frac{4P_E}{c\alpha S}[1 - e^{-(c\alpha S/4V)t}] \tag{9.36}$$

The steady-state value of the energy density can be obtained by letting t become infinite. It is seen to be

$$W_{\text{s.s.}} = \frac{4P_E}{c\alpha S} \tag{9.37}$$

Actually the energy density will reach this value closely within a short time. For the equation of decay, we assume that the source has been active for a long enough time that the steady state has approximately been reached, and that at a certain instant the source is "turned off." The value of P_E in the differential equation (9.33) thus becomes zero, since during the decay the power emanating from the source is zero. However, when $t = 0$, $W = (4P_E)/(c\alpha S)$, where P_E now represents the power of the source *before* it was turned off. The solution for the decay of sound is thus

$$W = \frac{4P_E}{c\alpha S} e^{-(c\alpha S/4V)t} \tag{9.38}$$

so that we have $c\alpha S/4V$ for the decay rate. From the above development it may be shown that the growth of *acoustic pressure* is given by the equation

$$p = 1{,}300 \frac{P_E}{a} [1 - e^{-(ca/4V)t}]^{1/2} \tag{9.39}$$

where p is in dynes per square centimeter, P_E is in watts, V is in cubic feet, c is in feet per second, a is in square feet units of absorption, i.e.,

$$a = S_1\alpha_1 + S_2\alpha_2 + \ldots$$

where $S_1 = $ surface area having absorption coefficient α_1, $S_2 = $ surface area having absorption coefficient α_2, etc.

The only difficulty in the derivation of Eq. (9.39) from Eq. (9.36) is the combination of cgs and English units, and the relation between energy density and pressure, which we have covered in Chapters 3 and 4.

Problem: Derive Eq. (9.39) from Eq. (9.36).

The steady-state equation for pressure is

$$P_{\text{s.s.}} = 1{,}300 \left(\frac{P_E}{a}\right)^{1/2} \tag{9.310}$$

which can be obtained from Eq. (9.39) by letting t approach infinity.

Sabine defined reverberation time T as the time during which the energy density falls from its steady-state value to $1/10^6$ of this value. We then have

$$e^{-(ca/4V)T} = 10^{-6} \tag{9.311}$$

$$T = \frac{4V}{ca} \ln_e 10^6 = \left(\frac{4\ln_e 10^6}{c}\right)\frac{V}{a} \tag{9.312}$$

The value of the constant $4 \ln_e 10^6/c$ depends upon whether English or metric units are used. In English units at 20°C, $c = 1{,}130$ ft/sec; therefore, the constant is

$$\frac{4 \times 2.3026 \times 6}{1{,}130} = 0.049, \qquad T = 0.049 \frac{V}{a} \tag{9.313a}$$

In metric units, $c = 343$ m/sec at 20°C, and we have for the constant,

$$\frac{4 \times 2.3026 \times 6}{343} = 0.161, \qquad T = 0.161 \frac{V}{a} \qquad (9.313b)$$

Equations (9.312) and (9.313) agree with the values experimentally measured by Sabine for small coefficient of attenuation. We may find the decay rate directly in decibels per second from Eq. (9.313a). We shall derive it in English units. Since the sound falls 60 db in time $T = 0.049 V/a$, the fall in unit time will be

$$\frac{60}{T} = \frac{60}{0.049} \cdot \frac{a}{V} = 1,230 \frac{a}{V} \text{ db/sec} \qquad (9.314)$$

where a is in square feet, and V is in cubic feet.

It is often important to know the power necessary to produce a pressure level in decibels re 0.0002 dyne/cm². We have

$$\text{pressure level} = 20 \log_{10}\left(\frac{p}{0.0002}\right) = 20 \log_{10} p + 74$$

$$= 20 \log_{10}\left[1,300\left(\frac{P_E}{a}\right)^{1/2}\right] + 74 = 10 \log_{10}\frac{P_E}{a} \qquad (9.315)$$

$$+ 136 \text{ db}$$

9.4 The Rate of Absorption of Sound by the Walls of an Enclosure

In the preceding article, we employed the equation

$$A = \frac{\alpha W c S}{4} \qquad (9.41)$$

for the rate of absorption of energy by the walls of an enclosure in which the energy density is homogeneous and of value W. It is the object of the present article to prove this relation. We first consider the radiation of energy from an elementary volume dV within the enclosure toward an elementary surface element dS of the wall (Fig. 9.41a). Since the volume is radiating energy equally in all directions with velocity c, the amount of radiation which impinges on dS will be proportional to the projection of dS on the sphere of radius r surround the volume element. The surface element will therefore receive a fraction of the total radiation of the volume element equal to

$$\frac{dS \cos \theta}{4\pi r^2} \qquad (9.42)$$

where θ is the angle between the normal to dS and the radius vector of dV.

We locate the volume element with respect to the surface element by a spherical coordinate system, Fig. 9.41(b). The coordinates of the volume element are r, θ, and ϕ, and the edges of the volume element have the values dr, $r\,d\theta$, and $r\,\sin\theta\,d\phi$. This infinitesimal volume may be taken as a rectangular parallelepiped to infinitesimals of the first order, and the volume may be written

$$dV = r^2 \sin\theta\, d\theta\, d\phi\, dr \qquad (9.43)$$

We therefore have for the energy of the infinitesimal volume,

$$dE = Wr^2 \sin\theta\, d\theta\, d\phi\, dr \qquad (9.44)$$

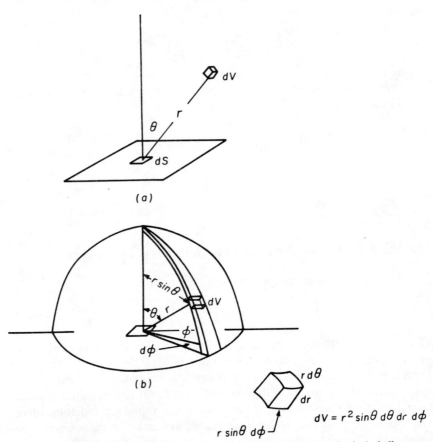

Fig. 9.41. Radiation toward a wall-surface element from a spherical shell within an enclosure.

Let us now find the total energy contribution to dS of a hemispherical shell of radius r and thickness dr by integrating with respect to θ and ϕ, remembering that the contribution of any element contains the factor $\cos\theta$. We first add contributions from the volume elements in a slice between two meridians. Over this integration, θ varies from 0 to $\pi/2$. Then we add the contributions of such slices over the surface of the hemisphere (ϕ varies from

0 to 2π). We then have for the contribution of a hemispherical shell of radius r and thickness dr,

$$dE = \frac{W \, dS}{4\pi} \int_0^{2\pi} \int_0^{\pi/2} \sin \theta \cos \theta \, d\theta \, d\phi \, dr = \frac{W \, dS \, dr}{4} \qquad (9.45)$$

The energy from this shell travels toward the surface element with velocity c. Therefore it strikes the surface element in the time interval dt, where $dt = dr/c$. The *rate* at which the energy arrives at the surface element is therefore

$$\frac{dE}{dt} = \frac{W \, dS \, dr}{4} \cdot \frac{c}{dr} = \frac{Wc \, dS}{4} \qquad (9.46)$$

The energy content is homogeneous and constant throughout the enclosure, and therefore the energy emission is also constant and continuous. Of all the energy that is emitted from all the volume elements in the room at a chosen instant, the energy from only a particular shell of thickness dr will impinge on the surface element in a particular time element dr/c. Therefore the expression (9.46) represents the rate at which energy is received by the surface element ds.

The intensity at any point of the wall is therefore $Wc/4$, and the total power received by the interior surface of the room is $WcS/4$, where S is the total wall surface. Since we have assumed the surface to be homogeneous, and have defined the rate of absorption A to be the product of the absorption coefficient α, and the rate at which energy is brought up to the walls, we have finally,

$$A = \frac{\alpha WcS}{4}$$

Problem: Show that all hemispherical shells with their centers at dS supply equal rates of energy, as long as they have equal thickness.

9.5 Eyring's Reverberation Theory

If we refer to Eq. (9.313) for Sabine's formula for the reverberation time, we can readily see that the theory is incorrect for a large value of absorption, for the equation predicts, when $\alpha = 1$, a finite value of 0.049 V/S for the reverberation time, whereas it should give a value of zero. Experimentation shows that when the coefficient of absorption is greater than about 0.2, the reverberation time predicted by Sabine's equation is seriously in error, and the error increases as α increases. In addition, Sabine's assumption of uniform energy density has been challenged by several physicists. For this reason Eyring,[5] among others,[3] proposed a somewhat different attack based on the method of images. His analysis is too lengthy for inclusion in this text, but we shall derive his equation by a method which is essentially equivalent, though less rigorous.

Let us suppose that all the sound energy of the room is carried by one ray which is successively reflected by the walls of the room. A purely geometrical analysis shows that the mean free path (average distance traversed between two reflections) is $4V/S$. Figure 9.51 shows that the distance between two reflections for ray 1 is L, and for ray 2 is $L/\sqrt{2}$. For a cube, $L = 6V/S$, so that the mean free path of the second ray is about $4.3V/S$. Comparison of the two rays shows that the mean free path decreases as the path of the ray becomes more irregular, and it is plausible that it approaches the value of $4V/S$ for the average ray.

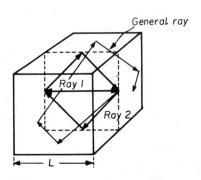

If the mean free path (mfp) equals $4V/S$, the average time interval between two reflections will have the value

Fig. 9.51. Mean free path of a sound ray in a cubcial enclosure.

$$\tau = \frac{\text{mfp}}{c} = \frac{4V}{Sc} \qquad (9.51)$$

The number of impacts which this ray makes with the walls in any time t will be

$$n = \frac{t}{\tau} = \frac{Sct}{4V} \qquad (9.52)$$

If the ray loses a fraction α of its intensity at each impact, the intensity of the ray after n impacts will be

$$I = I_0(1 - \alpha)^n = I_0(1 - \alpha)^{(Sc/4V)t} = I_0 e^{\ln(1 - \alpha)^{(Sc/4V)t}} \qquad (9.53)$$

$$= I_0 e^{[(Sc/4V)\ln(1 - \alpha)]t} \qquad (9.54)$$

Thus $(Sc/4V)[-\ln(1 - \alpha)]$ is the decay rate, and the reverberation time is

$$T = \frac{4V}{Sc[-\ln(1 - \alpha)]} \ln_e 10^6$$

$$= 0.049 \frac{V}{S[-\ln(1 - \alpha)]} \qquad \text{in English units}$$

$$\qquad (9.55)$$

$$= 0.161 \frac{V}{S[-\ln(1 - \alpha)]} \qquad \text{in metric units}$$

In the derivation we have merely shown that the value $4V/S$ is a plausible value for the mean free path. However, we can correlate this value with the analysis of the previous article.

Since the ray contains all the sound energy in the room, it will bring up energy VW at each impact. In the previous article, we have derived the expression $WcS/4$ for the power flow toward the walls. Let N equal the average number of impacts per unit time,

$$NVW = \frac{WcS}{4}$$

and therefore

$$N = \frac{cS}{4V}$$

If N is the average number of impacts per unit time, the average distance traversed between impacts must be

$$\text{mfp} = \frac{c}{N} = c\left(\frac{4V}{Sc}\right) = \frac{4V}{S}$$

Since the computation of reverberation time by Eyring's formula is complicated by the presence of the logarithmic function, which necessitates the use of a table of logarithms, it is the practice to construct graphs giving the reverberation time directly in terms of the absorption coefficient, the volume, and the surface area. The graph of Fig. 9.52 gives the reverberation time

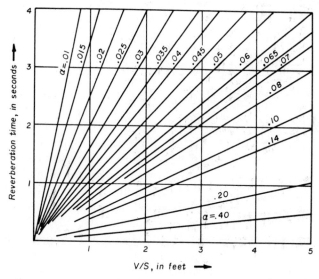

Fig. 9.52. Reverberation time in seconds, in terms of V/S and α.

within about 3 per cent of the value that would be computed from the Eyring formula.

It should be noted that Eyring's equation for reverberation is similar to Sabine's, differing only in that the absorption coefficient is replaced by a logarithmic function of the absorption coefficient. Indeed, since

$$\lim_{\alpha \to 0} \left[-\ln(1 - \alpha)\right] = \alpha$$

the two formulas approach the same value as the absorption becomes less. Thus for "live" rooms, it matters little which is used.

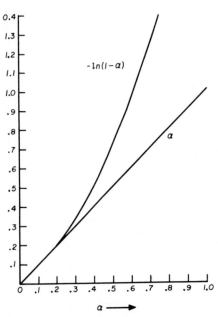

Fig. 9.53. The functions α and $-\ln(1-\alpha)$ plotted against α, showing that Eyring's function approaches ∞ for unity coefficient of absorption.

On the other hand, as we have noted, Sabine's formula is incorrect for an absorption coefficient of unity, whereas Eyring's formula gives the correct value of zero reverberation time. Figure 9.53, which is a plot of the factors α and $-\ln(1-\alpha)$, shows the comparison between the two values, and also enables one to compute the reverberation time very easily once the volume, surface area, and absorption coefficient are given.

Both formulas are likely to give results seriously in error with experiment when the absorption is not uniform over the entire surface. Likewise, in the case of bad focusing, one cannot expect the predicted values to compare with those determined experimentally. However, their failings should not be overstressed. Generally speaking, they have been highly successful for the acoustical designing of rooms.

The formulas of Sabine and Eyring by no means represent the ultimate in reverberation theory. Millington and Sette have offered a third geometric approach which is superior in some respects, while Knudsen, Morse, Bolt, and others have gone far beyond the geometrical theory in their investigation of sound waves in enclosures based on wave acoustics (Art. 9.2). It is hoped that the theory developed in the previous sections gives at least some understanding of the reverberation problem in architectural acoustics. We now turn to an application of these principles in the design of rooms, and the test methods which can be used to establish the degree of acoustical worth of rooms.

9.6 Air Absorption

In the interests of simplification, absorption in air has heretofore been neglected. This is not generally permissible. Knudsen[3] has developed a fomula for reverberation time which includes the effect of air absorption:

$$T = \frac{0.049V}{-S\ln(1-\alpha) + 4mV} \tag{9.61}$$

According to Knudsen, Eq. (9.55) can be used for calculating reverberation times for all frequencies below about 2,000 cycles, but Eq. (9.61), with the appropriate value of m, should be used for all higher frequencies. It is necessary to include air absorption for all frequencies above about 1,000 cycles in large auditoriums, especially if the humidity is below 50 per cent. The variation of m with frequency and humidity are shown in Fig. 9.61. Aside from their use in architectural acoustics, these curves are of interest to the physicist for a fundamental reason. The absorption which Knudsen observed in air was from 10 to 100 times that which would be expected from classical

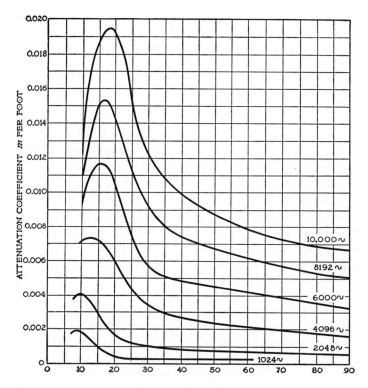

Fig. 9.61. Values of the absorption coefficient m as a function of relative humidity for different frequencies. [After Knudsen.]

absorption theory, in which absorption is explained by viscosity and heat conduction. Knudsen[6] and Kneser[7] ultimately proved that the absorption in this case is *molecular* in origin. The theory of molecular absorption is of great importance in modern sound theory and will be discussed in detail in Chapter 11. It is worth remarking that the curves of Fig. 9.61 represent one of the earliest experimental measurements showing this phenomenon. The curves are also of practical importance in investigations of sound propagation in the atmosphere. Knudsen[8] has compared propagation in the hot dry summer air of the desert and the cold winter air of the arctic. The differences are striking. The attenuation in the oxygen of desert air is so great that if it were not for the nitrogen, communication by unamplified speech would be impossible over distances in excess of about 40 m. Conversely, he has termed the arctic air "acoustically transparent." If one assumes that the absorption is *negligible*, that by shouting one can produce a sound pressure level of 84 db at a distance of 1 m, and that there occurs a 6 db drop in intensity level for each doubling of distance, the range would be in the neighborhood of 2^{14} m, or several miles, in the arctic. While the example is perhaps extreme, it indicates that air absorption is not to be treated lightly.

9.7 The Relation of Reverberation to Intelligibility

In Art. 9.3 we have developed the Sabine expression for the decay rate:

$$1,230\frac{S\alpha}{V}\, db/sec \qquad (9.71)$$

Let us now make use of the decay rate to study the influence of the absorption coefficient on intelligibility. Consider a succession of syllables each having the same power level, each lasting 0.15 sec, and each separated by a silent period of 0.05 sec, so that a new syllable is enunciated each 0.20 sec. The history of the sound level in the room will be a series of rise curves and decay curves, as shown in Fig. 9.71. The relation of this figure to intelligibility presents a fairly involved problem, but we can derive important information by calculating how much the peak of each syllable stands out above the sound remaining from the previous syllable. Choosing the purely arbitrary criterion of the decibel difference between the peak value of any syllable and the level of the decaying sound from the previous syllable at that instant, we shall compare the results obtained for values of absorption coefficients of 0.1, 0.2 and 0.4, respectively, for a V/S ratio of 4.5 ft, e.g. a room $32 \times 32 \times 20$ ft.

The functions which govern the rise time and decay time show that the decay curve is purely exponential if the intensity is plotted linearly, whereas the rise curve is not. If the intensity is plotted on a logarithmic scale, the decay curve becomes a straight line, but the rise time does not. However, the actual rise curve is not nearly so important as the intensity reached at the end of the syllable. Rather than attempt to plot the rise curve in detail, we make use of the concept of time constant, which is the time during which the sound level grows to a fraction $(1 - 1/e)$ of its saturation value. This fraction turns out to be 63 per cent, which is about 2 db below the steady-state value. Since the general shape of the rise curve is known, once the time constant is found the rise curve can be drawn with sufficient accuracy. When the end of the syllable is reached, the rise curve ceases and the decay curve begins. In all cases, for the room constants chosen, the rise curve has reached within 2 db of its

saturation value when the syllable ends. We are now in a position to plot rise
and decay curves for the chosen values of absorption. It must be remembered
that the larger the absorption, the lower the saturation value of the sound level
in the room. Consequently, the peak of the rise curve will be 3 db lower on

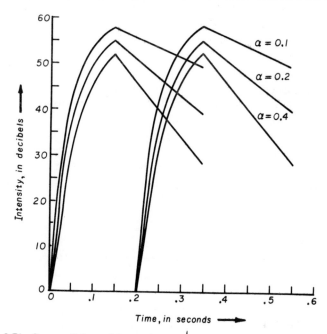

Fig. 9.71. Curves of rise and decay of sound level in a room in which $V/S = 4.5$
as a function of absorption coefficient. Saturation value of intensity for $\alpha =$
0.1 taken as 60 db.

the $\alpha = 0.2$ curve than on the $\alpha = 0.1$ curve, etc. (Eq. 9.37). The decay rates
for the absorption constants 0.1, 0.2, and 0.4 are computed from Eq. (9.71)
and drawn for several syllables in Fig. 9.71. It will be noted that the decay
curves have fallen from their peaks by the following amounts in the 0.2 sec
interval between syllables.

α	Difference
0.1	8 db
0.2	16 db
0.4	24 db

If the ambient noise level in the room is 40 db, the curve for $\alpha = 0.2$ is
just at the ambient noise level at the peak of the next syllable, the curve for
$\alpha = 0.1$ is still well above the noise level, and the curve for $\alpha = 0.4$ has fallen
to the noise level soon after the *start* of the succeeding syllable. It is evident
that the masking effect of the previous syllable is negligible for the highest
absorption, while it might be quite appreciable for the smallest absorption.

The simplicity of the assumption precludes a judgment on what absorption coefficient is needed for acceptable intelligibility. The example is given to show the fundamental principles upon which intelligibility depends in its relation to the decay of sound in a room.

The above example has shown somewhat of an inverse relation between intelligibility and reverberation time, and thus indicates that the addition of absorptive material to the walls will improve the characteristics of the auditorium for the intelligibility of speech. To a certain extent this fact was true before Sabine's experiments, since most listening chambers had extremely low absorption coefficients, and therefore the reverberation times were almost always inordinately large. As a result, increasing the absorption generally improved intelligibility. After a certain point, however, the consequent decrease in the sound level per unit of power from the source becomes an important factor, and in present design, where almost any reasonable value of absorption may be achieved, it is found that the optimum is something less than total absorption, at least for unamplified speech. This had led to the

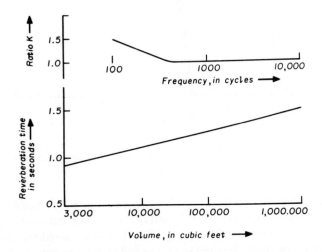

Fig. 9.72. Optimum reverberation time as a function of volume of an auditorium. The lower curve is Knudsen's latest curve of optimum reverberation time for rooms used about equally for music and speech, and is for a frequency of 1,000 cycles. The upper graph relation is used to find optimum reverberation time at other frequencies. "Ratio K" is the ratio between the optimum reverberation time at frequency f and that at 1,000 cycles.

criterion of *optimum reverberation time*. The criterion is influenced by the fact that the original source power may be increased by amplification, and also that the optimum decay rate for speech is somewhat different from that preferred for music. The curve given in Fig. 9.72 for optimum reverberation time is therefore somewhat a matter of compromise.

9.8 Room Design

Knowing the volume and surface area of a room, we can use Fig. 9.72 to find the optimum reverberation time at any frequency, and the curves of Fig. 9.52 to find the required absorption. However, a study of the characteristics of absorbing material shows that the absorption coefficient in most cases is highly frequency dependent. For instance, a certain brand of acoustical plaster applied to brick or concrete to a thickness of $\frac{1}{2}$ in. has the following absorption coefficients (when applied to metal laths it is much more absorptive at 128 cycles, possibly as much as 0.20):

	Frequency
0.06	128 cycles
0.36	512 cycles
0.72	2,048 cycles

The reverberation time for an auditorium in which $V/S = 5$, obtained from Eq. (9.55) or from the curves of Fig. 9.52 for this acoustical plaster, has the following values:

	Frequency
4.0 sec	128 cycles
0.6 sec	512 cycles
0.2 sec	2,048 cycles

Such an auditorium would have an exceptionally *boomy* response, since the higher frequencies would disappear very quickly, whereas the lower frequencies would linger. Many common absorptive materials have absorption coefficients which follow the same general trend with frequency as the acoustical plaster, although the plaster cited is an extreme example. Therefore other means often must be taken to introduce absorption at the low frequencies. This is frequently done, especially in certain European countries, by making use of the principle of the Helmholtz resonator. Open spaces of dimensions such that they resonate to low frequencies are included behind perforated wall panels. The energy enters these resonating chambers, and much of it is absorbed. Thin wood panels offer another, and usually more practical, means for increasing the absorption at low frequencies.

It was mentioned that the geometric theory of room acoustics assumed a homogeneous dispersion of the sound energy density throughout the auditorium. Whether this assumption is made or not, such a homogeneous sound field is desirable. It is found that such dispersion is aided by random arrangement of absorptive material on the walls. The effect is further enhanced if the patches of absorbing material and of other materials have convex surfaces. (The convexity of the surface, of course, applies to reflecting surfaces as well as absorbing surfaces.) This problem would not arise if it were always possible to cover the entire wall surface with a material which had the absorption coefficient necessary to produce the required total absorption for the desired reverberation time. However, it may turn out that when the absorbing material has been chosen, perhaps with regard to economic factors, only a fraction of the wall surface need be covered.

9.9 Effect of Audience on Reverberation and Echo

The presence of an audience causes a decrease in the reverberation time, since each person adds a rather large amount of absorptive material. This effect may be troublesome if the same auditorium is used for widely different attendance, and is not equipped with upholstered chairs. Obviously, it is most serious if the audience is expected to provide a significant fraction of the total absorption.

At first it is rather surprising to find that the harmful effects of *echo* may be even more serious in a filled, than in an empty, auditorium. If we remember, however, that *echo* is characterized by discrete reflections, while reverberation is the result of diffuse and multiple reflections, it is plausible that the discrete reflections will be less affected by a general increase in absorption. The echo peaks will therefore stand out more noticeably above the over-all sound level.

9.10 Intelligibility Ratings of Auditoriums

An articulation test for judging intelligibility was described in Art. 8.9. If a percentage articulation of 85 is achieved, only 3 words out of 100 will be misunderstood, and conditions are very good. This has been set as the minimum acceptable standard *when a sound amplification system is used*, although not many auditoriums meet this standard. If the percentage articulation is 75, then 6 words out of 100 will be misunderstood, and conditions are rated as satisfactory, but attentive listening is required. With a percentage articulation of 65, 10 words out of 100 are missed, and conditions are barely tolerable and very fatiguing to the listener. Below 65 per cent conditions are unsatisfactory.

The major factors which contribute to high percentage articulation are favorable room shape, low room noise, short reverberation time, and adequate speech level (the optimum is about 75 db at the position of the auditor). Knudsen[2] has attempted to isolate each of the four factors mentioned above and to give it a quantitative rating. He then proposes a formula for percentage articulation as a function of these four factors:

$$PA = 96 k_s k_n k_r k_l$$

where k_s = reduction factor for room shape, k_n = reduction factor for room noise, k_r = reduction factor for reverberation, k_l = reduction factor for insufficient loudness. Essentially, each of these factors is obtained by making the remaining factors optimum, and conducting a percentage articulation test for different values of the factor to be rated.

Figure 9.101 shows the result of such tests for the factors k_n, k_r, and k_l. For all these tests, the shape of the room was such that the value of k_s could be assumed to be unity. In deriving the curve for k_r, the room noise was held to a value well below the interference level, and an optimum value of loudness was provided. The reverberation time was then varied by the addition of absorbing material, and a PA test was conducted for several values of reverberation

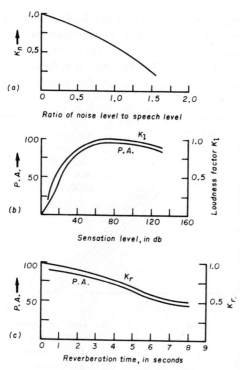

Fig. 9.101. (a) Noise reduction factor. (b) PA and k_1 as functions of sensation level. (c) PA and k_r as functions of reverberation time.

time. The PA curve rises toward a value of 96 for zero reverberation time, and therefore the k_r curve is given a value of unity for zero reverberation. In general, the value of k_r is about 4 per cent higher than the PA for the same reverberation time. In deriving k_l, the test was conducted with low noise and short reverberation time, so that both k_n and k_r could be assumed to be approximately unity, but the speech level was varied. The PA approached 96 at about 75 db, and k_l was assigned a value of unity at this value. Finally, k_n was derived by using a room with short reverberation time, varying the noise level while keeping the speech level constant, and graphing the PA versus the ratio of noise level to speech level. The shape factor K_s must be estimated. Knudsen took it as unity for the average room. Where bad focusing is present, it will be considerably less than unity. Conversely, where the walls and ceiling have been designed to obtain beneficial reflections, it may be somewhat greater than unity.

For many auditoriums, especially if the noise is at a low level, the product of k_s and k_n is about 0.96, and one can concentrate on the effects of speech level and reverberation by using the shortened formula

$$PA = 92k_ik_r$$

It was in the experimentation suggested by this formula that Knudsen developed the concept of optimum reverberation time for unamplified speech. Figure 9.102(a) shows the PA of an *average* speaker in auditoriums of various sizes and reverberation times. The influence of reflection in conserving the power of the speaker's voice is shown by the fact that the maximum point on

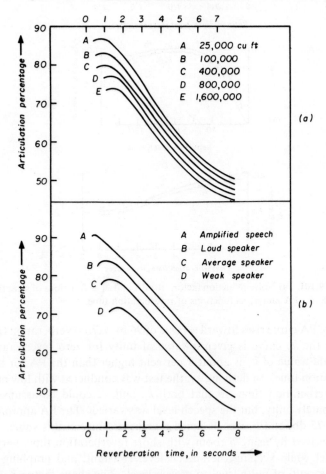

Fig. 9.102. (a) Percentage of articulation of an *average* speaker for auditoriums of various sizes. (b) Percentage of articulation for various speaker powers for an auditorium of 400,000 cu. ft.

the curves moves to the right for larger auditoriums. This set of curves can be directly related to the curve of optimum reverberation time.

The curves of Fig. 9.102(b) show the combined effect of loudness and reverberation in an auditorium of 400,000 cu ft. These curves show the benefit to be derived from an amplification system. Curve *A* is above the minimum acceptable value for PA for reverberation times of zero to 2 sec. Curve *B* barely reaches the minimum acceptable value (for speech amplification systems) at its optimum reverberation time of 1 sec. Curve *C* is never more than just satisfactory, and curve *D* is in the range where listening is fatiguing. The curves are for hearing conditions averaged throughout the auditorium. The PA will be less than average in the rear sections and more than average in the front sections of the auditorium.

9.11 The Use of Sound Amplification Systems in Room Design

We have mentioned in a previous article that there is a certain conflict between the benefit to be derived from a fast decay rate and the consequent lowering of the speech level in an auditorium. Before the advent of sound amplification systems, the benefit to be derived from reducing the reverberation had to be assessed against the lowering of the speech level which results. It is obvious, for example, that if the sound level at a certain point in an auditorium is below the masking level of the ambient room noise, it makes no difference if the masking effect of the previous syllable is negligible.

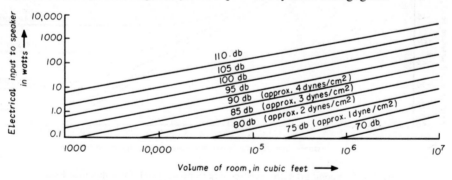

Fig. 9.111. Electric power required to provide correct sound level, assuming optimum reverberation time and efficiency of 5 per cent.

With present-day sound amplification systems, relatively unlimited source power can be provided. Therefore the design begins with a choice of the optimum reverberation time for the dimensions of the auditorium. The required absorption is then found from Fig. 9.52. When this has been done, the necessary source power for any pressure level can be computed from Eq. (9.315). A set of curves for such computation is shown in Fig. 9.111. The theory from which the curves of Fig. 9.111 are drawn is straightforward.

Since the volume is known, the optimum reverberation time in seconds can be obtained from Fig. 9.72. From a knowledge of surface area and volume, the necessary absorption can be found from Fig. 9.52. The source power needed for the desired sound level is then computed from Eq. (9.315). Finally, the electric power required of the speech system is computed from a knowledge of its efficiency.

9.12 The Sound Field in a Reverberant Room

Early reverberation theory assumed a uniform sound level throughout the enclosure, and working formulas for reverberation time are based on this assumption. However, it is common experience that in any room the sound level increases as one approaches the source, so that there exists an intermediate condition between the inverse square law of attenuation that would be found in the open air and the uniform level assumed by Sabine. As one would expect, the larger the absorption, the more closely the inverse square law is obeyed. Curves showing the pressure level against distance from the source are given in Fig. 9.121 for various values of the room constant R; the value

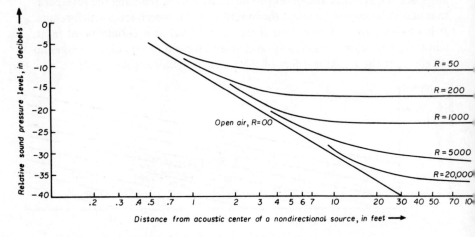

Fig. 9.121. Sound pressure level relative to power level, for a nondirectional source, for different values of the room constant R, as a function of the distance from the source.

of $R = \alpha S/(1 - \alpha)$, and is a function of frequency. These curves are for a nondirectional source.[9]

Most sources have a certain directivity. Often this directivity is utilized by the acoustical engineer in order to increase the ratio of the direct to the reflected sound, and to direct sound into those sections of the auditorium which might otherwise have inadequate sound levels. The curves of Fig. 9.122 show the pressure level against distance from the source as a function of the directivity of the source as well as the room constant. All these curves assume that there is no focusing of the sound in reflection.

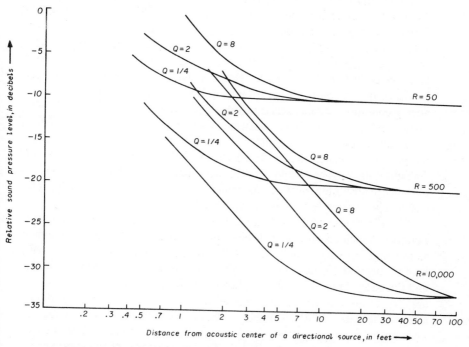

Fig. 9.122. Sound pressure level relative to power level, for a directional source, as a function of the distance from the source. The relationship is shown for three different values of the room constant R and directivity factor Q.

The directivity factor Q in these curves is the ratio between the sound-pressure level actually found at a point in the region of a source and the pressure that would be produced at the point by a nondirectional source of equal power in the absence of reflections. We arrive at a fractional value of Q if we have a directional source, such as a piston, and measure the pressure at some angle with respect to the axis of the sound beam. For instance, if a piston were radiating a wavelength smaller than its radius, the sound pressure would be quite small at an angle of 80° from the axis of the beam. The definition of Q coincides with that of the directivity factor D (see Art. 4.10) for points on the axis of the radiator.

9.13 The Anechoic Room

In Chapter 4, equations were developed for the power output of various sources, and the acoustic pressure to be expected as a function of this power output and the distance from the source. If experiments are conducted in the ordinary laboratory, the correlation between the predicted and the experimental results are so poor as to make the measurement practically worthless. As may be inferred from the previous article, most rooms have a sound field somewhere between the ideal Sabine assumption and the condition which obtains when the radiator is completely isolated from reflecting surfaces. While one might correct for the influence of the room by means of curves such as are given in Figs. 9.121 and 9.122 and arrive at a fair estimate of the performance of the source, it is far better to reduce reflections to a minimum. Such a condition is approached by open-air testing, and such testing is often carried out. However, it is somewhat unsatisfactory to be at the mercy of wind and weather, and even under ideal weather conditions, reflections from the ground influence the performance of both radiator and pickup, and ambient noise further complicates the measurements. With the increasing importance of absolute acoustic measurements, the desirability of a soundproofed chamber with completely absorptive boundaries becomes apparent.

The anechoic chamber at Cruft Laboratory, Harvard University, is a good example of such construction.[10] First of all, the chamber is large, the dimensions being 38 × 50 × 38 ft. The wall material is mineral wool, which has a high absorption coefficient. The material is cut into long narrow pyramids, and the base of the pyramid is applied to the wall. In this way two purposes are served: the wall surface is increased many times over the exterior dimensions of the walls, and the geometry is such that sound waves striking the wall must be reflected many times from a highly absorptive material before they can re-enter the interior of the room. The leading edges of the pyramids are sharp, and arranged at different angles to one another to assist the trapping of the sound within the honeycomb. All four walls, floor, and ceiling are similarly treated, and the working floor consists of a grill in which the open space greatly exceeds the solid structure. The instrumentation is also treated with absorbing material, as well as the interior of the tightly fitting entrance door.

For noiseproofing, the anechoic chamber is constructed as a "room within a room," the inner room being vibration-mounted from the outer. In such a room a noise level of 0 db can readily be obtained.

The ideal in an anechoic room is to achieve an inverse-square characteristic. A tentative and purely arbitrary criterion of a 1 db departure from this law has been set as a practical goal. Another suggested criterion is that the reflected sound at a point be 20 db below the direct sound from the radiator, as measured with a highly directive microphone; i.e., that the effective absorption coefficient of the room be greater than 0.99.

Olson[11] has constructed a somewhat less expensive chamber by hanging Ozite baffles 1 ft apart on all six surfaces of the room. These baffles are 1 in. thick. Alternate baffles are 7 ft and 4 ft wide, respectively. The absorption coefficient of Ozite is as follows: 128 cycles, 0.09; 256 cycles, 0.19; 512 cycles,

0.28; 1,024 cycles, 0.51; 2,048 cycles, 0.56; 4,096 cycles, 0.47. Olson remarks that it is comparatively easy to obtain the inverse-square characteristic in the mid-frequency region, but that the low and high frequencies present problems for different reasons. The absorption of the wall begins to fail at low frequencies where the wavelength approaches the width of the wall material (in his case, 7 ft) and at the high frequencies because of reflections from the floor grille and the instrumentation. He has also measured the absorption coefficient at different frequencies with a highly directive microphone. Curves giving the absorption and the departure from the square law are shown in Figs. 9.131 and 9.132.

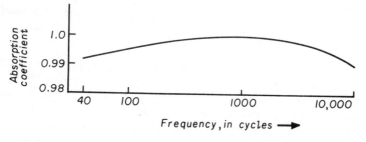

Fig. 9.131. Absorption coefficient as a function of frequency in an anechoic room.

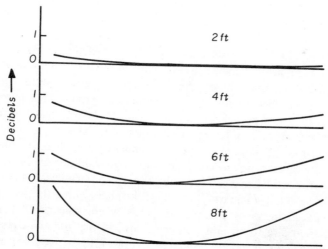

Fig. 9.132. Departure from square law as a function of distance and frequency in an anechoic room.

9.14 Noise Reduction

We have discussed noise in several articles in the last two chapters, and it is safe to conclude that from all points of view, noise is very undesirable. We have seen that pains are taken to design favorable room shapes, to provide the correct absorption on the walls, and to secure a sufficient loudness of source, even if this must be aided by an amplification system. We now consider the steps that are taken to insulate a room or building from external noise.[2, 3]

The first requirement in the design is to know the characteristics of the ambient external noise, and also the desired noise level in the room. The difference of these two levels gives the number of decibels by which the noise must be reduced. For example, if a broadcasting studio (desired level, 30 db) were to be constructed on the main street of a city, where the average traffic noise might be 75 db, the problem would be to introduce at least 45 db of attenuation. It might be necessary to introduce several decibels more to insulate against peak values (see Art. 8.11). In addition, insulation must be provided not against external noise only but also against noise originating in other parts of the building.

The main avenues of noise transmission are openings, transmission through partitions, conduction through solids, and diaphragm action of walls. Even a small space around a door or window opening may be the source of a surprising amount of noise. As an example, suppose the space under a door is only $\frac{1}{1000}$ of the total area of the door. Then even if the door itself is a perfect sound insulator (and diffraction through the crack under the door is neglected), the closing of the door introduces only a 30 db drop in the sound level. This may not be enough if the level outside the door is very high. For this reason, tightly sealed openings are the rule where noiseproofing has been put into effect.

Very little sound energy is transmitted to a *rigid* partition directly from the air because the reflection coefficient between air and any solid is very close to unity. This is not the case, however, in transmission between water and solids, a case that is extremely important in naval tactics. What is much more likely, however, is that the external sound source will set the wall panels into vibration in the manner of a sounding board on a piano. This is what is meant by diaphragm action of walls. The sound transmission may then be quite appreciable. Noise that is borne by conduction through solids, or *solid-borne* noise, becomes noticeable when it sets into vibration some large surface in the room. It is well known that sound can travel large distances with little attenuation in solids. Thus heating pipes, etc., provide paths by which mechanical vibration may be carried directly from a distance source to the listening chamber.

Perhaps the most troublesome sources of noise are openings for ventilating ducts. These ducts may carry noise originating in the ventilating machinery room, they may carry noise from room to room, and lastly, solid-borne noise may be transmitted through the walls of the duct. Among the means of combating such noise are the use of slow-speed, quiet fans and blowers, and the introduction of a large amount of absorption in the motor room to keep the sound energy density down. (This is an example in which absorption assists insulation. In the majority of cases, however, the two are quite distinct.

Absorption is primarily a *surface* phenomenon, while transmission involves the entire body of the material.) Ventilating ducts, especially those of naval vessels, are often designed as low-pass filters, and in addition, the walls are heavily damped for the double purpose of absorbing the air-borne sound in the duct and damping the solid-borne sound carried through the walls. In addition, flexible duct lengths may be installed so that the solid-borne noise originating in the machinery vibration will not be transmitted.

It has already been mentioned that the diaphragm action of walls is the major source of transmission through walls. It is found that the *reduction factor* measured in decibels is approximately proportional to the mass of the panel. Representative factors are 23 db for 1 lb/ft², 36 db for 10 lb/ft², and 52 db for 100 lb/ft². It usually is not economical to secure the desired reduction factor by building up the mass (making the wall thicker). It is often the practice to introduce discontinuities. Thus three rigid partitions separated by air spaces in which are hung blankets of hair felt give a much greater reduction factor than a single partition, even though the total mass of the latter is much greater.

Vibration insulation is another important item in noise reduction. When all efforts to reduce the vibration of a piece of machinery to acceptable levels have failed, the vibrations must be prevented from reaching the main frame of the structure. This is done by the use of resilient mounts. In effect, we then have a system of coupled masses, one active and one passive, and it may be shown that the ratio between the amplitude of the active mass and that of the passive mass is a function of the constants of the system; chiefly the two masses and the compliance and damping of the mount. Above the resonant frequency of the system, the ratio between the two amplitudes falls off swiftly. The rise at resonance is, of course, flattened by damping. If a mounting material can be found to make the resonant frequency of the order of 5 cycles per second, only a small amount of vibration will be transmitted through the resilient mount in the audible frequency range.

References

1. Morse and Bolt, *Revs. Mod. Phys.*, **16**, 69, 152 (1944).
2. Knudsen, *Architectural Acoustics*, Wiley, New York, 1932.
3. Knudsen and Harris, *Acoustical Designing in Architecture*, Wiley, New York, 1950.
4. Morse, *Vibration and Sound*, 2d ed., McGraw-Hill, New York, 1948.
5. Eyring, *J. Acoust. Soc. Am.*, **1**, 217 (1930).
6. Knudsen, *J. Acoust. Soc. Am.*, **3**, 126 (1931); **5**, 64, 112 (1933); **6**, 199 (1935).
7. Kneser, *J. Acoust. Soc. Am.*, **5**, 122 (1933).
8. Knudsen, *J. Acoust. Soc. Am.*, **18**, 90-96 (1946).

9. Peterson and Beranek, *Handbook of Noise Measurement*, General Radio, Cambridge, 1953.
10. Beranek and Sleeper, *J. Acoust. Soc. Am.*, **18**, 140-150 (1946).
11. Olson, *J. Acoust. Soc. Am.*, **15**, 96 (1943).

Problems

1. (a) Draw rise and decay curves for the following values of V, S, and α. $V/S = 4.5$, $\alpha = 0.1$; $V/S = 4.5$, $\alpha = 0.2$; $V/S = 9$, $\alpha = 0.2$.

(b) For each combination, find the source power output in watts acoustical to provide a level of 70 db in the chamber, assuming with Sabine that the energy is homogeneously distributed.

(c) In each case, find the decay rate and the reverberation time.

2. Assuming the free path to be given by the expression $4V/S$, find the mean free path for the auditorium which has dimensions $100 \times 100 \times 20$. Find the number of reflections per second. Assume that 1 db is lost on each reflection, and compute the decay rate and the reverberation time. Compute the value of α corresponding to a loss of 1 db at each reflection. Find the values of α corresponding to losses of 2 and 3 db per reflection and the corresponding decay rates and reverberation times, and check against the Eyring and Sabine formulas.

3. Assume that the average speaker has an output of 50 μw. A lecture hall is to be designed to effect the best compromise between loudness level and reverberation time. The dimensions are $30 \times 60 \times 10$ ft. Find values of loudness level and reverberation time for several values of α and choose the best combination. Assuming values of unity for the noise factor and the shape factor, what will be the percentage articulation in each case?

4. An auditorium of dimensions $40 \times 60 \times 20$ ft has an average absorption coefficient of 0.2. Find the loudness level, reverberation time, and PA for a source output of 15 μw. Find the LL, RT, and PA if the source power is increased 30 db by an amplification system.

5. Develop the equation for the sound pressure level in a room in terms of the source power and the total absorption.

6. Find the average decay rate in decibels per second by Eyring's theory.

7. An auditorium of length 100, width 50, and height 20 ft has an absorption coefficient which has the following frequency characteristics: $\alpha = 0.5$ at 128 cycles, $\alpha = 0.7$ at 512 cycles, $\alpha = 0.6$ at 1,024 cycles. The absorption coefficient may be assumed to be homogeneous. Compute the source power at each of the above frequencies so that the ambient level in the auditorium may be 40 phons and 70 phons, respectively. What are the corresponding loudnesses in sones?

8. A decay curve shows an echo pulse 6 db above an average decay of 18 db. If $V/S = 4.5$ for the auditorium, find the value of a which characterizes the absorption of the auditorium. Find the per cent by which a must be decreased so that the echo peak no longer stands out above the decay curve, assuming that the echo is unaffected by the over-all decrease in absorption. Find the old and new values cf reverberation time, and comment upon the relative advantages and disadvantages of decreasing the absorption in the auditorium.

9.   At what rate is energy being absorbed in an auditorium in which the steady-state energy density is 1 erg/cm³, the velocity is 34,400 cm/sec, the surface area is 10^7 sq cm, and the average coefficient of absorption is 0.2?

10.   Show how the curve of optimum reverberation time can be plotted from the experimental results contained in Fig. 9.102.

11.   A room has a volume of 10^6 cu ft and a $V/S = 4.5$. Design the room for a speech level of 70 db and optimum reverberation time.

Chapter 10

ACOUSTIC MEASUREMENTS AND
MEASUREMENT APPARATUS

At the start of the chapter on acoustic measurements it is well to redefine sound as an alteration in pressure, stress, particle displacement, or particle velocity in an elastic medium, or the superposition of such propagated alterations. Acoustic measurements, then, are quantitative investigations of this alteration. We have seen that the assumption of a continuous elastic medium gives rise to the prediction of a definite velocity of propagation, with which the sound wave travels through the medium. Accordingly the most fundamental sound measurements are the velocity of propagation and the intensity of the sound—or more precisely, of the various frequency components of the sound. Since the intensity is directly related to the displacement, particle velocity, and acoustic pressure, any of these may be subjects of measurement.

Along with the above fundamental measurements, we have secondary measurements, which in many cases are performed more often by acousticians than the primary measurements. These include measurements of intensity distribution from sources, acoustic impedances of media, microphone sensitivities, and the like. These secondary measurements, however, are only applications of the fundamental measurements to particular problems. Therefore we shall in this chapter restrict our considerations to fundamental measurements, chiefly velocity, intensity, and the composition of complex sounds.

10.1 Velocity Measurements

The measurement of sound velocity is relatively simple. Quite accurate measurements of the velocity of sound in air were made as far back as the seventeenth century, Mersenne arriving at a value of 1,038 ft/sec. Early measurements were made directly by noting the delay between the production of a sound pulse at one point and its arrival at a distant point. Since it takes approximately 5 sec for sound to travel a mile, the time intervals involved are large enough to permit good accuracy with only the most rudimentary apparatus. For instance, by watching the flash of a gun on a distant hill and timing the delay until the arrival of the report with an ordinary watch, one can obtain the velocity with only a small percentage of error.

More accurate laboratory measurements can be made with the *acoustic interferometer*. Standing waves are formed in a fluid column if the column length bears a simple relation to the wavelength. The standing-wave phenomenon can be easily recognized by a number of methods. By obtaining the standing-wave phenomenon for any column length and then changing the column length a known amount until the standing-wave pattern is again achieved, a very accurate measurement of the wavelength and hence of velocity can be made, since there exist methods of measuring frequency with extreme accuracy. It may be shown theoretically, and it has been checked many times experimentally, that the dispersion of sound (change of velocity with frequency) is negligible except in special cases. Hence velocity measurements made at high frequencies, where the experimental conditions are favorable, may be assumed to hold at any frequency. Velocity measurements have been made at ultrasonic frequencies by the interferometer for all the more common gases and liquids. Results obtained are shown in Table 10.11. The discussion of the interferometer itself is contained in Chapter 11.

TABLE 10.11
Velocity of Sound in Typical Gases and Liquids

GASES

Gas	Speed, m/sec at 0°C	
Air	331.45	
Carbon dioxide	258.0	(low freq.)
	268.6	(high freq.)
Helium	970	
Hydrogen	1269.5	
Nitrogen	337	
Oxygen	317.2	

LIQUIDS

Liquid	Temperature, °C	Velocity, cm/sec
Alcohol, ethyl	12.5	1.24×10^5
Benzene	20	1.32×10^5
Ether, ethyl	20	1.01×10^5
Glycerin	20	1.92×10^5
Water, fresh	17	1.43×10^5
Water, sea	15	1.505×10^5
Castor oil	20	1.50×10^5

10.2 Intensity Measurements

Of all the characteristics of sound, its intensity is probably the most fundamental. Although the intensity has been measured directly, by Clapp, Firestone and Emms, Rayleigh, King, and others, the usual practice is to measure either the pressure or the pressure gradient, which in many cases is proportional to the particle velocity. Measurements of particle displacement have been made by observing the motion of smoke or dust particles in a microscope, but their importance is minor. Most microphones are pressure-sensitive devices, and it may be said that the ordinary measurement of sound intensity is usually accomplished by the measurement of acoustic pressure.

We have seen, in the chapter on microphones, that the sensitivity of the microphone may be theoretically computed if its parameters are known. However, an independent experimental check, if at all possible, is always desirable; and as a consequence, a great number of experiments have been performed on the calibration of microphones. Out of this experimentation has evolved a technique called reciprocity calibration, which at the present time appears to be a very accurate method of absolute calibration. Intensity measurements have thus become largely identified with microphone calibration.

For many years (roughly from 1885 to 1920) the Rayleigh disk was the standard method for the absolute measurement of sound intensity. Rayleigh noticed that a light disk, suspended in a sound field, experienced a torque, and much research was done on the relation between the torque and the intensity of the sound field. The Rayleigh disk has great historical importance, and is by no means obsolete as a method of intensity measurement. However, the theory is quite complicated, and since the current emphasis is on the reciprocity method, the Rayleigh disk will not be further discussed.

It was perceived by Arnold, Crandall, Wente, and others that microphone calibration could be effected if an acoustic pressure of a known value could be produced. Their work led to the development of the thermophone, an instrument in which the acoustic pressure in a closed cavity can be accurately predicted from the heating effect of an alternating current in a metal foil within the cavity, and the resultant pressure increase. Although the computation of the pressure is rather involved, and many correction factors must be used, it was felt that the predicted value was reliable. A somewhat similar device is the pistonphone, in which the pressure within a closed cavity is produced by the oscillations of a closely fitting piston. As in the thermophone, the microphone to be calibrated is subjected to the acoustic pressure within the cavity. The theory of the pistonphone is somewhat more straightforward than that of the thermophone, but the method is basically similar.

The reciprocity technique will be described only in its essential principles. In actual practice, great care must be used, since there are several limitations in its employment. These details will be suppressed in the following treatment.

Electrostatic Actuator. The electrostatic actuator is similar in principle to the thermophone and pistonphone, except that it utilizes electrostatic forces between two conducting surfaces. It can be used along with the reciprocity method for obtaining absolute response curves of microphones. The reciprocity method is used for absolute calibration of the actuator, and the actuator is then used to get the over-all response curve (see Brüel and Kjaer, *Instruction and Applications—Condenser Microphone and Microphone Apparatus*, Brüel and Kjaer, Naerum, Denmark).

10.3 The Principle of Reciprocity

The principle of reciprocity has an important place in the design of electric, acoustic and electroacoustic systems. The principle was defined for acoustic systems in a general way by Rayleigh, and further by Helmholtz. Ballantine applied the principle to electroacoustic systems. Though the reciprocity theorem does not hold for all classes of transducers, it is valid for most of the ordinary transducers, and in particular for the electrodynamic transducer, which we shall use to illustrate the principle. Reciprocity can be illustrated in an elementary manner by an example from circuit electricity. Consider the circuit of Fig. 10.31(a) consisting of two meshes. If a voltage generator is inserted in mesh I and a current meter in mesh II, the ratio between the voltage

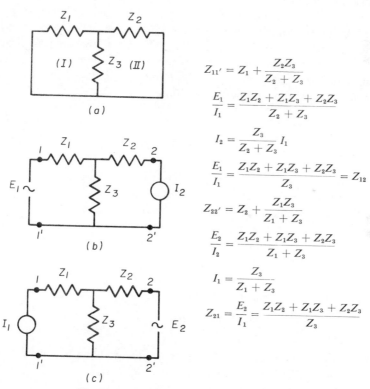

$$Z_{11'} = Z_1 + \frac{Z_2 Z_3}{Z_2 + Z_3}$$

$$\frac{E_1}{I_1} = \frac{Z_1 Z_2 + Z_1 Z_3 + Z_2 Z_3}{Z_2 + Z_3}$$

$$I_2 = \frac{Z_3}{Z_2 + Z_3} I_1$$

$$\frac{E_1}{I_1} = \frac{Z_1 Z_2 + Z_1 Z_3 + Z_2 Z_3}{Z_3} = Z_{12}$$

$$Z_{22'} = Z_2 + \frac{Z_1 Z_3}{Z_1 + Z_3}$$

$$\frac{E_2}{I_2} = \frac{Z_1 Z_2 + Z_1 Z_3 + Z_2 Z_3}{Z_1 + Z_3}$$

$$I_1 = \frac{Z_3}{Z_1 + Z_3}$$

$$Z_{21} = \frac{E_2}{I_1} = \frac{Z_1 Z_2 + Z_1 Z_3 + Z_2 Z_3}{Z_3}$$

Fig. 10.31. Reciprocity in an electric network.

E_1 and the current I_2 is called the *transfer impedance* Z_{12} [Fig. 10.31(b)]. If the positions of the generator and meter are reversed as in Fig. 10.31(c), the ratio E_2/I_1 is called the transfer impedance Z_{21}. It may be shown by elementary circuit theory that these two *transfer impedances* are *equal*, each having the value $(Z_1 Z_2 + Z_1 Z_3 + Z_2 Z_3)/Z_3$. If we assume that the voltage source and the current meter are connected respectively between the terminal pairs 1-1' and 2-2', we may state the broad principle that applies to many electric networks: "The transfer impedance between two terminal pairs is independent of the position of source and receiver."

Lest the theorem be misunderstood as trivial, it does *not* say that the input impedance between 1 and 1' is equal to that between 2 and 2'. This would be so only if the network were symmetrical, i.e. if $Z_1 = Z_2$. It is easy to see that different expressions are obtained in general for the *input* impedances between 1 and 1' and 2 and 2', respectively.

Helmholtz's expression of the principle of reciprocity for acoustic systems is essentially as follows: "The acoustic pressure produced at point 2 by a sound source at point 1 is equal to the pressure produced at point 1 with the sound source at point 2." If we remember that source strength is defined as a product of area and surface velocity, we can readily generalize this statement in the following manner: "The ratio between the pressure at point 2 and the volume current (of a source) at point 1 equals the ratio between the pressure at point 1 and the volume current at point 2." Volume current, in this definition, is used synonomously with the source strength of chapter 4. The principle may be expressed by the equation

$$\frac{P_2}{U_1} = \frac{P_1}{U_2} \tag{10.31}$$

One of the more important purely acoustical results of the principle of reciprocity is that the directivity of a reversible piston transducer working as a microphone is the same as its directivity when working as a source.

Because the electromagnetic coupling constant* has the same numerical value for an electrodynamic speaker and an electrodynamic microphone, the reciprocity theorem can be further extended. The speaker "source strength" is given in terms of the current by the equation

$$U_1 = \frac{A D I_1}{Z_m} \tag{10.32}$$

where I_1 is the driving current in abamperes,

   A is the surface area of the source,

   D is the coupling constant,

while the open-circuit output of the microphone in abvolts will be given in terms of the free-field pressure by the equation

$$E_1 = \frac{P_1 A D}{Z_m} \tag{10.33}$$

Substituting for U_1 and P_1 in Eq. (10.31),

$$\frac{P_2}{I_1} = \frac{E_1}{U_2} \tag{10.34}$$

---

* This applies to other coupling constants as well.

This is one statement of the principle of electroacoustic reciprocity. In words, it states that the ratio of the pressure at point 2 to the driving current (of the transducer working as a speaker) at point 1 equals the ratio of the open-circuit voltage at point 1 (of the transducer working as a microphone) to the volume current (or volume velocity) at point 2 (Fig. 10.32). Each side of the equation may be considered as a kind of generalized transfer impedance. Although we have proved this relation only for the electrodynamic transducer, analysis shows that most important common transducers obey the reciprocity relation. As a matter of fact, our analysis was intended more to illustrate the meaning of the equation than to offer a general proof. Once understood, the relation has a certain plausibility, so that we may accept it (on a tentative basis if necessary), and turn our attention to its use as a means of microphone calibration. Before considering microphone calibration as such we shall, in the next article, define and explain the *response ratio* of a reciprocal transducer.

I_1

P_2

Transducer as speaker

E_1

U_2

Transducer as microphone

Fig. 10.32. $P_2/I_1 = E_1/U_2$.

10.4 The Response Ratio of a Reciprocal Transducer

In the following treatment we shall make the assumption that we are dealing with purely spherical waves. Consider the transducer as a source and assume it to be of dimensions small enough to produce a spherical field in its vicinity. If we consider it as a microphone we shall assume that it picks up the radiation from a simple source, and that the dimensions are such that it is completely nondirective. We can then make use of the fundamental expression for the pressure at a distance r from a simple source in terms of the source strength:

$$P_1 = \frac{\rho c \, k \, U_2}{4\pi r} = \frac{\rho c}{2\lambda r} \, U_2 \qquad (10.41)$$

We now define the *response of a radiator* as the ratio between the pressure produced at a distance r from the source to the driving current in the radiator, i.e.,

$$S = \frac{P_2}{I_1} \quad \text{or} \quad \frac{P_1}{I_2}$$

It should be noted that this ratio is just the left-hand member of Eq. (10.34). We are now interested in comparing this response with the conventional microphone response M given by the relation E/P, where E is the open-circuit voltage and P is the free-field pressure. By the use of Eq. (10.41), we can replace the denominator of the second term in Eq. (10.34) by its equivalent.

We then have

$$\frac{P_2}{I_1} = \frac{\rho c}{2\lambda r} \cdot \frac{E_1}{P_1} \tag{10.42}$$

$$S = \frac{\rho c}{2\lambda r} M \tag{10.42a}$$

This equation states that the ratio between the response of the transducer as a speaker to its response as a microphone is a constant independent of the constants of the transducer. Actually, if a fixed distance were to be used in specifying speaker sensitivity, the ratio would be a function only of the wavelength and the characteristic impedance of the medium.

10.5 The Reciprocity Method of Microphone Calibration (*Free-Field Method*)

The apparatus required for the calibration of a microphone by the reciprocity technique is the following:
1.   A sound source (loudspeaker) S.
2.   A reciprocal transducer (loudspeaker-microphone) T.
3.   The microphone to be calibrated M.
4.   A voltmeter for the measurement of open-circuit voltages produced in the sound receivers.
5.   A current meter for the measurement of the driving currents in the transducer used as source.
6.   A scale for the measurement of the distance between the source and the sound receiver.

Procedure for reciprocity calibration. The procedure consists of three steps:

Step 1. With the loudspeaker radiating (at point A), the transducer is set at a distance d (point B), and used as a microphone. The transducer open-circuit voltage E_2' is measured (Fig. 10.51).

Step 2. With the loudspeaker driven by the same current as in step 1, the transducer is replaced by the microphone at the same point (point B). The open-circuit voltage of the microphone E_2'' is measured.

Step 3. The loudspeaker is replaced by the transducer at point A. The driving current, I_1, in the transducer and the open-circuit voltage in the microphone, E_2''' are measured.

Steps 1 and 2 serve to give the ratio between the microphone response and the transducer response (as a microphone):

$$\frac{M_T}{M_M} = \frac{E_2'}{E_2''} \tag{10.51}$$

In the third step we have for the open-circuit voltage of the microphone,

$$E_2''' = M_M P_2''' = M_M S_T I_1 \tag{10.52}$$

where the second equivalence is written from the definition of the response of a source.

Dividing Eq. (10.52) by Eq. (10.51), we get

$$I_1 M_M^2 \frac{S_T}{M_T} = \frac{E_2'' E_2'''}{E_2'} \tag{10.53}$$

But from Eq. (10.42) $S_T/M_T = \rho c/2\lambda d$, and therefore we have for the microphone response,

$$M_M^2 = \frac{2\lambda d}{\rho c} \cdot \frac{E_2'' E_2'''}{E_2' I_1} \tag{10.54}$$

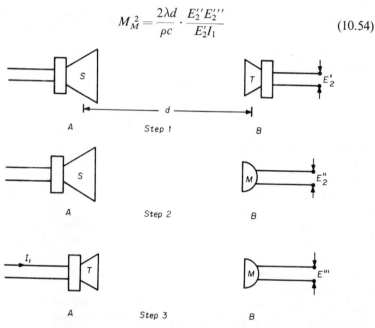

Fig. 10.51. Reciprocity method of microphone calibration.

From this exceedingly important equation, the response of a microphone can be found from purely electric measurements, which can be made with great precision. Reciprocity calibration has become the accepted standard method.

In the method of reciprocity calibration which we have described, the expression used for the pressure on the microphone depends on the existence of the inverse square law for the intensity. This law will be followed fairly closely in the open air, if all reflecting surfaces are distant, and there are no winds. It also holds fairly well in a large room if the intensity of the radiation is kept low, and the source is close to the microphone. In anechoic rooms, as we have noted, the departure from the inverse square law is almost negligible. However, because of the expense involved in the construction of these rooms, a second method of reciprocity calibration called the *chamber method* has been developed, in which the source and microphone are coupled by a small enclosed chamber. The experimentation is roughly similar to the free-field method except that the chamber pressure, rather than the inverse square pressure, enters the computations. Since it is essential that the spacing between the source and the microphone be much less than the wavelength of the sound if lumped-circuit theory is to be used, hydrogen gas is used for high-frequency calibration. It is possible to employ chambers in which the dimensions are not small compared with the wavelength, but the analysis is quite involved.

Although reciprocity measurements have actually been made at the limits of the audible range, by the exercise of great care, there exists an alternative method of obtaining the absolute response of the microphone which is much simpler in practice, and is actually capable of greater accuracy. The electrostatic actuator has been mentioned in Art. 10.2 as a device by which absolute measurements have been made in the past. The limit of absolute accuracy has been estimated to be about ± 1.5 db, the uncertainty being due primarily to the difficulty of estimating the effective distance between the two closely-spaced surfaces between which electrostatic forces exist. However, the electrostatic force, though uncertain, will be independent of frequency, and excellent *relative* measurements of response can be made as long as the spacing is small compared with the wavelength at the upper limit of the frequency region. Thus the electrostatic actuator can, in effect, be calibrated at one frequency by a microphone whose response has been obtained at that frequency by the reciprocity method, and then used to calibrate the microphone at all other frequencies. In practice, as a check on the actuator, the microphone is calibrated by the reciprocity method for several frequencies in the mid-frequency region.

The Chamber Method of Reciprocity Calibration. Suppose a pair of microphones obeying the law of reciprocity to be coupled by a cavity of dimensions small compared with the wavelength of the tone at which calibration is to be performed (Fig. 10.52). Let V be the volume of the cavity. The acoustic

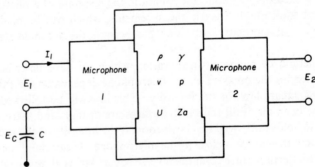

Fig. 10.52. Electroacoustic network for reciprocity calibration.

impedance of the cavity will be $B/j\omega V$, and if we assume the adiabatic law for propagation, this can be written $Z_A = \gamma p_0/j\omega V$, where p_0 is the ambient pressure.

From the fundamental relation between the acoustic pressure and the volume velocity ($P = Z_A U$), we have

$$P = \frac{\gamma p_0}{j\omega V} U \qquad (10.55)$$

In this case, P is the acoustic pressure produced within the cavity by the microphone which is working as a transducer, and being driven by a current I.

The second microphone will have for its open-circuit voltage,

$$E_2 = M_2 P = M_2 \frac{\gamma p_0}{j\omega V} U \qquad (10.56)$$

But by the principle of electroacoustic reciprocity applied to the cavity, the ratio of the cavity volume current to the electric driving current equals the response of the transducer working as a microphone, where in this case the cavity pressure is used in the response equation. That is,

$$\frac{I_1}{U} = \frac{P}{E_1} = \frac{1}{M_1} \qquad (10.57)$$

Substituting the value $U = M_1 I_1$ from Eq. (10.57) in Eq. (10.56),

$$M_1 M_2 = \frac{j\omega V}{\gamma p_0} \frac{E_2}{I_1} \qquad (10.58)$$

The product of the sensitivities has been obtained. The ratio M_1/M_2 can easily be measured by subjecting the two microphones to the same cavity pressure and comparing their outputs, as in free-field calibration.

It is difficult to measure the driving current directly. In practical measurements, a capacitor is connected in series with the transmitting microphone, and the voltage across this capacitor is measured. It is necessary that the capacitance be accurately known. The product of the sensitivities is then given by the equation

$$M_1 M_2 = \frac{V}{\gamma p_0 C} \cdot \frac{E_2}{E_C} \qquad (10.59)$$

where C is the capacitance of the auxiliary capacitor.

The normal response of most capacitor microphones is in the neighborhood of -50 db re 1 volt dyne^{-1} cm^2. For reciprocity calibration of a capacitor microphone, it is therefore convenient in practical measurements to choose the ratio $V/\gamma p_0 C$ so that $E_2 = E_C$ when both transmitter and receiver microphones have a response of exactly -50 db (it is assumed that both are capacitor microphones). A short calculation will show that this means choosing V and C such that $(V/\gamma p_0 C) = 10^{-5}$. The American Standards Association prescribes that the cavity coupling the two microphones have a volume of 19.5 cm^3. Atmospheric pressure may be taken to be 1.013×10^6 dynes/cm^2 and γ to be 1.402. To obtain the capacitance in farads, the volume must be written in m^3, and the pressure in newtons/m^2. (1 newton $= 10^5$ dynes). It is left to the reader to show that the necessary value of the capacitance C is approximately 0.130 μf.

Let us assume that the above parameters have been chosen, and that an actual measurement shows E_2 to be n db below E_C (e.g. if $E_2 = \frac{1}{2}E_C$, $n = 6$). It can readily be shown that the average response of the two microphones is then $-50 - (n/2)$. It remains only to find the response of the individual microphones, which is done by exposing them separately to the same pressure.

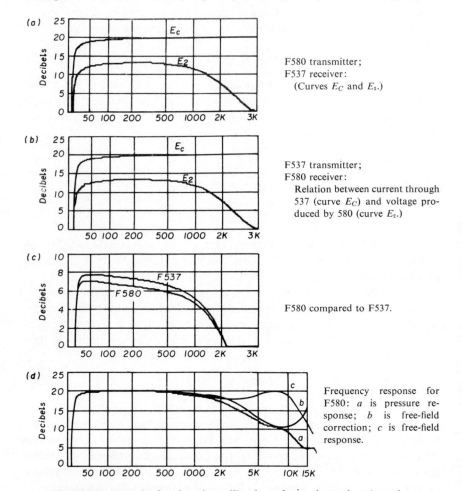

(a) F580 transmitter;
F537 receiver:
(Curves E_C and E_2.)

(b) F537 transmitter;
F580 receiver:
Relation between current through 537 (curve E_C) and voltage produced by 580 (curve E_2.)

(c) F580 compared to F537.

(d) Frequency response for F580: a is pressure response; b is free-field correction; c is free-field response.

Fig. 10.53. Record of reciprocity calibration of capacitor microphone by chamber method.

Let us assume that this measurement shows microphone M_1 to have a sensitivity m db greater than that of microphone M_2. The absolute sensitivities of the two microphones are then

$$M_1 = -50 - \frac{n}{2} + \frac{m}{2} \qquad M_2 = -50 - \frac{n}{2} - \frac{m}{2}$$

The data obtained in a typical measurement are shown in tabular form. The records of the test, obtained with a Brüel and Kjaer Model 2310 graphic level recorder, are shown in Fig. 10.53. Curves (a) and (b) show the output voltage E_2 of each of the microphones compared to the voltage E_C across the capacitor in series with the input. Curve (c) shows the output voltages of the microphones when subjected to equal cavity pressures. Curve (d) is the frequency response of the less sensitive microphone, obtained with an electrostatic actuator.

Calculation of Microphone Sensitivities by Reciprocity Method

Cycles:	100	500	1,000	2,000
Curve (a):				
F537 transmitter				
F580 receiver				
E_2/E_C in db............	− 6.2	− 6.6	− 8.0	−12.6
Curve (b):				
F570 transmitter				
F537 receiver				
E_2/E_C in db............	− 6.2	− 6.4	− 7.9	−12.6
Average of curves				
(a) and (b)	− 6.2	− 6.5	− 8.0	−12.6
Average sensitivity				
$50 − n/2$ db............	−53.1	−53.2	−54.0	−56.3
Curve (c):				
M_{537}/M_{580}, db	1.0	0.8	0.6	0.2
Absolute sensitivity, F537				
$50 − n/2 + m/2$	−52.6	−52.8	−53.7	−56.2
Absolute sensitivity, F580				
$50 − n/2 − m/2$	−53.6	−53.6	−54.3	−56.4
Curve (d):				
Frequency response, F580	...	...	...	...

It has already been noted that the chamber method gives the *pressure response* of the microphone, rather than the free-field response. The two responses differ by the free-field correction. However, this correction can be accurately computed from the dimensions of the microphone. If a filter having the frequency characteristics of the free-field correction is inserted in the output circuit of the microphone, the free-field response can be obtained automatically. The lower of the two curves of (d) shows the pressure response of the microphone, and the upper curve shows the free-field response.

10.6 Sound Spectra

The reciprocity method, with consequent absolute calibration of microphones, gives a precision measurement of sound pressure, probably the most fundamental acoustic measurement. However, the complete character of a complex sound cannot be revealed by a single reading of pressure or intensity, since a complex sound is made up of a number of component frequencies. It is therefore necessary to analyze the sound into its component frequencies, and to measure the pressure or the intensity of each. The plot of intensity (or pressure) against frequency is called a sound spectrum, and the procedure employed in obtaining sound spectra is called sound analysis.

Sound analysis may be divided into steady-state and nonsteady-state analyses. In the steady-state case, the intensities of the various frequency components are constant with time. In the latter case, both the relative and the absolute value of these components may vary with time, and a "three-dimensional" presentation of amplitude-frequency-time is necessary to describe the character of the sound completely. We shall describe first the analysis of a steady-state sound.

Several principles have been used in the construction of sound analyzers. Some of these employ the straightforward method of recording the wave shape of the instantaneous pressure, and subsequently analyzing the wave by a Fourier series method to find the amplitudes of the various frequency components. The more modern methods employ electric filters and associated electronic circuits to measure the components directly. We shall restrict the discussion to the electronic type. There are three types of design, the "constant-band-width" analyzer, the "constant-percentage-band-width" analyzer, and the octave-band analyzer.*

All involve electric filters of the band-pass type. In such analyzers, the "center frequency" of the filter, or the limits of the pass band, may be changed at will, and in some, the *selectivity* of the filter is also variable. The selectivity is a measure of the ability of such filters to select a particular frequency and discriminate against others. The response of a *constant-band-pass filter* will fall off by a certain percentage if the frequency introduced differs by a number of cycles from the frequency to which it is tuned, regardless of the frequency region in which it is operating. As an example, its selectivity may be described as "down" 3 db, 20 cycles off the center frequency. If the frequency scale (abscissa) is linear, the response curve will occupy the same area, regardless of the center frequency; but if the abscissa is scaled logarithmically, as is usually the case, the area decreases with frequency. On the other hand, the response of the *constant-percentage-band-width filter* is described as "down" so many decibels at a frequency 1 or 5 per cent off the center frequency. Such a curve will have the same shape for different center frequencies if the frequency axis is plotted logarithmically (Fig. 10.61).

Both of the above analyzers are generally included in the term "narrow-band" analyzers. The octave-band filter has a band pass which is relatively wide compared with the center frequency and hence is called a "wide-band" analyzer. Half-octave and third-octave filters are also used, the third-octave

---

* Half-octave and third-octave analyzers are also used.

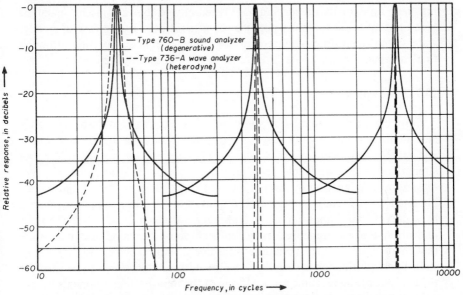

Fig. 10.61. Selectivity curves for degenerative (solid curves) and heterodyne (dashed curves) analyzers. [Courtesy of General Radio Co.]

filter having several advantages for noise analysis. The pass bands of a third-octave filter are shown in Fig. 10.62.

For direct analysis of a steady-state sound, the sound is picked up by a microphone and converted to an electric signal. The electric signal is delivered to the analyzer input, and a voltage-measuring device is connected to the

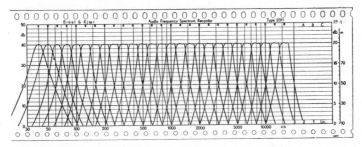

Fig. 10.62. Pass bands for a Brüel and Kjaer third-octave analyzer, Type 2109. [Courtesy of Clevite Brush.]

analyzer output. The center frequency of the analyzer is then changed either manually or by motor drive, and the output voltage is recorded either by noting the meter reading as the frequency changes or by recording the voltage automatically with a graphic level recorder.

Often a high-fidelity recording is made of the sound, and the record is played back into the analyzer-graphic level-recorder combination. Disk, magnetic tape, or film recording may be employed, but at present, magnetic tape appears to be the most popular for general use. In the case of steady-state sound, recording is more of a convenience than a necessity, although there are many cases where direct analysis would be impractical.

10.7 Transient Analysis

Suppose we wish to analyze sound in which the distribution of frequency and intensity is continually varying with time. Examples are speech, music, and machinery noise. We may wish to obtain a record that will show the strength of each component at each instant of time, as in speech analysis. We may wish only an average amplitude-frequency plot, similar to the record obtained for the steady-state sound. But even in the latter case, a single scan by a narrow-band analyzer may yield a record which is an extremely poor indication of the average frequency composition of the sound. Let us assume that there is a 3 per cent variation in the speed of a machine and that a constant-band-width analyzer having a band width of 20 cycles is to be used for the analysis of the machine noise. If one of the important components has an average frequency of 1,200 cycles, it may be outside the band of the analyzer when the analyzer frequency indicates 1,200 cycles. In this case this important component may be missed, especially if a sharp change in speed occurs just previous to the examination of the 1,200 cycle band by the analyzer.

An alternative is to analyze several short samples of the recording, running the entire sample through the analyzer for each frequency band to be analyzed. This is done by cutting out a portion of the tape recording and joining it together at the ends to make a continuous loop. If the analysis is to be made automatically, a constant-band-width type of analyzer should be used. Then the rotational speeds of the tape and analyzer are set so that the tape rotates once each time the analyzer center frequency changes by an amount equal to its band width.

Another example is a frequency analysis of the sound field in a reverberant room. Such a room has definite standing-wave patterns, and if the recording microphone were held at a fixed point in the room, the recording might be a poor indication of the over-all sound field, since frequencies which had nodes at this point would be discriminated against, while those having antinodes would be enhanced. Accordingly, a "microphone traverse" is made; that is, the recording microphone is moved about in a random manner, the intention being to average out the point-to-point variations in the sound field. The recording made from such a traverse is essentially similar to a record of machinery noise, and the loop method is used here also.

If the analysis of such a record were to be made with a constant-percentage-band-width analyzer, the tape speed of the playback would be required to vary logarithmically with frequency; otherwise the high frequencies should be favored over the lows. However, it is possible to effect a conversion to the true spectrum from readings obtained with the constant-percentage-band-width analyzer by converting the readings to spectrum levels. Charts for converting data taken with octave-band and constant-percentage-band-width

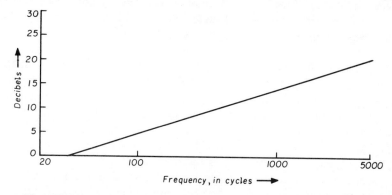

Fig. 10.71. Plot showing number of decibels to be subtracted from type 760-B narrow-band analyzer to obtain spectrum level. [Courtesy of General Radio Co.]

analyzers to spectrum levels are shown in Table 10.71 and Fig. 10.71. The use of this conversion involves assumptions that the sound level is continuous within the measured band, and that there are no pure tone components. Each type of analyzer involves some uncertainty when used for analysis of sound of general characteristic, and the theory of analysis turns out to be quite complex when all factors are taken into account. Analyzers will be discussed at greater length in subsequent articles.

TABLE 10.71

Band (cycles)	Decibels	Geometric Mean Frequency (cycles)
20-75	18	39
75-150	19	106
150-300	22	212
300-600	25	425
600-1,200	28	850
1,200-2,400	31	1,700
2,400-4,800	34	3,400
4,800-10,000	38	6,900

Table 10.71 shows the number of decibels to be subtracted from the General Radio Type 1550-A octave-band analyzer readings to obtain spectrum level. It will be observed that these correspond to the k values of Art. 8.9.

Speech analysis, in which an amplitude-frequency-time record is achieved, is a further development of the loop method. This is the method by which the spectrograms of Fig. 8.21 were obtained. One further problem must be overcome, namely, that of achieving a three-dimensional record on a two-dimensional surface. If we take the horizontal axis for the time and the vertical axis for the frequency, we might plot a series of points in our frequency-time "space" indicating which frequency components were present at each instant of time. If, further, the density of these points can be made proportional to the amplitude of the frequency components, a "three-dimensional" plot which contains the desired information, has been achieved.

We shall describe an analyzer of this type which was developed by the Bell Telephone Laboratories for the purpose of visible speech portrayal. Again a sample is obtained as in the continuous-loop method and played continuously through an analyzer whose scanning rate is synchronized with the rotation frequency of the sample. In this case, however, the output of each rotation is plotted separately as a line of variable density, each line representing an amplitude-time plot. This is done as follows (Fig. 10.72).

A sensitized paper is placed on the surface of a cylindrical drum which is mounted on an axle common to the drum containing the magnetic tape. A sharp metallic stylus is mounted perpendicular to the surface of the sensitized

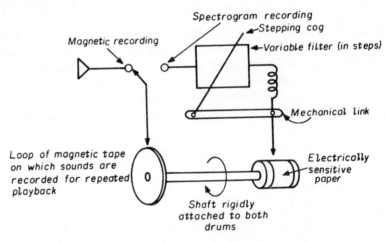

Fig. 10.72. Sound spectrograph.

paper, so that the paper revolves once beneath the stylus for each revolution of the axle, and therefore for each playback of the speech sample. The metallic stylus is fed with voltage by the analyzer, whose input is the playback signal from the reproducing head of the magnetic recorder.

A stepping cog moves the stylus parallel to the axis of the drum on each revolution of the drum. Simultaneously, it shifts the center frequency of the constant-band-width analyzer. Consequently, on each revolution, the sensitive paper is impressed with an amplitude-time trace of a single frequency band of the speech sample. As a simple example, if the early part of the sample consisted predominantly of low-pitched components, and the latter part of high-pitched components, the lower left-hand portion and the upper right-hand portion of the record would be much darker than the remainder. A close study of the speech spectrograms of Fig. 8.21 will help in an understanding of the process.

10.8 The Sound Level Meter

The sound level meter is a convenient device for making measurements of loudness, loudness level, or sound intensity, where the fluctuations of the sound level do not exceed about 20 db in a short period of time. The over-all range is from 25 db to 140 db. In use, the level is obtained with a step attenuator and a zero-centered meter which reads approximately 10 db either side of center. The meter circuit is approximately logarithmic, any departure from the logarithmic response being compensated by the ruling of the meter face. The other elements of the sound level meter are a calibrated microphone and an amplifier which can be given any one of three gain-vs.-frequency characteristics. These gain characteristics are inverse to the auditory response of the 40-, 70-, and 120-phon curves of Fig. 8.31. This is done in an attempt to make the reading of the meter correspond approximately to the psychological loudness level of the sound. For most measurements, the 40-phon characteristic should be used in the range from 25 to 55 phons, the 70-phon characteristic from 55 to 85, and 120-phon characteristic above readings of 85 db. Since the 120-phon characteristic is essentially flat, readings taken with this scale will correspond approximately to the over-all sound pressure level.

Since the sound level meter is not designed primarily as an absolute measuring instrument, but rather as an easy-to-use indicator of psychological loudness, most of the theory centers on the best design of the compensated amplifier circuits. For example, the use of the phon curve for compensation has been criticized because these curves were arrived at with steady pure tones, while most measurements are made on sounds of a much more complex and transient character, such as noise. The proposed modifications were arrived at by the analysis of many types of sound, and subsequent mathematical treatment. Such mathematical treatment is outside the scope of this text. In nature, it is roughly similar to the methods by which the masking spectrum of room noise and resultant change in threshold level are obtained (Art. 8.5). From this discussion, it should be evident that absolute measurements inevitably demand that analysis be performed.

10.9 The Constant-Band-Width Analyzer

An extremely selective electric band-pass filter can be constructed with an arrangement of quartz crystals. It is possible to design such a filter with a center frequency of 100,000 cycles, relatively constant response from 10 cycles below to 10 cycles above this frequency, and a sharp falling off above and below this 20 cycle band (Fig. 10.91). From the viewpoint of sound analysis, such a crystal element lacks two desirable properties: its response is above the upper limit of audible sound, and its resonant frequency is fixed. As we have seen in the study of combination tones, however, when two frequencies are mixed in a

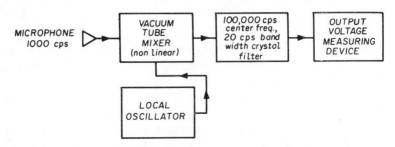

Fig. 10.91. Block diagram of the constant-band-width analyzer. The local oscillator supplies a 101,000-cycle signal, its dial being calibrated to 1,000-cycle units. The output-voltage measuring device provides a meter reading proportional to the strength of the frequency component.

nonlinear device, frequencies equal to the sum and difference of the component frequencies are produced. Thus if a 105,000 cycle frequency is mixed with a 5,000 cycle frequency, the difference frequency is at the center frequency of the crystal filter. The principle of mixing two frequencies to produce the sum or difference frequency is called the heterodyne principle, and the constant-band-width analyzer works on this principle. The electric signal generated in the microphone is delivered to the input of an electric "mixer" circuit, and a variable-frequency *local oscillator* generates a frequency which may vary from 80,000 to 100,000 cycles or 100,000 to 120,000 cycles, depending on whether the sum or difference frequency is to be used. The mixer output is delivered to the quartz filter element. If high outputs are obtained from the quartz element when 101,000, 102,000, and 105,000 cycles are fed from the variable oscillator, we may conclude that the sound contains strong component frequencies at 1,000, 2,000, and 5,000 cycles. Furthermore, the over-all circuit may be designed so that the output is proportional to the strength of the frequency component. With the heterodyne principle in mind, the oscillator dial may be numbered zero when the oscillator is generating a frequency of 100,000 cycles, and 20,000 when it is generating a frequency of 120,000 cycles, so that the oscillator dial reads directly the component frequency of the sound being analyzed. In this way, the frequency spectrum may be obtained by turning the oscillator dial slowly through its range, and graphing the meter reading against the dial reading. A better method is to employ a frequency-changing motor drive which is synchronized with a graphic level recorder.

10.10 The Constant-Percentage Band-Width Analyzer

Although *resonant* circuits, in the accepted use of the term, demand inductance and capacitance, it is possible to construct resistance-capacitance circuits which are frequency sensitive. One of the better known is the Wien bridge. The essence of the Wien bridge circuit (Fig. 10.101) is that a null (zero) voltage is obtained at the output if the input voltage has the frequency

$$f = \frac{1}{2\pi RC}$$

where R and C are values of resistive and capacitive elements of the bridge, and the remaining elements have values shown in Fig. 10.101. The output voltage, plotted against frequency, approaches the null along a curve not

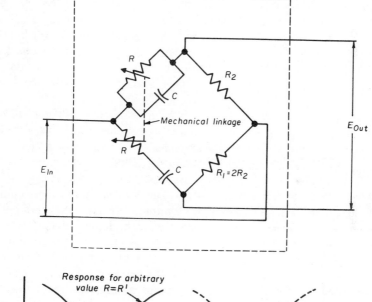

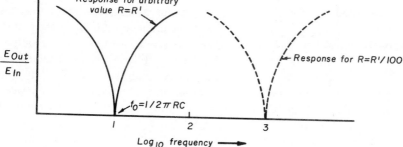

Fig. 10.101. At top, a Wien bridge null network. If the resistors in the R-C branches are always equal and $R_1 = 2R_2$ the bridge will have zero output at frequency $f_0 = 1/2\pi RC$. Note that the capacitors in the R-C branches are fixed and equal. At bottom is shown the response of a Wien bridge.

unlike the resonance curve of an L-C circuit, although the effective Q is of the order of unity, as compared with the order of a hundred in the L-C resonant circuit. However, as will be explained, an auxiliary electronic amplifier performs a function of increasing the selectivity of the bridge which has been termed "Q-multiplication," as well as providing an output proportional to the strength of the voltage component at the null frequency of the bridge. Since high-quality variable resistances may readily be obtained with values necessary for audio frequencies, this circuit has become the basis of a very useful frequency analyzer. Since the effective Q of the bridge-amplifier circuit is essentially constant with frequency, and since the percentage band width is proportional to the effective Q, such an analyzer is called a *percentage bandwidth analyzer*.

To describe the operation of this analyzer, it is necessary to consider the principle of *degenerative feedback*. (The use of degenerative feedback has already been mentioned in connection with the electrodynamic cutterhead used for disk recording, in which a flat frequency characteristic is obtained by feeding back a portion of the output voltage out of phase with the input voltage.)

(a)   Amplification $= \dfrac{E_0}{E_i} = K$

(b)   Amplification $= \dfrac{E_0}{E_i} = \dfrac{K}{1+\beta K}$

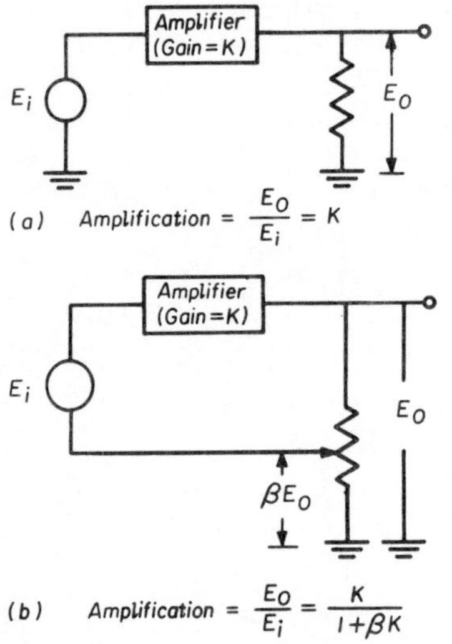

Fig. 10.102. Elementary amplifier and degenerative feedback amplifier.

Consider the circuit of Fig. 10.102(a), which consists merely of an electronic amplifier of intrinsic gain K, fed by a voltage E_i, and delivering across an output potentiometer a voltage $E_0 = KE_i$. The construction of the amplifier is such that the output voltage is out of phase with the input voltage, but this fact is immaterial for most applications. Now consider the modification in (b) of the figure, in which a portion of the output voltage is fed back in series with the input voltage. Since the amplifier has an intrinsic gain K, the output voltage is still the factor K times the *net* input voltage, which has the value $E_i - \beta E_0$. We are most interested, however, in computing the ratio between E_0 and E_i, which is called the *over-all amplification*, A, of the amplifier with degenerative feedback.

$$E_0 = K(E_i - \beta E_0) \qquad (10.101)$$

$$E_0(1 + K\beta) = KE_i$$

$$A = \frac{E_0}{E_i} = \frac{K}{1 + \beta K} = \frac{1}{1/K + \beta} \qquad (10.102)$$

There are two important limiting conditions. Consider the case in which β is much greater than $1/K$. The over-all gain is then given closely by the value $1/\beta$. As an example, if the gain K of the purely electronic portion is 500, while $\beta = 0.1$, the over-all gain is very close to 10. Further, even if K should change by a factor of say 20 per cent, say from 500 to 400, the over-all gain will be little affected. The *stability* of the gain has thus been made to depend on the constancy of resistor values rather than the characteristics of vacuum tubes. This is a general application of the principle of degenerative feedback.

In our application, we are also interested in the contrary condition, namely, that in which β is greatly reduced. We then find that the over-all gain approaches the value K. If β actually becomes equal to zero, we have the equality $A = K$.

If we now interpose the Wien bridge circuit between the output potentiometer and the input, as in Fig. 10.103, the effective feedback ratio can be made to vary from approximately unity to approximately zero, and the corresponding over-all gain from approximately unity to approximately K. Ideally then, a frequency to which the null circuit is tuned enjoys the full amplification of

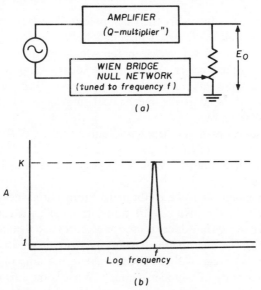

Fig. 10.103. (a) Block diagram of constant-percentage band-width analyzer. (b) Gain of analyzer as a function of frequency.

the system, whereas components outside the tuning range are amplified with only small gain (approximately unity). We have already given the experimental response curves in Fig. 10.61.

One practical use of the degenerative analyzer is in the analysis of machinery noise and other sounds of shifting frequency characteristic. Since the frequency shift is usually on a percentage basis, there is much less likelihood that important frequency components will be missed, though slight inaccuracies may be made in frequency measurement. This is not usually objectionable, since other methods of measurement can be employed once the important components have been located.

References

Beranek, *Acoustic Measurements*, Wiley, New York, 1949.
General Radio Co. Catalog.
Brüel and Kjaer Catalog, obtainable from the Brush Electronics Co., Cleveland, Ohio.

Problems

Note: For use in the problems the following conversion factors from c.g.s. to practical electrical units are necessary:

$$1 \text{ volt} = 10^8 \text{ abvolts}, \quad 1 \text{ amp} = 0.1 \text{ abampere}$$

1. Identical transducers are used as source and receiver, with a separation of 1 m. Assume that the inverse square law holds. A driving current of 0.1 amp at a frequency of 344 cycles in the source produces an open-circuit voltage of 1 μv in the receiver. What are the source strength, response ratio, and microphone sensitivity? If the diaphragm area is 10 cm^2, and the coupling constant D is 10^4, what is the mechanical impedance of the transducer? *Note:* $c = 34,400$ cm/sec.

2. A transducer used as source has a source strength of 10 cm^3/sec. When used as a microphone it has a voltage sensitivity of -60 db. What is its driving current when used as source? What is its response ratio at 1 m for a wavelength of 25 cm?

3. A microphone is to be calibrated. From initial measurements, it is determined that its sensitivity is 10 times as great as a certain reversible transducer. When the transducer is used as a source at a distance of 1 m (from the microphone), the microphone has an open-circuit sensitivity of 10 μv at a frequency of 344 cycles with a driving current of 1 amp in the transducer. What is the sensitivity of the microphone? What is the rms pressure on the microphone?

4. An amplifier has an intrinsic gain of 200. Find the over-all gain of a feedback amplifier employing this intrinsic gain for the following values of β: 1.0, 0.9, 0.5, 0.1, 0.01, 0.001, 0.0001. From the results, show that the important design consideration is the existence of a good "null" at the critical frequency, rather than a sharp approach to the "null."

5. Figure P10.5 is illustrating a curve showing the addition of two sounds of different levels, showing the sum level as an addition to the stronger sound.

Find the absolute over-all noise level if the following components are obtained in a noise analysis: 300 cycles, 80 db; 500 cycles, 72 db; 600 cycles, 72 db; 700 cycles, 72 db; 1,000 cycles, 77 db; 1,500 cycles, 78 db; 2,000 cycles, 75 db.

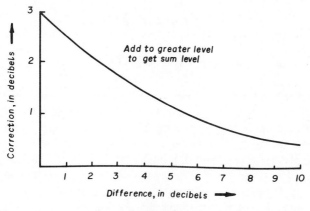

Fig. P10.5.

Find the loudness in sones corresponding to this over-all level at a frequency of 1,000 cycles. Then find the over-all loudness in sones by adding the loudnesses of each of the tones.

6. Discuss the plotting of the curve for the addition of noise levels.

7. A sound-level meter gives the following readings on the C (flat) weighting network: 100 cycles, 60 db; 200 cycles, 50 db; 300 cycles, 40 db; 500 cycles, 40 db; 1,000 cycles, 25 db; 3,000 cycles, 36 db. What would be the approximate readings at these frequencies on the A (40-phons) weighting network?

8. Taking the normal pressure to be 1.013×10^6 dynes/cm^2 and the density to be 1.98×10^{-3} g/cm^3, show that the low-frequency ratio of specific heats of CO_2 is approximately 7/5, while the high-frequency ratio is approximately 8/6.

9. Given $C_p = C_v + R$, where C_p is the specific heat at constant pressure, C_v is the specific heat at constant volume, and R is the universal gas constant, find the value of C_v for the low-frequency and high-frequency specific heats. If each "active degree of freedom" of the molecule contributes energy $R/2$ to the specific heat at constant volume, how many degrees of freedom are active in CO_2 at low and at high frequencies?

Chapter 11

ULTRASONICS

Ultrasonics is defined as the study of sound waves which have frequencies greater than the upper frequency limit of human audition. To the physicist, this dividing line is quite arbitrary, since physical sound is, in a sense, a subject completely independent of human audition. When one considers that compressional waves in material media have been produced up to a frequency of 1,000 megacycles, it becomes quickly evident that the audible frequencies are an insignificant part of the sound spectrum, and that acoustics, in the sense of the relation between physical sound and audition, is a very limited field. Yet the relation between sound and hearing has definitely influenced the development of sound theory. As an example, it is general practice to neglect the influence of absorption in theoretical treatments of the propagation of sound waves. For one thing, the analysis is much simplified, and for a second, absorption is of minor importance in most applications. It is true that the absorption of the higher-frequency audible sounds by air is a factor in archi-tectural acoustics, but not a fundamental factor, except at high frequencies in dry air. Thus considerations of absorption are usually added onto the primary treatment, in which results are obtained by considering the absorption negligible.

The theory of sound is based on three fundamental equations: (1) the equation of continuity, $s = -\partial\xi/\partial x$; (2) the dynamic equation $\rho\, \partial^2\xi/\partial t^2 = -\partial p/\partial x$; (3) the relation between stress and strain $p = Bs$. It is the third of these equations that tacitly assumes that the medium is dissipationless. In the field that has become known as "ultrasonics" but which might more rightly be termed "general sound theory," the problem of the propagation of com-pressional waves in a material medium is attacked in a much more general manner. Assumptions that are allowed because they give results which check theoretically at frequencies below 20,000 cycles are re-examined because they fail to explain the propagation of sound waves at higher frequencies. The more general theories which are projected to explain sound propagation at ultrasonic frequencies have an important by-product; they necessitate the hypothesizing of a mechanism which will explain the propagation of a sound wave at *any* frequency. If this mechanism is successful in the prediction of results, it often gives a better knowledge of the structure and energy relations in the medium.

Occasionally, these hypotheses may appear to do violence to concepts which have been established in the earlier chapters of this text. However, basic physical concepts are accepted because they agree with experience. It is often possible to state certain laws with greater simplicity by omitting qualifications which have only slight importance in a particular application, and which are often more burdensome than helpful to the student. These laws lead to simple models which have great value in pursuing the implications of the laws. Once these models have become familiar, there is a tendency to consider as contradictory any hypothesis which does not agree with the familiar model. In the next three articles we shall be engaged in formulating hypotheses and constructing models to explain results *which the simpler hypotheses and simpler models have failed to explain.* Therefore we must be willing to make assumptions freely, as long as no self-contradiction is involved. We can withhold our judgment as to the worth of these assumptions until we arrive at the conclusions. If these conclusions are confirmed by experiment, we can feel satisfied that our assumptions are justifiable.*

11.1 Stokes's Theory of the Propagation of Sound

In the preceding chapters, we have often used the fundamental relation $p = Bs$. It is now necessary to examine this relation and its ramifications more closely. The bulk modulus is measured mechanically by what is called a *static method.* For such a measurement, the pressure and volume of a sample of gas are measured initially, the pressure is slowly changed, and the static pressure and volume are measured again. No measurements are made while the change is taking place. The bulk modulus is then computed by comparing the pressure change with the volume change. Either the isothermal or the adiabatic bulk modulus can be measured by controlling the conditions under which the pressure change takes place. Now there is no a priori reason why a dynamic process should obey the same law as a static process. That is to say, we have not proved in our static measurement of the bulk modulus that the pressure is instantaneously proportional to the relative density (condensation) but only that the initial and final values of the two are proportional. Thus our use of the relation as an instantaneous relation is itself an assumption. When we introduce the static value of the bulk modulus into certain equations, the results which we obtain agree very closely with measured values of *velocity* in the audible range (Art. 3.6), and the assumption seems justifiable. However, as we have stated previously, when this relation is used with Newton's law and the equation of continuity, it predicts that the propagation of sound should be dissipationless. Stokes, therefore, decided to generalize the pressure-density relation, by assuming that a change in pressure influences not only the

---

* A considerable portion of this chapter is based on J. J. Markham, R. T. Beyer, and R. B. Lindsay, "Absorption of Sound in Fluids," *Revs. Mod. Phys.*, **23**, 353-411 (1951).

ultimate change in density, but also *the rate at which the change takes place.* His assumed pressure-density relation may be written

$$p = B_A s + \zeta \frac{\partial s}{\partial t} \tag{11.11}$$

where B_A is the *static* adiabatic bulk modulus, and ζ is a constant of the medium. To assist in an understanding of this relation, we give an analogous mechanical system. This system consists of a spring obeying Hooke's law and a frictional mechanism called a *dashpot* (Fig. 11.11). The lower end of the spring and the cylinder of the dashpot are attached to an immovable base. The force required to move the piston is proportional to the velocity of the

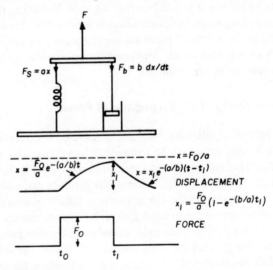

Fig. 11.11. Relation between displacement and force for a system consisting of a spring and dashpot.

piston, and of course the force required to move the spring is proportional to the extension of the spring. The upper end of the spring and the piston of the dashpot are attached to a rigid bar constrained to remain parallel to the base. Inasmuch as both the reactive force in the spring and the reactive force of the dashpot unite in opposing the impressed force, the dynamic equation of the system will be

$$F = ax + b \frac{dx}{dt} \tag{11.12}$$

From this mechanical model, we can derive a knowledge of the concept of *retardation time,* or *relaxation time.*[*] Suppose a square force pulse is applied

---

[*] The equations of this article are similar to those of the rise and decay of sound in an enclosure (Chapter 9).

to the mechanical system. From the time t_0 to the time t_1, the displacement increases according to the law

$$x = \frac{1}{a} F_0 (1 - e^{-at/b}) \tag{11.13}$$

At the time t_1, the force falls to zero, and the displacement decreases at the rate

$$x_1 e^{(-a/b)(t - t_1)} \tag{11.14}$$

where x_1 is the "value" of the displacement at the end of the pulse. From Eqs. (11.13) and (11.14), we have for the displacement from t_1 to ∞,

$$x = \frac{1}{a} F_0 (1 - e^{-at_1/b}) e^{-(a/b)(t - t_1)} \tag{11.15}$$

We have already used the concept of *time constant* in Chapters 1 and 9, namely, the time during which a variable falls to a fraction $1/e$ of its initial value. In the present instance this is the meaning assigned to the relaxation time. We have for the relaxation time,

$$\tau = \frac{b}{a} \tag{11.16}$$

Since Stokes's equation is entirely similar to Eq. (11.12), we have for the relaxation time in an acoustic process,

$$\tau = \frac{\zeta}{B_A} \tag{11.17}$$

The mechanical model of Fig. 11.11 and the accompanying analysis were given primarily to introduce the idea of a time constant (relaxation time). We shall now develop the propagation of a plane compressional wave in an elastic medium as determined by the three equations,

$$-\frac{\partial p}{\partial x} = \rho \frac{\partial^2 \xi}{\partial t^2} \tag{11.18}$$

$$s = -\frac{\partial \xi}{\partial x} \tag{11.19}$$

$$p = B_A s + \zeta \frac{\partial s}{\partial t} \tag{11.11}$$

Equations (11.18) and (11.19) are precisely those used to develop the equation of the plane wave in Art. 3.2. The third is Stokes's equation, repeated for convenience.

If we substitute the relation between condensation and displacement (Eq. 11.19) in Stokes's equation,

$$p = -B_A \frac{\partial \xi}{\partial x} - \zeta \frac{\partial^2 \xi}{\partial x\, \partial t} \tag{11.110}$$

Differentiation with x gives

$$-\frac{\partial p}{\partial x} = B_A \frac{\partial^2 \xi}{\partial x^2} + \zeta \frac{\partial^3 \xi}{\partial^2 x\, \partial t} \tag{11.111}$$

Equating the right-hand members of Eqs. (11.18) and (11.111), we get

$$B_A \frac{\partial^2 \xi}{\partial x^2} + \zeta \frac{\partial^3 \xi}{\partial x^2\, \partial t} = \rho \frac{\partial^2 \xi}{\partial t^2} \tag{11.112}$$

In Arts. 3.18 and 5.8 we have been successful in solving equations of this general type by assuming for the solution the equation of an attenuated wave. Therefore we shall again assume an equation of this form.

Let
$$\xi = \xi_0 e^{j\omega t}\, e^{-(\alpha + j\beta)x} \tag{11.113}$$

Then
$$\frac{\partial^2 \xi}{\partial x^2} = (\alpha + j\beta)^2 \xi, \quad \frac{\partial^3 \xi}{\partial x^2\, \partial t} = j\omega(\alpha + j\beta)^2 \xi, \quad \frac{\partial^2 \xi}{\partial t^2} = -\omega^2 \xi$$

Substituting in the differential equation gives

$$B_A(\alpha + j\beta)^2 + \zeta j\omega(\alpha + j\beta)^2 = -\omega^2 \rho$$

$$(\alpha + j\beta)^2 (B_A + j\zeta\omega) = -\omega^2 \rho$$

$$(\alpha + j\beta)^2 = \frac{-\omega^2 \rho}{B_A + j\zeta\omega} = -\frac{\rho}{\zeta} \cdot \frac{\omega^2}{B_A/\zeta + j\omega} \tag{11.114}$$

We have already noted that the relaxation time which arises from Stokes's hypothesis has the value ζ/B_A. If a square pulse were to be imposed on a system governed by Eq. (11.12) and the active time of this pulse were very long compared with the relaxation time, both the rise time and the relaxation time would be such that the system would effectively follow the impulse; that is, the strain would be essentially proportional to the force throughout the active time of the pulse. On the other hand, if the active time of the pulse were short compared with the relaxation time, the instantaneous values of the strain would differ significantly from the instantaneous values of the force. Analogously, if an alternating pressure is imposed on a medium governed by Stokes's pressure-density relation (Eq. 11.11), the condensation is effectively *in phase* with the pressure for periods long compared with the relaxation time, whereas a phase lag occurs if the period is short compared with the relaxation time. The frequency B_A/ζ at which the period of the wave equals the relaxation time is therefore a critical frequency in the propagation of sound waves as determined by Stokes's theory. We shall accordingly substitute ω_V for the term B_A/ζ in Eq. (11.114). Making this substitution and rationalizing,

$$(\alpha + j\beta)^2 = -\frac{\rho}{\zeta} \cdot \frac{\omega^2(\omega_V - j\omega)}{\omega_V^2 + \omega^2} \tag{11.115}$$

Separating each side of the equation into real and imaginary parts gives

$$\alpha^2 - \beta^2 + 2\alpha\beta j = -\frac{\rho}{\zeta} \cdot \frac{\omega^2 \omega_V}{\omega_V^2 + \omega^2} + j\frac{\rho}{\zeta} \cdot \frac{\omega^3}{\omega_V^2 + \omega^2}$$

$$\beta^2 - \alpha^2 = \frac{\rho}{\zeta} \cdot \frac{\omega^2 \omega_V}{\omega_V^2 + \omega^2} \tag{11.116}$$

$$2\alpha\beta = \frac{\rho}{\zeta} \cdot \frac{\omega^3}{\omega_V^2 + \omega^2} \tag{11.117}$$

We divide Eq. (11.116) by Eq. (11.117) to obtain

$$\frac{\beta}{\alpha} - \frac{\alpha}{\beta} = 2\frac{\omega_V}{\omega}$$

We shall examine this equation for two limiting frequencies. If $\omega \ll \omega_V$, the right-hand member of the equation approaches infinity and therefore $\beta \gg \alpha$. Conversely, if $\omega \gg \omega_V$, the right-hand member approaches zero, so that $\beta = \alpha$, and therefore we can make the following approximations.

At low frequencies,

$$\beta^2 \approx \frac{\rho}{\zeta} \cdot \frac{\omega^2}{\omega_V} \approx \frac{\rho}{B_A} \cdot \frac{B_A}{\zeta} \cdot \frac{\omega^2}{\omega_V} \approx \frac{1}{c_0^2} \omega^2$$

where

$$c_0 = \sqrt{B_A/\rho}$$

or

$$\frac{\omega^2}{\beta^2} = c^2 = c_0^2$$

Therefore at low frequencies (frequencies much less than ω_V) the velocity should be essentially independent of frequency. The absorption coefficient becomes

$$\alpha = \frac{1}{2\beta} \cdot \frac{\rho}{\zeta} \cdot \frac{\omega^3}{\omega_V^2 + \omega^2} \approx \frac{1}{2\beta} \cdot \frac{\rho}{\zeta} \cdot \frac{\zeta^2 \omega^3}{B_A^2}$$

$$\approx \frac{c_0}{2\omega} \frac{\rho^2 \zeta \omega^3}{\rho B_A^2} \approx \frac{\zeta \omega^2}{2\rho c_0^3}$$

Stokes analyzed the propagation of a compressional wave in a viscous medium and concluded that the constant ζ should be directly proportional to the mechanical viscosity. He gave the relation: $\zeta = \frac{4}{3}\eta$, where η is the mechanical viscosity. Accepting Stokes's value for ζ, we have for the coefficient of absorption,

$$\alpha = \frac{2\eta\omega^2}{3\rho c_0^3} \tag{11.118}$$

Kirchhoff added a term due to heat conduction which is appreciable for gases and negligible for most liquids. The sum of Stokes's and Kirchhoff's term is called the *classical value of the coefficient of absorption for fluids.*

At high frequencies,

$$2\alpha^2 \approx \frac{\rho}{\zeta}\omega, \quad \alpha = \left(\frac{\rho}{2\zeta}\omega\right)^{1/2} \tag{11.119}$$

and since $\beta = \alpha$,
$$\beta = \left(\frac{\rho}{2\zeta}\omega\right)^{1/2} \tag{11.120}$$

Thus we have for the velocity,

$$c = \frac{\omega}{\beta} = \left(\frac{B_A}{\rho} \cdot \frac{2\zeta}{B_A}\omega\right)^{1/2} = c_0 \left(\frac{2\omega}{\omega_V}\right)^{1/2} \tag{11.121}$$

The conclusions that follow for the equality $\beta = \alpha$ are rather startling. Such an attenuation coefficient means that the amplitude will decrease by the factor $e^{-2\pi}$ in each wavelength! Sound propagation, as we ordinarily understand it, no longer exists. Nevertheless, the predictions of Stokes's theory have been checked approximately in helium gas above the critical frequency!

To clarify the theoretical values of velocity and absorption as predicted by Stokes's hypothesis, velocity and absorption are plotted versus frequency in Fig. 11.12. To simplify the graph, we plot α/ω^2 rather than α.

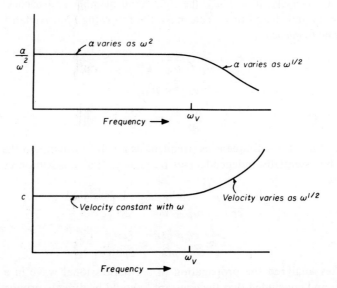

Fig. 11.12. Variation of absorption coefficient and velocity with frequency, according to Stokes's hypothesis.

Although the Stokes hypothesis is a more general viewpoint than that taken in elementary sound theory, it is only one of the viewpoints which have been taken concerning the stress-strain relation. By contrast, the Maxwell hypothesis makes the condensation proportional to the sum of the pressure and the rate of change of pressure. (Note that the Stokes hypothesis makes the pressure proportional to the sum of the condensation and the rate of change of the condensation.) When the Maxwell hypothesis is used alone, the results are not at all in accord with experiment, whereas the Stokes hypothesis, though not always predicting the correct absolute values of velocity and absorption, at least predicts the variation with frequency, so much so that it is the custom in quoting absorption coefficients, to give the value α/ω^2. It is remarkable that this value is constant with frequency in a great number of fluids.

Since the bulk moduli and viscosities of liquids and gases can be measured by mechanical methods, the critical frequency ω_V can be calculated independently of acoustic measurements. It turns out to be an extremely high frequency, even for gases, and for liquids to be practically unattainable by experiment. We give it below for air and water.

For air: 6,000 *megacycles* at normal pressure
For water: 2×10^6 megacycles

In gases, one reduces the bulk modulus by reducing the pressure (Art. 3.6), whereas the viscosity is relatively independent of pressure. In this way the critical frequency can be greatly lowered. Actually, this is the common method in measurements of the propagation constant in gases. Since it is difficult to change the frequency (our discussion of the interferometer will show why this is so), variation of the propagation constant is graphed against pressure changes.

11.2 Additional Theories of Sound Propagation

Besides Stokes, several other physicists have put forward observations of a theoretical nature. Among these is Kirchhoff's theory of absorption of sound by a fluid as a result of heat conduction. The absorption predicted by Kirchhoff's theory added to that predicted by Stokes's theory gives the *classical value* of the coefficient. We shall not derive Kirchhoff's absorption coefficient, but the classical value of the absorption coefficient is given in Art. 11.5 with a discussion of experimental results.

In addition to the classical theory of sound propagation, several newer theories have been projected which are known by the generic term of *relaxation theories*. In contrast, Stokes's theory is known as a *viscosity* theory. Relaxation theories, in general, hypothesize definite structural arrangements in the medium. Herzfeld and Rice have proposed a theory of *thermal or molecular relaxation*, in which they show that the rapid variations of pressure at ultrasonic frequencies cause the specific heat to be a function of frequency, and that this should lead to dispersion and a critical dependence of absorption on frequency. The computation of the critical frequencies of the molecular relaxation theory would entail the use of several thermodynamic coefficients, and it will not be possible for us to find their values, as we were able to do for Stokes's critical frequency. However, it is important to state that the critical frequencies arrived at by relaxation theory are much lower than Stokes's critical frequencies, so that they are subject to experimental verification.

Hall and others have considered a relaxation of another type, which they call *structural relaxation*. Hall assumed that in addition to the solid, liquid, and gas states there exists "substates" which are characterized by different structural arrangements. If a certain "region" of a liquid differs in state from a neighboring region, energy interchange may take place between these regions, similar to the energy interchange within molecules which characterizes Herzfeld's theory of molecular relaxation. Hall has applied this theory to water, and has succeeded in giving a plausible explanation of the measured value of the coefficient of absorption. We shall illustrate the idea of relaxation by a simplified treatment of molecular relaxation.

11.3 Molecular Relaxation

In elementary gas theory, the molecules are considered to be perfectly elastic spheres, and the pressure on the walls of a container can be derived in terms of the *energy of translation* of the molecules. When the structure of the molecule is taken into account, it is found that the molecule may possess *internal* energy of rotation and vibration, in addition to the energy of translation. In the classical interpretation, the energy of the molecule is assumed to be evenly distributed among the active *degrees of freedom* of the molecule. If we assume an ideal gas, we can easily show that the difference between the specific heat at constant pressure C_p and that at constant volume C_v should equal the universal gas constant R (Art. 3.6). If it is assumed that each degree of freedom has an associated energy $RT/2$, where T is the absolute temperature, a monatomic gas should obey the equation $C_v = \frac{3}{2}R$, since it has three degrees of freedom (three axes of translation). Following from this $C_p = C_v + R = 5R/2$, and we have for the ratio of specific heats,

$$\gamma = \frac{C_p}{C_v} = \frac{5}{3}$$

This value has been found experimentally in measurements of specific heat of monatomic gases.

Diatomic molecules may have three *internal* degrees of freedom, due to rotation about two axes orthogonal to the molecular axis and vibration along the molecular axis. Often, the vibrational mode is not excited at lower temperatures. Thus the molecule should have five degrees of freedom at lower temperatures and six at higher temperatures. Many common molecules are diatomic, and the experimental value of γ at normal temperature and pressure is found to be close to $\frac{7}{5}$ for these diatomic molecules, which indicates that five degrees of freedom are present. Thus we may say that the hypothesis of equal energy distribution among the various degrees of freedom has been well checked by experiment.

If the mechanism by which energy enters the internal degrees of freedom is considered, it is natural to assume that a sudden compression of the gas should at first excite the translational degrees alone, but that, as a result of intermolecular collisions, the translational energy would be gradually converted into internal energy until a state of equilibrium was reached (until each degree of freedom had equal energy $RT/2$). It takes, on the average, a definite time for the gas to obtain this equilibrium state, as one can show on the basis of statistical reasoning. Equilibrium is approached exponentially, as in other similar processes, and the time constant of the process is defined as the *molecular relaxation time*. This relaxation time turns out to be of the order of microseconds or milliseconds.* We consider the propagation of a sound wave through the gas. For low frequencies, the relaxation time is much smaller than the period of the wave, and equilibrium among the various degrees of freedom exists virtually at all times. However, as the period of the wave decreases with increasing frequency, it eventually becomes less than the relaxation time, and little or no energy conversion takes place from the translational to the internal degrees of freedom. For high frequencies, then, the specific heat at constant volume is determined entirely by the translational modes, and the ratio of specific heats approaches the value $\frac{5}{3}$ for all molecules. Let us call C_0 the specific heat at zero frequency, and C_∞ the specific heat at infinite frequency. The specific heat at intermediate frequencies should be a function of the relaxation time. We can even think of the gas as having an *instantaneous specific heat* given by the expression,

$$C_v = C_\infty + C_i(1 - e^{-t/\tau}) \qquad (11.31)$$

It is obvious that $C_0 = C_\infty + C_i$. For example, if we take a diatomic gas with the vibrational mode not excited, $C_\infty = 3R/2$, $C_i = R$, and $C_0 = 5R/2$.

We can also write Eq. (11.31) in the form

$$C_v = C_\infty + (C_0 - C_\infty)(1 - e^{-t/\tau}) \qquad (11.32)$$

However, we are not so much interested in the instantaneous specific heat as in the *effective specific heat* as a function of the frequency of a harmonic variation. As an aid to the interpretation of this quantity, let us consider the circuit of Fig. 11.31, in which the numerical values of the capacitances are given by C_∞ and $(C_0 - C_\infty)$, and the numerical value of the resistance by $\tau/(C_0 - C_\infty)$. If a step voltage E is imposed on this circuit, the instantaneous capacitance, defined by ratio of the instantaneous charge to the voltage, will be

$$C = C_\infty + (C_0 - C_\infty)(1 - e^{-t/\tau})$$

which is similar to Eq. (11.32). Let us now find the *effective capacitance* of the circuit for an alternating voltage. We have for the current,

$$I_0 e^{j\omega t} = \left(j\omega C_\infty + \frac{1}{1/j\omega C_i + \tau/C_i} \right) E_0 e^{j\omega t} \qquad (11.33)$$

Since $i = dq/dt$, we can show that the charge will be

$$Q_0 e^{j\omega t} = \left(C_\infty + \frac{C_i}{1 + j\omega\tau} \right) E_0 e^{j\omega t} \qquad (11.34)$$

---

* According to Herzfeld, any value may exist. Knudsen has found large values in air.

By analogy, we can assume that the *effective specific heat* at constant volume will be

$$C_v = C_\infty + \frac{C_0 - C_\infty}{1 + j\omega\tau} \tag{11.35}$$

Fig. 11.31. Effective capacitance of a network comprised of an *R-C* branch in parallel with a pure capacitance.

Having generalized the expression for specific heat, we must also generalize the relation between the adiabatic and isothermal bulk moduli:

$$B_A = \gamma B_I = \frac{C_p}{C_v} B_I = \left(1 + \frac{C_p - C_v}{C_v}\right) B_I = \left(1 + \frac{R}{C_v}\right) B_I \tag{11.36}$$

If we substitute in Eq. (11.36) the generalized expression for specific heat (Eq. 11.35) we have, after rationalizing,

$$B_A = B_I \left[\frac{(R + C_0)C_0 + (R + C_\infty)C_\infty\tau^2\omega^2}{C_0^2 + C_\infty^2\tau^2\omega^2} + j\frac{RC_i\tau\omega}{C_0^2 + C_\infty^2\tau^2\omega^2} \right] \tag{11.37}$$

Our ultimate objective is to obtain expressions for velocity and absorption from Eq. (11.37). We rewrite Newton's law and the equation of continuity for convenience:

$$-\frac{\partial p}{\partial x} = \rho \frac{\partial^2 \xi}{\partial t^2} \tag{11.38}$$

$$-\frac{\partial \rho'}{\partial x} = \rho \frac{\partial^2 \xi}{\partial x^2} \tag{11.39}$$

Now from the fundamental definition of the bulk modulus,

$$B = \rho \frac{\partial p}{\partial \rho'}$$

The subscript has been omitted for the present, since no conditions of the condensation process have been stated. Evidently

$$\frac{\partial p}{\partial x} = \frac{\partial p}{\partial \rho'} \frac{\partial \rho'}{\partial x} \qquad (11.310)$$

Substituting Eq. (11.310) in Eq. (11.38),

$$-\frac{\partial p}{\partial \rho'} \frac{\partial \rho'}{\partial x} = \rho \frac{\partial^2 \xi}{\partial t^2} \qquad (11.311)$$

Dividing Eq. (11.311) by Eq. (11.39),

$$\frac{\partial p}{\partial \rho'} = \frac{\partial^2 \xi / \partial t^2}{\partial^2 \xi / \partial x^2}$$

Let us make the additional assumption that we have an attenuated wave given by the equation

$$\xi = A e^{j\omega t} e^{-(\alpha + j\beta)x} \qquad (11.312)$$

Then

$$\frac{\partial^2 \xi}{\partial t^2} = -\omega^2 \xi$$

$$\frac{\partial^2 \xi}{\partial x^2} = (\alpha + j\beta)^2 \xi = (\alpha^2 + 2j\alpha\beta - \beta^2)\xi$$

If we assume that $\alpha \ll \beta$, we have for the pressure-density relation,

$$\frac{\partial p}{\partial \rho'} = \frac{\omega^2}{\beta^2 - \alpha^2 - 2j\alpha\beta} \approx \frac{\omega^2}{\beta^2}\left(\frac{1}{1 - 2j\alpha/\beta}\right) \approx \frac{\omega^2}{\beta^2}\left(1 + 2j\frac{\alpha}{\beta}\right) \quad (11.313)$$

Our assumption that α is small compared with β is in accord with the remarks made after Eq. (11.21) with regard to equality of α and β. The partial derivative $\partial p/\partial \rho'$ of Eq. (11.313) is a complex number. Let us write it in general fashion as $U + jW$.

We then have for the relation between the velocity and the real part of the complex $(\partial p/\partial \rho')$:

$$U = \frac{\omega^2}{\beta^2} = c^2 \qquad (11.314)$$

and for the relation between the coefficient of absorption and the imaginary part of the complex $\partial p/\partial \rho'$:

$$W = \frac{2\omega^2 \alpha}{\beta^3}$$

$$\alpha = \frac{W\beta^3}{2\omega^2} = \frac{\beta}{2c^2}W = \frac{\omega}{2c^3}W = \frac{\omega}{2c} \cdot \frac{W}{U} \qquad (11.315)$$

We shall now assume that the partial $(\partial p/\partial \rho')$ in Eq. (11.313) is the *adiabatic* bulk modulus divided by ρ. We shall further assume that, however the bulk modulus B_A is obtained, *its real part U gives the square of the wave velocity, and its imaginary part W, multiplied by the factor $\omega/(2cU)$, gives the coefficient of absorption.* With these assumptions, we have from Eq. (11.37),

$$c^2 = B_I \left[\frac{(R + C_0)C_0 + \omega^2\tau^2(R + C_\infty)C_\infty}{C_0^2 + \omega^2\tau^2 C_\infty^2} \right] \qquad (11.316)$$

$$\alpha = \frac{\omega}{2c} \left[\frac{\omega\tau R(C_0 - C_\infty)}{(R + C_0)C_0 + \omega^2\tau^2(R + C_\infty)C_\infty} \right] B_I \qquad (11.317)$$

The coefficient α is the attenuation *per unit length*. It is often more useful to know the absorption in a wavelength. If we define a new constant, $A = \alpha\lambda$, then

$$A = \frac{\omega\lambda}{2c} \left[\frac{\omega\tau R(C_0 - C_\infty)}{(R + C_0)C_0 + \omega^2\tau^2(R + C_\infty)C_\infty} \right]$$

$$= \left[\frac{\pi\tau R(C_0 - C_\infty)\omega}{(R + C_0)C_0 + \omega^2\tau^2(R + C_\infty)C_\infty} \right] \qquad (11.318)$$

We shall restrict our considerations to the character of the variation of A and c with frequency. It is then sufficient to write Eqs. (11.316) and (11.318) in simpler forms by use of single constants K, L, M, N, P, and Q.

$$c^2 = \frac{K + L\omega^2}{M + N\omega^2}, \qquad A = \frac{\omega}{P + Q\omega^2}$$

It is obvious that c^2 approaches limiting values at zero and infinite frequencies.

$$\lim_{\omega \to 0} c^2 = \frac{K}{M} = \left(\frac{R + C_0}{C_0} \right) B_I = \left(1 + \frac{R}{C_0} \right) B_I \qquad (11.319a)$$

$$\lim_{\omega \to \infty} c^2 = \frac{L}{N} = \left(\frac{R + C_\infty}{C_\infty} \right) B_I = \left(1 + \frac{R}{C_\infty} \right) B_I \qquad (11.319b)$$

We can show by differentiating A and equating to zero that the absorption per wavelength has a critical value which is a maximum. The critical value is

$$\omega^2 = \frac{P}{Q}, \qquad A_{Max} = \frac{1}{2P^{1/2}Q^{1/2}} \qquad (11.320)$$

Since $C_0 > C_\infty$, the velocity at very low frequencies is lower than that at very high frequencies. The theoretical curve is shown in Fig. 11.32. The ratio

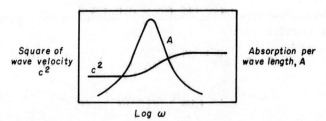

Fig. 11.32. Variation of velocity and absorption with frequency, as predicted by relaxation theory.

P/Q for the frequency of maximum absorption per unit wavelength is too complicated to be useful in the present discussion. However, it is of fundamental importance, in that it enables one to estimate the relaxation time of the molecule. Key experiments in ultrasonics were the discovery of dispersion and absorption in carbon dioxide as predicted by the curves of Fig. 11.32.

11.4 The Ultrasonic Interferometer

Velocity and absorption can be measured by interferometric, optical, and pulse methods. Because it can be handled most readily within the sphere of fundamental acoustics, we choose the interferometric method to describe in detail. We have already mentioned in Art. 3.18 that the use of an acoustic interferometer involves the reaction of a fluid column on a piston transducer. In the ultrasonic interferometer [Fig. 11.41(a)] the "piston" is a quartz crystal driven in thickness vibration by a constant voltage generator. The crystal current is a function of the equivalent electric impedance of the crystal, which is in turn influenced by the loading effect of the fluid column.

The electric equivalent circuit of any transducer is derived by a method essentially similar to our derivation for the dynamic transducer. Since the piezoelectric crystal operates on a different principle, it is not surprising that the equivalent circuit differs somewhat from that of the dynamic transducer. The interferometer and the quartz equivalent circuit are shown in Fig. 11.41(b), where C_1 is the dielectric capacitance, L, R, and C are the equivalent motional elements of the unloaded crystal, and R' and C' are the constants modified by the loading of the fluid. We have

$$R' = R + dSr_s, \qquad \frac{1}{C'} = \frac{1}{C} + d\omega Sx_s$$

where d is a piezoelectric constant, S is the surface area of the crystal, r_s is the specific acoustic resistance of the fluid column, x_s is the specific acoustic reactance of the fluid column.

If an unloaded quartz crystal is fed by a constant voltage generator through a series inductance, and the circuit constants are such that $L_1C_1 = LC$, a type of curve called the *crevasse curve* is obtained as the generator frequency is varied (Fig. 11.42). A variation of this type occurs because $L \gg L_1$, $C \ll C_1$, and R is comparatively small. Consequently, the motional branch of the equivalent circuit has a very high reactance and has little influence on the circuit unless the frequency is very close to resonance. Therefore, as the generator frequency is varied toward the frequency $f_0 = 1/2\pi\sqrt{L_1C_1} = 1/2\pi\sqrt{LC}$, the crystal voltage rises toward the maximum that it would have if the crystal were a pure dielectric capacitance C_1. However, at the frequency f_0, the motional branch becomes a resistance R which is of the order of R_1, and the crystal voltage falls to a small fraction of the generator voltage (Fig. 11.42). With the generator frequency fixed at f_0, the voltage across a loaded crystal

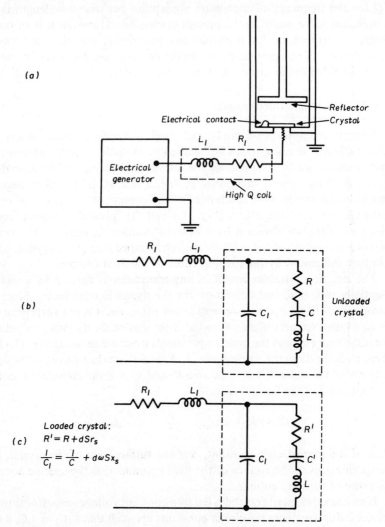

Fig. 11.41. Ultrasonic interferometer and equivalent circuits of unloaded quartz crystal and crystal loaded by a fluid column.

will vary with variation of the loading, and the quartz crystal becomes a very sensitive detector of variations in the input impedance of a fluid column. Reference to Fig. 3.103 will show the type of variation of input impedance to be expected with variation of reflector distance (column length). The curves of Fig. 3.103 are drawn for a dissipationless fluid, and are perfectly cyclic. If absorption is present in the fluid, there is a gradual decrease in the maximum values of r_s and x_s and a gradual rise in the minimum value of r_s. For large distances, x_s will approach zero, and r_s will approach ρc. This result may be

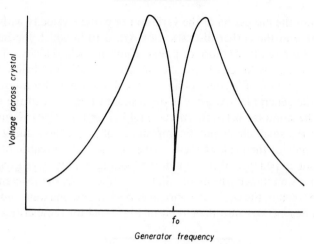

Fig. 11.42. Crystal crevasse curve. Crystal crevasse frequency $f_0 = 1/2\pi\sqrt{LC}$
$= 1/2\pi\sqrt{L'(C' + C_0)}$.

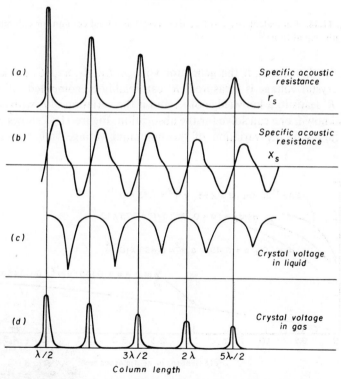

Fig. 11.43. Variation of specific acoustic resistance, specific acoustic reactance, crystal voltage in liquid, and crystal voltage in gas for a fluid column of variable length.

inferred from the discussion of the variation of particle velocity with distance in Art. 3.18 and the earlier discussion of Art. 3.10 in which the impedance curves were derived from those of pressure and particle velocity. The variations of r_s and x_s with length are shown in Fig. 11.43, and below them are shown the variation of crystal voltage with column length for a liquid and a gas when the generator frequency is the resonant frequency of the unloaded crystal. The contrast between curves 11.43(c) and 11.43(d) is interesting. Because of the small characteristic impedance of a gas, the loading becomes significant only at the peak of the r_s curve. Conversely, because of the high characteristic impedance of the liquid, the loading is quite large *except* where r_s and x_s are simultaneously small. Since, in either case, the reactance of the motional branch of the equivalent circuit is zero at both maxima and minima, the crystal degenerates into the circuit of Fig. 11.44 for these critical column

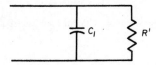

Fig. 11.44. Equivalent circuit of quartz crystal and fluid column for column lengths equal to $n\lambda/4$.

lengths. In this circuit, if the generator voltage, L_1, R_1, and C_1 are known, and the crystal voltage is measured, R' can readily be computed. A knowledge of R' leads to a knowledge of r_s, and if the variation of r_s with column length is known, one can solve for the absorption. Figure 11.45 shows experimental curves of the variation of the minimum voltage values in several liquids.

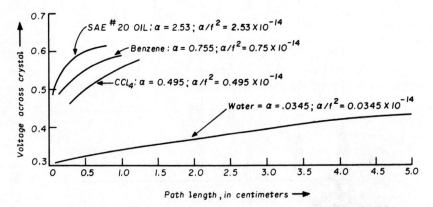

Fig. 11.45. Experimental absorption curves and values of α. *Note:* The value of $\beta = \omega/c$ is about 400 for these liquids at 10 megacycles, so the assumption $\alpha = \beta$ is justified.

11.5 Ultrasonic Experimentation

The combined Stokes-Kirchhoff expression for absorption is

$$\alpha = \frac{\omega^2}{2\rho C_0^2}\left(\frac{4}{3}\eta + \frac{\gamma-1}{C_p}K\right) \tag{11.51}$$

For a gas, we have the equality $\gamma p_0 = \rho c_0^2$ and the Stokes-Kirchhoff formula for absorption becomes

$$\frac{\alpha}{f^2} = \frac{2\pi^2}{\gamma p_0 C_0}\left(\frac{4}{3}\eta + \frac{\gamma-1}{C_p}K\right) \tag{11.52}$$

In this equation, p_0 is the mean pressure on the gas, and K is the thermal conductivity. The combined Eq. (11.52) is commonly known as the equation of the *classical absorption coefficient*. For liquids, the Kirchhoff heat-conduction term is negligible compared with the Stokes viscosity term.

This equation is borne out by experimental results for two categories of fluids: monatomic gases and liquids, and highly viscous liquids. Most other gases and liquids have a value of measured absorption much higher than predicted by the Stokes-Kirchhoff equation. The difference between the Stokes-Kirchhoff value and the measured value is called *the excess absorption*, and it is customary to ascribe excess absorption to molecular relaxation. Relaxational effects seem fairly well established in diatomic hydrogen, and very well established in oxygen and triatomic carbon dioxide. In general, it is agreed that observed effects in gases are rather well accounted for by the Stokes-Kirchhoff and relaxation theories. On the other hand, liquids are classified as *normal* or *abnormal* depending on the ratio of the measured value of absorption to the classical value. We have already mentioned that normal liquids include monatomic and highly viscous liquids. To these should be added the liquid phases of common elements which are gases at normal temperature and pressure: oxygen, nitrogen, and hydrogen. The anomalous liquids can be divided into three classes which are characterized by comparison of the experimental value of the absorption coefficient α_e and the classical value α_c. These classes are: (1) water and the alcohols, or associated polyatomic liquids; (2) unassociated polyatomic liquids such as benzene, carbon tetrachloride, and carbon disulfide; (3) organic acids and esters. The first group is characterized by a comparatively low α_e/α_c ratio (1.5 to 3). The coefficient α_e decreases with temperature, while α_e/α_c is virtually independent of temperature; the second and third groups are characterized by highly abnormal experimental values (3 to 5,000). The second group has an absorption coefficient which increases with temperature, while the absorption coefficient of the third group depends critically on the temperature. It is almost certain that the absorption in the second group is the effect of molecular relaxation.

Besides pure gases and liquids, measurements have been made in gases with impurities deliberately added and in liquid solutions. A knowledge of the mechanism of absorption in solutions is important because sea water is a solution of sodium chloride, magnesium sulfate, and traces of other elements. Although absorption measurements may be carried out in the open sea, the sources of error in open sea measurements are very great, as we shall see in the discussion of underwater sound. Measurements on magnesium sulfate solutions under the controlled conditions of the laboratory have been valuable aids to a knowledge of sea water absorption.

The more important of the results mentioned in the above paragraph are portrayed in a series of graphs in Figs. 11.51 to 11.55. Before concluding the discussion with these graphs it is necessary to describe the technique of measurements in gases. In Eq. (11.52) we have expressed the coefficient of absorption in terms of the frequency and the pressure. In our theoretical discussion we have been primarily concerned with the variation of the absorption coefficient with frequency. Unfortunately, it is a difficult matter to conduct ultrasonic measurements at many different frequencies. The quartz crystal must operate at its resonant frequency or at some harmonic thereof, and therefore only discrete points on the absorption vs. frequency curve can be obtained. Further, employing a crystal at a harmonic is not nearly so reliable as at its fundamental, so that one faces the possibility of changing to another transducer for each absorption test. Often this requires the disassembly of fairly complicated apparatus. For this reason, it was decided to make use of the fact that the theoretical absorption is also a function of the pressure. It is often useful to plot the function $\alpha p_0/f^2$ as ordinate vs. f/p_0 as abscissa. Examining the Stokes-Kirchhoff equation, it is evident that the function $\alpha p_0/f^2$ is a constant, and therefore should give a straight horizontal line when plotted, no matter what the abscissa. It turns out that the use of f/p_0 for the abscissa brings out most clearly the existence of relaxation effects. Conversely, if a straight horizontal line is obtained, the Stokes-Kirchhoff hypothesis is confirmed.

Figure 11.51 is a modified plot of $\alpha p_0/f^2$ vs. f/p_0 obtained in helium gas. For convenience $\alpha_e p_0/f^2$ will be abbreviated to α_e', and $\alpha_c p_0/f^2$ abbreviated to α_c'. It will be noted that α_e'/α_c' is constant out to a critical frequency, and then drops off proportionally to the frequency, exactly as predicted by the Stokes theory described in Art. 11.1.

Figure 11.52 shows the ratio of experimental to classical values for mercury, glycerin, and castor oil. In this figure, $\alpha_e' = \alpha_e/f^2$, and $\alpha_c' = \alpha_c/f^2$. It will be noted that the experimental points of the mercury and glycerin cluster about the line $(\alpha_e'/\alpha_c') = 1$, whereas the points for castor oil fall below this value above 4 megacycles, indicating that the relaxation frequency is about 4 megacycles. Although this bears out the general shape of the curve predicted by Stokes, the critical frequency computed from Stokes's theory is about 300 megacycles.

Figure 11.53 shows a relaxational effect in hydrogen determined by a velocity measurement. In this figure the square of the ratio of experimental to classical velocities is plotted against the frequency-pressure ratio.

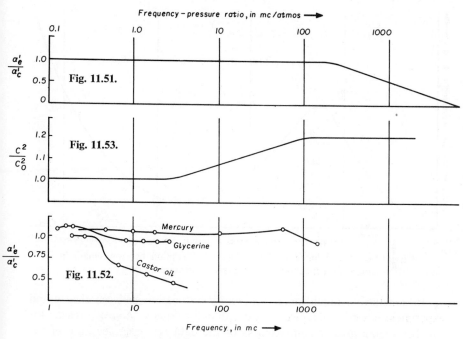

Fig. 11.51. Absorption-frequency variation of ratio of experimental to classical values in helium: $\alpha'_e = \alpha_e p_0/f^2$; $\alpha'_c = \alpha_c p f^2$.

Fig. 11.53. Velocity variation in hydrogen, showing relaxation effect from 10 to 100 megacycles/atmos: c = velocity at any frequency; c_0 = limiting velocity at zero frequency.

Fig. 11.52. Variation of experimental to classical ratio with frequency, for three "normal" liquids: mercury, glycerine, and castor oil.

Figure 11.54 is the result of one of the most famous of ultrasonic experiments. It shows the existence of both molecular relaxation and Stokes's viscosity in carbon dioxide. The relaxational peak occurs at about 20 kc for standard temperature and pressure. (If the carbon dioxide contains small traces of impurities, the peak is at higher frequencies.) Above the relaxation region, which is quite broad, there is a steady climb as predicted by the Stokes-Kirchhoff equation. In this figure, the absorption per wavelength is plotted against the frequency-pressure ratio. The relaxation was found by Fricke, and the classical region by Zartman. Knudsen and Fricke found that the presence of impurities changed the relaxation time.

The curves of absorption vs. frequency in fresh water, open sea water, and a magnesium sulfate solution of strength equal to that of sea water are shown in Fig. 11.55. These curves make the presumption very strong that absorption in sea water is caused by relaxation of the magnesium sulfate molecule. It should also be mentioned that a very strong relaxational effect in oxygen is shown by the curves of figure which was discussed in Chapter 9.

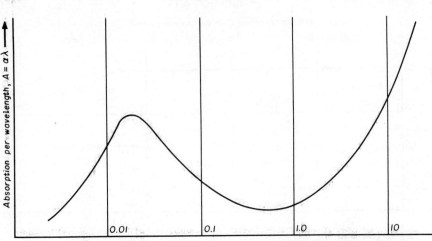

Fig. 11.54. Approximate relative values of absorption per wavelength in carbon dioxide as a function of the frequency-pressure ratio.

In conclusion, much more satisfactory correlation between theory and experiment has been obtained for gases than for liquids. A strong reason for this lies in the greater completeness of the data for gases, because of the possibility of pressure variation as contrasted with the laborious experimentation entailed in measurements in liquids at different frequencies. Some of it

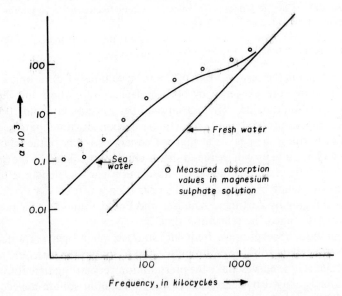

Fig. 11.55. Absorption in fresh water, open-sea water, and magnesium sulphate solution.

may be because a gas is a simpler structure than a liquid. On the whole, the theory of propagation of sound in gases is considered to be quite well established, whereas the theory of propagation in liquids is of a more tentative nature.

11.6 Waves of Finite Amplitude

In Art. 11.1, one of the simplifying assumptions of acoustic theory was suppressed, namely the relation $p = Bs$. This simple assumption was replaced by one in which the pressure was supposed to vary not only with the condensation, but also with the rate at which the condensation was taking place. In the discussion of waves of finite amplitude in perfect fluids, it is again assumed that the pressure is proportional to the condensation, but recognition is given to the fact that the bulk modulus will vary with the instantaneous pressure. A glance at the pressure-density curve of an adiabatic change in a gas (Fig. 11.61) will show that this is so. The bulk modulus is effectively given by the expression $B = \rho(\partial p'/\partial \rho')$, and it is evident that the slope of the curve is greater for high pressures than for low pressures. Therefore in the expression $p = Bs$, the value of B must be taken as variable with the pressure.

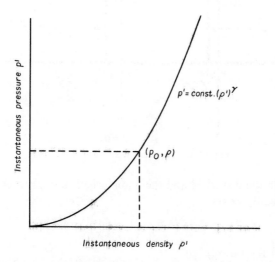

Fig. 11.61. Pressure-density curve of an adiabatic change in a gas.

The mathematical analysis of wave propagation becomes quite complicated when B is a function of the density and it will not be possible to give a rigorous treatment of the propagation of sound under this general condition. Indeed, though Rayleigh, Lamb, Rankine, Riemann, Earnshaw, and several other leading workers in the fields of acoustics and hydrodynamics have treated this problem, none of them has succeeded in deriving general equations sufficiently simple to be useful in an introductory treatment of the subject. In fact, the rigorous mathematical treatment of waves of large amplitude is very complex even when limited to the case of plane waves. The treatment to be followed, therefore, will investigate the fundamental relations to a degree sufficient to derive an equation that, up to a certain point, is an exact equation for the propagation of a compressional wave of any amplitude. This equation will then be discussed on a plausibility basis with two main objects in view: (1) to show that the velocity of propagation of disturbances of finite amplitude will increase with amplitude; (2) to show that distortion of the wave must occur, the wave tending to pass from a sinusoidal form to a form having a vertical front. Experimental results and examples will then be given to show that the theory is borne out.

The figure on which the analysis of waves of infinitesimal amplitude was based can also be used for waves of finite amplitude. It is repeated for convenience (Fig. 11.62). Since the same mass is included between the bounding

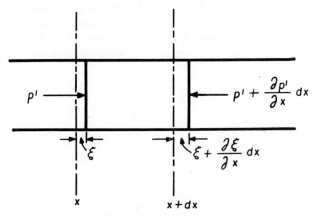

Fig. 11.62. Element of strained medium.

planes in both the disturbed and the undisturbed states, it is evident that the following equality exists:

$$\rho = \rho' \left(1 + \frac{\partial \xi}{\partial x}\right) \tag{11.61}$$

This gives for the ratio (ρ'/ρ),

$$\frac{\rho'}{\rho} = \left(1 + \frac{\partial \xi}{\partial x}\right)^{-1} \tag{11.62}$$

We therefore have for the condensation,

$$S = \frac{\rho' - \rho}{\rho} = \frac{1}{1 + \partial \xi/\partial x} - 1 = -\frac{\partial \xi/\partial x}{1 + \partial \xi/\partial x} \tag{11.63}$$

which is similar to that obtained in Art. 3.2, except for the additional term in the denominator.

For the dynamic equation, we first investigate the unbalanced force. As in the analysis of the third chapter, the expression $-S(\partial p/\partial x)dx$ is obtained. For the mass we have either $S\rho/dx$ or $S\rho'[1 + (\partial\xi/\partial x)]dx$. Let $(\partial^2\xi/\partial t^2)$ be the average particle acceleration over the element. The use of the average acceleration as a close approximation for the acceleration of each particle does not necessitate that the displacements are infinitesimal, but only that the length of the volume element is infinitesimal. We therefore arrive at the same dynamic equation derived in the third chapter:

$$\rho \frac{\partial^2\xi}{\partial t^2} = -\frac{\partial p}{\partial x} \tag{11.64}$$

It is thus seen that the somewhat more general expression for the condensation is the only mathematical complication that arises from the more general assumptions. This is enough, however, to make the subsequent analysis decidedly more difficult, simply because no well-known and easily interpreted solution can be obtained from the equations which develop from the combination of Eqs. (11.63) and (11.64).

Let us assume that the pressure, though a variable function of the density, is at least a function only of the density. For the partial derivative $(\partial p/\partial x)$ we can write

$$\frac{\partial p}{\partial x} = \frac{\partial p}{\partial \rho'} \frac{\partial \rho'}{\partial x}$$

From the relation between ρ' and ρ we obtain

$$\frac{\partial \rho'}{\partial x} = -\rho\left(1 + \frac{\partial\xi}{\partial x}\right)^{-2} \frac{\partial^2\xi}{\partial x^2}$$

and finally:

$$-\frac{1}{\rho}\frac{\partial p}{\partial x} = \left(\frac{\rho'}{\rho}\right)^2 \frac{\partial^2\xi}{\partial x^2} \frac{\partial p}{\partial \rho'} \tag{11.65}$$

It is now necessary to obtain an expression for $(\partial p/\partial \rho')$. We shall assume the adiabatic law:

$$\frac{p'}{p_0} = \left(\frac{\rho'}{\rho}\right)^\gamma$$

We therefore have

$$\frac{\partial p}{\partial \rho'} = \frac{\gamma p_0}{\rho}\left(\frac{\rho'}{\rho}\right)^{\gamma-1} \tag{11.66}$$

Substituting the appropriate equations in Eq. (11.64) we obtain

$$\frac{\partial^2\xi}{\partial t^2} = \frac{\gamma p_0}{\rho} \cdot \frac{\partial^2\xi/\partial x^2}{(1 + \partial\xi/\partial x)^{\gamma+1}} \tag{11.67}$$

This last equation may, with small approximation, be written,

$$\frac{\partial^2\xi}{\partial t^2} = \left[\frac{\gamma p_0}{\rho}(1 + s)^{\gamma+1}\right]\frac{\partial^2\xi}{\partial x^2} \tag{11.68}$$

In this form, it resembles the elementary equation (Eq. 3.23) in which the coefficient of the second space partial is a constant equal to the square of the wave velocity. Actually, Eq. (11.68) is not strictly a wave equation at all.* However, though it cannot be solved formally in any convenient fashion, it may be interpreted to give the most important properties of finite amplitude waves without formal solution. It states that *each part* of the progressive disturbance possesses its own proper velocity of propagation and that this velocity of propagation is a function of the magnitude of the condensation at the point. It is immediately evident that the wave will be propagated faster in high-pressure regions than in regions of lower pressure, and that therefore the wave must become distorted as it advances. Several authors have shown that the wave should become very steep as it progresses, theoretically approaching a vertical front. A. B. Wood has pointed out that this is almost exactly what happens when sea waves approach a beach. Because the forward velocity of the crests is greater than that of other parts of the waves, the wave fronts become steeper and steeper, until they curl over and break.

If the change in form is ignored, and the factor in the brackets on the right side of Eq. (11.68) is interpreted as the square of the wave velocity of a finite amplitude wave (e.g. suppose a compressive pulse), the equation predicts that the velocity should increase rapidly with the value of condensation. Some very interesting confirmations of this prediction have been obtained by W. Payman, H. Robinson, and W. C. F. Shepherd, who photographed a pressure pulse emerging from the mouth of a tube, the pulse being generated by the explosion of a gaseous mixture in the tube. They obtained instantaneous

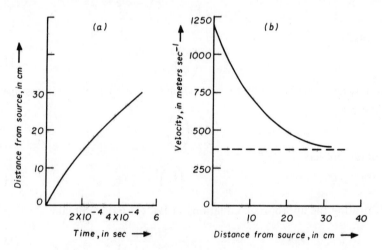

Fig. 11.63. Velocity of a sound pulse of finite amplitude.

---

* At least, not in the sense that we have used the term heretofore. Our definition implied that the shape of the traveling disturbance remained unchanged.

spark photographs of the pressure pulse at different instants after leaving the tube, and were thus able to compute the velocity at any instant. The computations showed a steady fall in the velocity of propagation of the pulse, which would be expected, since the amplitude is diminishing by spreading of the wave front, as well as by frictional losses. A plot of their raw data is shown in Fig. 11.63(a) and the velocity computed from these data is plotted in (b) of the figure. It will be noted that the velocity for the high amplitudes that occur as the pulse is just leaving the tube, while it approaches the small-amplitude value as the distance from the source increases, is about three times the measured small-amplitude velocity in air.* Cole has given a very complete modern treatment of the propagation of large amplitude waves, such as shock waves and explosive waves, in his text *Underwater Explosions*, Princeton University Press, Princeton, 1948.

11.7 Dispersion and Group Velocity

Dispersion may be described as the variation of velocity of propagation with the frequency of a sinusoidal wave. In general, a disturbance may consist of several frequencies, as white light consists of a mixture of all visible frequencies. It is known that dispersion accounts for the fact that white light can be split by a prism into its various components, because the various components travel at different speeds through the material of the prism, and hence are refracted at different angles. Let us assume that we have a complex sound wave, consisting of several frequency components in the frequency region of carbon dioxide in which a variation of velocity with frequency occurs, and consider how this complex wave will be propagated through the carbon dioxide. For simplicity, it will be sufficient to consider the propagation of *two* components which have different velocities of propagation. We say that each frequency component has a different *wave velocity*. This indicates that the crests of each frequency component are propagated through the gas with their proper velocity, a velocity that has been thoroughly discussed in the earlier chapters of this text. However, the superposition of the two waves will give a sum wave, in which crests occur at varying points, since only occasionally will it happen that a crest of one component will be coincident with the crest of the other. Let us consider the velocity with which a crest of the compound wave will propagate through the gas. If many frequency components were considered, the components would be called a "group", and the velocity of the crests of the group would be called the "group velocity." It is somewhat trivial to call the pair of components under consideration a "group," but it will be seen that if the two extreme frequencies are considered, and the situation examined for this pair, the main essentials of the problem will have been taken into account. The analysis of an entire group of frequencies proceeds

* That is, 34,500 cm/sec.

similarly to the analysis of noise, which was discussed in Chapter 8, and need not concern us here. The present discussion is not unlike that of "beats" in Art. 1.14, and indeed there are many similarities, both mathematical and physical. For example, it is implicit in both cases that the frequency difference of the components is small compared with the mean frequency. To emphasize the similarity with beats, we shall first analyze the beat effect between two *waves* of different frequencies, but having the same velocity. It will be remembered that our former analysis of beats involved two *vibrations* of different frequencies, and hence the space element was missing in the problem. If we suppose that the two waves are plane waves proceeding in the positive-x direction, we have for the sum wave,

$$\xi = A[\cos{(\omega_1 t - k_1 x)} + \cos{(\omega_2 t - k_2 x)}] \qquad (11.71)$$

By trigonometric identities, this can be converted to the form,

$$\xi = 2A \cos{\left(\frac{\omega_1 - \omega_2}{2}t - \frac{k_1 - k_2}{2}x\right)} \cos{\left(\frac{\omega_1 + \omega_2}{2}t - \frac{k_1 + k_2}{2}x\right)} \quad (11.72)$$

The second cosine factor represents a wave very similar to the original waves, whose frequency and wavelength are an average of the two initial values, and which moves with a velocity $(\omega_1 + \omega_2)/(k_1 + k_2)$. This is practically the same as the original velocities, and indeed is the same if $\omega_1/k_1 = \omega_2/k_2$. But the first cosine factor, which changes much more slowly with respect to x and t, may be regarded as a varying amplitude. Thus we have for the resultant a wave of approximately the same wavelength and frequency, but with an amplitude which changes with time and distance. The appearance of the group at any instant will resemble the beat wave form of Fig. 1.141. The actual disturbance lies between the two profile curves, cutting the x axis at regular intervals, and touching alternately the upper and lower profile curves. Either profile curve has an equation of the form:

$$y = 2A \cos{\left(\frac{\omega_1 - \omega_2}{2}t - \frac{k_1 - k_2}{2}x\right)}$$

If the velocities of the two component waves are the same, so that $\omega_1/k_1 = \omega_2/k_2$, then the wave system shown in Fig. 1.141 moves forward steadily without change of shape. If this wave were to pass the ear of a listener, he would be aware of a frequency equal to the mean of the two component frequencies, but with an amplitude fluctuating with a frequency twice that of the profile curve. This frequency is just the difference of the two component frequencies.

If the velocities of the two component waves are not the same ($\omega_1/k_1 \neq \omega_2/k_2$), then the profile curves move with a speed $(\omega_1 - \omega_2)/(k_1 - k_2)$, which is different from that of the more rapidly oscillating part (the mean of the two component velocities). That is, the crests of the sum wave have a relative velocity with respect to the profile wave, so that each individual crest decreases and increases its amplitude as it moves along. This causes a gradual change in the shape of the profile itself, and it can be shown in general that the only wave form that can be propagated without change of shape in a dispersive medium is a purely sinusoidal wave form, and even this must be of infinitesimal amplitude, in view of the findings of the previous article.

The velocity of the profile curves in Fig. 1.141 is known as the group velocity U, of the pair of waves. If the two component velocities are almost equal, the differences $(\omega_1 - \omega_2)$ and $(k_1 - k_2)$ are of the order of infinitesimal quantities, and we can write

$$U = \frac{\omega_1 - \omega_2}{k_1 - k_2} = \frac{d\omega}{dk} \tag{11.73}$$

Since $k = 2\pi/\lambda$, this may also be obtained in terms of wavelength:

$$U = \frac{d\omega}{dk} = \frac{d(kc)}{dk} = c + k\frac{dc}{dk} = c + k\frac{dc}{d\lambda}\frac{d\lambda}{dk}$$

$$= c + k\left(\frac{-2\pi}{k^2}\right)\frac{dc}{d\lambda} = c - \lambda\frac{dc}{d\lambda} \tag{11.74}$$

Equation (11.74) shows that the group velocity is less than the mean wave velocity if the wave velocity increases with increasing wavelength, and is greater than the mean wave velocity if the wave velocity decreases with increasing wavelength. It is true that dispersion is not of great importance in ordinary applications of acoustics, but the distinction between wave velocity and group velocity is an important one in general wave theory. As an example, in optical measurements of the speed of propagation of light in a given medium, it is important to know whether the measurement made is one of wave velocity or group velocity. In the propagation of electromagnetic waves in wave guides, it is found that the wave velocity can exceed the velocity $c = 3 \times 10^{10}$ cm/sec, which Einstein assumed to be the absolute limit of velocity of propagation. However, it is found that where the wave velocity exceeds c, the group velocity will be less than c, and by the same ratio, such that the product of the wave velocity and the group velocity always equals the square of the velocity of propagation of electromagnetic waves in free space. It turns out that the group velocity is the velocity at which energy is carried forward in the guide, and this velocity is always less than c. Thus the concept of group velocity resolves a difficulty which apparently involves the contradiction of a fundamental physical law.

References

Vigoreux, *Ultrasonics*, Wiley, New York, 1952.

Kinsler and Frey, *Fundamentals of Acoustics*, Wiley, New York, 1950.

Markham, Beyer, and Lindsay, "Absorption of Sound in Fluids," *Revs. Mod. Phys.*, **23**, 353-411 (1951).

Cole, *Underwater Explosions*, Princeton University Press, Princeton, 1948.

Problems

1. A square force pulse of magnitude 10 dynes and duration 200 millisec operates on a system having a stiffness constant of 10^4 dynes/cm, and a damping constant of 10^2 dynes/sec. The system starts from rest. Find the equation of the instantaneous displacement and plot the displacement for the first 3 sec of motion. What is the value of the relaxation time?

2. (a) Find the theoretical value of the Stokes relaxation time for the substances listed in the table with their physical constants at standard temperature and pressure.

Substance	Bulk Modulus	Density	Viscosity, poises
Water	2.18×10^{10} dynes/cm^2	1.0 g/cm^3	0.01
Castor oil....	Approx. 2×10^{10}	0.95	10.00
Oxygen......	$1.40 \times 1.013 \times 10^6$	1.43×10^{-3}	1.9×10^{-4}
Helium	$1.66 \times 1.013 \times 10^6$	0.18×10^{-3}	1.9×10^{-4}

(b) Find the theoretical velocity and absorption in these substances as predicted by Stokes's theory for frequencies less than the critical value determined by the relaxation time, and at frequencies twice that of the relaxation times characteristic of the fluids.

(c) Find the relaxation times of oxygen and helium at 0.01 atmosphere.

3. (a) Develop Eq. (11.32) for the effective capacitance across the circuit consisting of a capacitor in parallel with an R-C circuit.

(b) Given a square voltage pulse of duration 1 μsec, plot the instantaneous charge across the circuit with the following values of the parameters: $\tau/C_i = 1$ ohm, $C_i = 1$ μf, $C_\infty = 1.5$ μf.

(c) With the same values of the parameters, find the phase angle between the voltage and current at 100 kc, 1 megacycle, 10 megacycles.

(d) Plot the instantaneous charge for pulses of 0.01 μsec and 100 μsec.

4. In the critical curves for carbon dioxide, the value of c_0 is 2.58×10^4 cm/sec and the value of c_∞ is 2.68×10^4 cm/sec. Show that these velocity values correspond approximately to the following values of the ratio of specific heats: $\gamma_0 = 8/6, \gamma_\infty = 7/5$. Carbon dioxide is a triatomic molecule. Discuss the modes of vibration which exist in carbon dioxide at high and low frequencies.

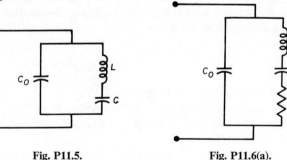

Fig. P11.5.   Fig. P11.6(a).

5. (a) Plot the reactance curve for the circuit of Fig. P11.5 if the circuit parameters have the values $C_0 = 50\ \mu\mu f$, $L = 1$ henry, $C = 0.01\ \mu\mu f$.

(b) Find the frequency at which the reactance is zero, and the frequency at which the reactance is infinite.

(c) Find the Q of the L-C branch if it contains a resistance of 30 ohms in series with the inductance and capacitance.

6. If a quartz crystal having the circuit of Fig. P11.6(a) is driven at its series resonant frequency, and resonates into a fluid column of resonant length, (i.e. such that the acoustic reactance of the column is zero), the effective resistance of the L-C-R branch will be increased by the amount dSr_s, where d is the effective coupling constant of the crystal, S is the effective area of the radiating surface of the crystal, and r_s is the specific acoustic resistance of the column. When a liquid is used in the interferometer, the added term is much greater than that caused by internal losses in the crystal, and may be taken as the total resistance. Further, if the crystal is driven at the frequency at which $X_L = X_C$, the circuit reduces to that of Fig. P11.6(b). Show that the circuit of P11.6(a) is equivalent to the series circuit shown in Fig. P11.6(c).

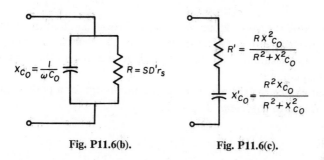

Fig. P11.6(b).   Fig. P11.6(c).

7. Show that, if $R \geq 10 X_{C_0}$ in the circuit of Fig. P11.6(b), the components of the equivalent series circuit have the values, accurate to 1 %: $X'_{C_0} = X_{C_0}$, $R' = X^2_{C_0}/R$. If $X_{C_0} = 100$ ohms, find R' for the following values of R: 1 megohm, 10^4 ohms, 10^3 ohms. *Ans.* 0.01 ohm, 1 ohm, 10 ohms.

8. (a) The circuit of Fig. P11.8 is tuned to the frequency at which $X_{L_0} = X_{C_0}$, and the values are chosen such that each of these reactances is 100 ohms. $R_0 = 2$ ohms. Find the value of the circuit Q if $R = \infty$. Find the

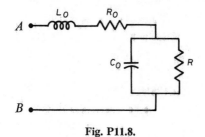

Fig. P11.8.

value of the circuit Q for values of R/X_{C_0} equal to 1,000, 100, and 10 respectively. *Ans.* 50, 47.6, 33.3, 8.3.

(b) If a voltage E at the frequency $f = 1/2\pi\sqrt{L_0C_0}$ is applied between the terminals A and B, the voltage across the capacitor C_0 is approximately QE as long as the condition $R \geq 10X_{C_0}$ holds. Plot the voltage across C_0 as a function of R for values of R greater than 1,000 ohms.

(c) If a water column of very great length loads the crystal, the radiation impedance will be approximately $1.5 \times 10^5 S$ (i.e. ρcS), where S is the effective area of the radiating surface of the crystal. If $S = 5$ cm² and the voltage across C_0 is $\frac{2}{3}$ that which would be obtained for $R = \infty$, find the value of the effective coupling constant d. *Ans.* $d = 1.33 \times 10^{-2}$.

(d) With the value of the coupling constant found in (c), find the value of r_s which will give an equivalent resistance R of 1,000 ohms. Find the voltage across C_0 for this value of r_s. *Ans.* $r_s = 0.1$ $\rho c = 1.5 \times 10^4$, $E_{C_0} = 8.3E$.

9. (a) Refer to the expression found for r_s in Problem 3.11 and show that the maximum and minimum values of r_s for unity reflection coefficient will be

$$r_{s_{Max}} = \rho c \frac{1 + e^{-2r\alpha}}{1 - e^{-2r\alpha}}, \qquad r_{s_{Min}} = \rho c \frac{1 - e^{-2r\alpha}}{1 + e^{-2r\alpha}}$$

(b) Assuming the same circuit values as in Problem 8, find the path length which will give the voltage found in part (d) of Problem 8, assuming a value of 0.5 for α, and assuming that this voltage is read at one of the minima of r_s. *Ans.* $r = 0.20$ cm.

(c) What will be the voltage reading at a minimum for a path length three times that found in (b)? *Ans.* $E_{C_0} = 24.9E$.

Chapter 12

UNDERWATER SOUND

The fundamental equations of acoustics which we have derived in the earlier chapters of this book are independent of the medium in which the sound is propagated. However, in most of our applications we have either tacitly or expressly taken air as the medium of transmission, since this is obviously the case of most frequent application. In Chapter 11 we have seen that several other substances have interest in ultrasonic experimentation. In this chapter we study the acoustic properties of the second practical medium of sound transmission, and the influence of these properties on underwater applications.

In contrast to the propagation of sound in air, the following are the most important points regarding the transmission of sound in water.

1. The velocity is about five times as high as in air. The wavelength for any frequency is proportionately greater, and directive elements need to be correspondingly larger to give the same directional patterns.

2. The characteristic impedance of sea water is greater than that of air by a factor of 3,700 to 1. In general this fact makes it easier to radiate larger powers into water than into air. However, for equal acoustic pressures, the intensities will be inverse by the same ratio.

3. The attenuation of sound in water is very much less than it is in air. Consequently, long-distance transmission is quite possible in water, and much consideration is given to making the range as great as practicable. This is not the case in transmission in air, where most important applications do not involve transmission over large distances. Paradoxically, this makes absorption an important consideration in underwater transmission.

4. Because of the distance of transmission possible in underwater sound, certain phenomena which can usually be neglected in air transmission have to be taken into account in underwater sound. The most important of these is *refraction*. Refraction is caused by bending of sound rays because of velocity changes which occur with changes of water temperature and pressure, the temperature changes being by far the more important of the two. Refraction in most cases causes the sound rays to curve away from the surface, and often decreases greatly the useful range of undersea transmission between two points near the surface.

5. Noise and reverberation are obstacles to reception of underwater signals, as in air. Noise sources are analogous to those prevalent in air, but

371

reverberation arises in a somewhat different manner, though it has about the same effect practically. Reverberation is most significant in *pulse* transmission and reception.

6. Unlike sound transmission in air, which is wide band in nature, underwater sound applications very often make use of a rather narrow transmission band.

The differences between water and air transmission may perhaps be illustrated most readily by comparing intensities, pressures, particle amplitudes, and particle velocities in the two media for typical sound levels, assuming plane waves.

Specific Acoustic Impedances:

Sea water: 153,500 g/cm² sec
Air: 41.5 g/cm² sec

Particle Velocity for Unit Acoustic Pressure (1 dyne/cm²):

Water: 6×10^{-6} cm/sec
Air: 2.4×10^{-2} cm/sec

Particle Amplitude at 800 cycles for Unit Acoustic Pressure:

Water: 1.2×10^{-9} cm
Air: 4.8×10^{-6} cm

Intensities for Unit Acoustic Pressure:

Water: 6×10^{-6} erg/sec/cm²
Air: 2.4×10^{-2} erg/sec/cm²

Pressure for Unit Intensity (1 erg/sec/cm²):

Water: 390 dynes/cm²
Air: 6.4 dynes/cm²

The foregoing will serve to emphasize the differences which will be found to exist between apparatus used in air and that used in water. Considering transmission, it will be found that large forces are not met with in air, but large motions must be produced to radiate intensities of any magnitude, while in water, it is the pressure which must be large for high intensity radiation, the displacements necessary being comparatively small. Therefore underwater apparatus is extremely rugged in character, and this is aside from the fact that it must also be able to withstand the high static pressures to which it will be subjected in undersea use. On the other hand, it does not have to permit the motion necessary in air apparatus.

In order to present the main topics of underwater sound in something approaching a connected fashion, we shall first describe what is probably the foremost application of underwater sound, that of echo ranging. The individual problems that are introduced in this discussion will then be investigated separately in subsequent paragraphs.

12.1 Echo Ranging

By echo ranging we mean the location of an undersea object, and the measurement of the distance between the object and the source. It is similar in many respects to the pulse method of velocity measurement, with the difference that the distance is known and the velocity is computed in the former, while the reverse is true in echo ranging. A narrow beam is used for azimuth measurement, this measurement being further refined by a device called a *split transducer*, which is similar in principle to the location of sound sources by binaural hearing.

Omitting for the moment consideration of practical details of precise timing circuits and devices for accurate localization, we shall first solve the problem of predicting the strength of the returning echo, given the source power and the directivity of the source. By this means, we can arrive at an idea of approximate ranges to be expected of the pulse method. The returning echo strength is a function of the following:

1. Divergence according to the inverse square law
2. The directivity index of the transducer
3. The attenuation due to absorption
4. An effective loss due to refraction
5. The size and material of the target

We shall first restrict the problem somewhat by considering only the divergence according to the inverse square law and the size of the target. Once this problem has been solved, the other effects can be considered without undue difficulty.

If we let I_0 be the intensity at unit distance (1 m) from the source, then I_0/r^2 is the intensity at distance r (meters) from the source. Let us suppose that there is at distance r a perfectly reflecting object of cross-sectional area S which reradiates the wave equally in all directions. The power intercepted by this obstacle will be $I_0 S/r^2$ and the intensity of the reflected wave at the source will be

$$I_e = \frac{I_0 S}{4\pi r^4} = \frac{I_0}{r^4}\left(\frac{d'}{4}\right)^2$$

where d' is the target diameter.

In decibel notation,

$$I_e = I_0 - 40 \log r + 20 \log d'/4$$

In this notation, the term $40 \log r$ is the loss due to divergence, and the term $20 \log d'/4$ is called *target strength T*. It is regarded as a transmission gain in the overall system.

Influence of Refraction, Absorption and Directivity. Because refraction in most cases causes a curvature of sound rays away from the surface, the returning echo is usually weaker than would be expected from the inverse square law. As we shall see in a subsequent paragraph, the refraction phenomenon is quite complicated, and it is almost impossible to give a general expression for this loss. Analytically, it is handled by adding in a certain number of decibels which depend primarily on the temperature gradient of the water.

The value of the absorption coefficient for sound waves in sea water is fairly well established. Once the frequency of transmission is known, the absorption loss can be written as $2\alpha r$, where α is the coefficient of absorption in decibels per meter, and r is the distance from the source to the obstacle.

In our study of radiation from a piston, we saw that the directivity factor is a function of the ratio between the radius of the piston and the wavelength of the sound, and is defined as the ratio between the intensity at a point on the axis of a directive source to the intensity that would exist at the same point for an isotropic source of the same power. The "directivity index" is the decibel expression of this ratio. Consequently the directivity index acts as a transmission gain.

Limitations on Transmitted Power. Atmospheric pressure at sea level is approximately 10^6 dynes/cm². It is quite possible to produce an acoustic pressure in water in excess of this figure. However, the result is a negative instantaneous pressure in the water, and since water will support very little tension, a phenomenon called cavitation takes place, which is very injurious to regular transmission of sound, and gives rise to noise. Consequently, it is not advisable to allow the instantaneous acoustic pressure to exceed 10^6 dynes/cm², which means that the maximum rms value is 0.7×10^6 dynes/cm², or 117 db re 1 dyne/cm².

Minimum Acceptable Strength of Reflected Signals. The average value of sea noise is a function of the state of the sea, but is of the order of 1 dyne/cm². While it is possible to recognize signals below the ambient background, we shall take this figure (1 dyne/cm²) as the criterion of acceptable received signal strength. Thus our problem is to achieve a strength of zero decibels (re 1 dyne/cm²) in the signal reflected back from an underwater target.

Over-all Equation for Echo Signal Strength. Taking account of all our gains and losses,

$$I_e = I_0 + d - 40 \log r - 2\alpha r - 2A + T$$

where I_e = signal strength of the echo signal in decibels, I_0 = intensity of the transmitted signal at a distance of 1 m from the source, d = directivity index, representing the number of decibels gain due to the directivity of the source, A = transmission anomaly, representing the number of decibels loss due to refraction, r = distance in meters to the target, α = absorption coefficient for sea water in decibels per meter, T = target strength, representing the number of decibels gain from the target.

Sample problem in echo ranging. Given a piston radiator of radius 30 cm emitting a 24 kc wave with an intensity of 110 db at a distance of 1 m from the source. Given a target with size comparable with that of a sphere of diameter 40 m. Neglect the transmission anomaly due to refraction. Calculate the strength of the echo signal for a range of 1,000 m and for a range of 10,000 m, taking a value of $\alpha = 3 \times 10^{-3}$ db/m for the absorption coefficient. Calculate the theoretical range if minimum usable echo strength is zero db re 1 dyne/cm².

Solution:

1. *Gains:*

    Target strength:

    $$T = 20 \log (d'/4) = 20 \text{ db}$$

    Directivity (see Eq. 4.105a):

    $$d = 10 \log D \approx 10 \log\left(\frac{4\pi^2 a^2}{\lambda^2}\right) \approx 10 \log 10^4 \approx 40 \text{ db}$$

    $$\left(\lambda \approx \frac{150,000}{24,000} \approx 6 \text{ cm}\right)$$

    Total gain, 60 db

2. *Losses:*

    Divergence:

    $$40 \log r = 120 \text{ db} \quad (1,000 \text{ m})$$
    $$= 160 \text{ db} \quad (10,000 \text{ m})$$

    Absorption:

    $$2\alpha r \quad = \; 6 \text{ db} \quad (1,000 \text{ m})$$
    $$= 60 \text{ db} \quad (10,000 \text{ m})$$

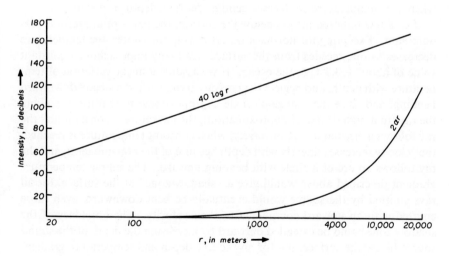

Fig. 12.11. Diffusion and absorption losses as a function of r, the distance from the source. The absorption coefficient $\alpha = 3 \times 10^{-3}$ db/meter.

3. *Echo signal strength:*

    $$I_e = 110 + 20 + 40 - 120 - 6 = 44 \text{ db} \quad (1,000 \text{ m})$$
    $$I_e = 110 + 20 + 40 - 160 - 60 = -50 \text{ db} \quad (10,000 \text{ m})$$

4. *Maximum range:*

Allowing I_e to be zero, we have:

$$(40 \log r) + 2\,(3 \times 10^{-3})r = 170$$

This may most readily be solved for r by plotting the functions $40 \log r$ and $2\alpha r$ and solving graphically as in Fig. 12.11. The range obtained from the plot is approximately 4,000 m. It must be remembered, however, that refraction was neglected, and this should not be taken as a typical range.

12.2 Refraction and the Transmission Anomaly

The propagation of sound in water is an extremely complicated phenomenon, principally because of the inhomogeneity of the medium. Whatever general formulas exist have been arrived at after simplifying assumptions which approximate the conditions found in practice. However, even with the simplifications which are introduced in an effort to emphasize the most significant factors, these formulas are still quite complex. Hence in our investigation we shall restrict the treatment to the two predominant causes of refraction, temperature and pressure, and shall further simplify by assuming that the velocity is a linear function of the temperature. The formula which we shall take for the velocity of sound in sea water is as follows:

$$c = 1{,}450 + 3.8t + 0.018h \text{ m/sec}$$

where t = temperature in degrees centigrade, h = depth in meters.

For a few hundred meters below the surface, the temperature term is predominant. Excepting for northern waters during the winter, the temperature decreases as one recedes from the surface, gradually approaching a constant value of about $-3.7°C$ in the ocean. If we assume a linear variation of temperature with depth, and neglect the pressure term, we find a steady downward bending, and since the change of angle is proportional to the distance along the ray (to a high degree of approximation), the curvature is constant and the ray follows a circular arc. Conversely, when constant temperature is reached, the velocity increases linearly with depth because of the pressure term, and the ray follows an arc of a circle with bending upward. The simple temperature gradient described above would give a "shadow zone" at the surface, for all rays emitted by the source would eventually be bent downward, even those emitted with an upward component to their velocity. The boundary of the shadow zone could be extended outward by increasing the depth of the sound source below the surface, but for any source depth and temperature gradient there would be some range beyond which no rays could penetrate, except those at great depths.

With more complicated temperature gradients, a great variety of shadow zones can be produced. Saby and Nyborg[*] have studied several temperature

---

[*] Saby and Nyborg, *J. Acoust. Soc. Am.*, **18**, 316-322 (1946).

gradients and have found that it is possible for complex shadow-zone structures to exist in which zones of silence are intermixed with zones of above-
normal transmission.

The above findings are based on geometric acoustics, and predict zero
radiation into the shadow zone. However, Pekeris* has broadened the problem to study the intensity of diffracted radiation which penetrates into the
shadow zone, and its dependence on distance from the source and on frequency. He finds that the intensity falls off essentially exponentially with
distance into the shadow zone. Evans (Fig. 12.21) remarks that the normal
effective limit for echo ranging as imposed by refraction is several thousand
yards, but that a large temperature gradient, such as is found in the tropics,
may restrict the range to less than 1,000 yards, while Kinsler and Frey give a

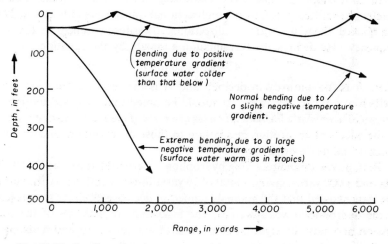

Fig. 12.21. Bending of underwater sound beams, caused by various water-
temperature gradients.

figure of 30 db as a typical drop within the shadow zone, and show how the
simple case of zero temperature gradient to a certain depth, and constant
temperature gradient beyond, give a zone of silence located vertically between
two zones of transmission, and extending within *900 yards* of the source.

Upward bending of the beam takes place when the surface water is colder
than the water below. This may actually be an advantage to echo ranging,
since the beam will be successively reflected from the water surface. In this
case, the only range limitation is that caused by spreading and absorption.

One instance of beneficial refraction is the phenomenon of deep sea ranging, in which abnormally high ranges may be achieved. If a ray is emitted at
the upper boundary of the constant-temperature level with a small upward

---

* Pekeris, *J. Acoust. Soc. Am.*, **18**, 295 (1946).

angle, it will ultimately be bent downward again because of the temperature gradient, while if it has a small downward angle it will be bent upward because of the pressure gradient. It may readily be shown that where there is a velocity gradient in a medium, any ray tends to the level of minimum velocity. The rays thus spread out in a circle rather than a sphere, and the attenuation due to spreading obeys the inverse first-power law for intensity rather than the inverse square law. This fact makes for tremendous ranges. The sound from a detonation at the minimum-velocity level can be picked up at distances of over a thousand miles by sensitive listening apparatus. The formation of sound channels can also occur closer to the surface if peculiar temperature gradients occur, and has been suggested as an explanation of abnormally good transmission.

In an attempt to make a systematic study of the transmission anomaly, Sheehy transmitted pulses from nondirectional transducers radiating at 24 kc, and picked them up with nondirectional transducers tuned to the same frequency. He defined the transmission anomaly by the equation

$$A = H - 20 \log r$$

where A is the anomaly in decibels and H is the total transmission loss in decibels at a range of r yards. It should be noted that by this definition, *the transmission anomaly includes all losses in excess of the inverse square loss*; that is, the effects of absorption in addition to those of refraction, and any other losses of unknown origin.

Both projector and receiving hydrophones were held at depths of 150, 300, 500, and 1,000 yards, giving a total of 16 variations in depth below the surface. The data showed that the anomaly tended to decrease as either the projector or the hydrophone was lowered. The following are averages of the transmission anomaly for eight combinations of emitter depth and hydrophone depth.

Hydrophone (ft)

Emitter (ft)	150	300	500	1,000
150	16	11	..	..
300	10	5	..	..
500	..	6	8	..
1,000	..	6	..	3

In this series of experiments, trials were also made with both emitter and hydrophone 16 ft below the surface. However, the temperature was so variable close to the surface that results obtained were judged to be completely unreliable. For instance, the depth at which the temperature was 0.3°F less than the surface temperature changed by as much as 45 ft during one of the measurement runs. Conversely, at depths of 500 and 1,000 feet, the thermal gradients are small and on the average probably exert little influence on transmission. It is likely that 3 db per 1,000 yd is close to the minimal value for the attenuation of 24 kc sound in the sea, while 16 db per 1,000 yd seems to be the highest that is likely to be encountered.

Two interesting cases showing the unpredictability of the transmission anomaly are shown in Fig. 12.22. In curve A, the anomaly increases rapidly out to 700 yd, but much less rapidly beyond this range. This phenomenon is very common for 24 kc sound near the surface under thermal conditions causing sharp downward refraction of the beam. In these cases sound is often

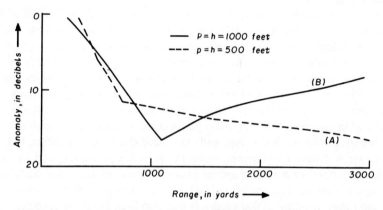

Fig. 12.22. An anomalous case, showing transmission by direct path, and a decreasing transmission anomaly beyond 1,000 yd. For curve B the projector and hydrophone were both 1,000 ft. deep. For curve A the projector and hydrophone were both 500 ft. deep. The sound frequency was 24 kc for both cases.

observed well into the shadow zone which would be expected to exist on the assumption of a ray theory of refraction. Although attempts have been made to explain this phenomenon by diffraction and by scattering from a deep-scattering layer, the results shown in curve A are 30-40 db higher than can be explained by scattering theory, and it is judged that some other mechanism, at present unknown, is responsible.

In curve B, the anomaly increases out to 1,000 yd, and then decreases out to 2,700 yd. This phenomenon has been noted in other studies of 24 kc transmission near the surface, and is believed to be associated with conditions which produce *sound channels*, thereby causing the energy to be relatively concentrated in certain regions.

12.3 Noise and Reverberation in the Sea

There is one type of noise that is always present at sea. This is the noise that arises from the turbulence characteristic of the sea itself, caused by the wind, weather, rain, and the action of the waves. Marine life is also a cause of noise. During the second World War, much attention was given to the noise level from this source, and naval sound men became highly aware of the noise caused by shrimp, croakers, and other marine animals. Seagoing traffic is a third cause of noise, although on the high seas this source is not likely to interfere greatly with the tactical use of echo-ranging systems. It has been stated that the average over-all value of sea noise may reach 15 db re 1 dyne/cm^2, and in especially quiet areas may be as little as -15 db. Special efforts are made to find areas with very low background noise for undersea tests of sound levels.

In addition to these external noise sources, there is the self-noise of the vessel, which may interfere with reception of the sound reflected from underwater obstacles. Finally there is the reverberation in the surrounding region caused by the emitted pulse. Reverberation is caused by reflections from the bottom and the surface, similar to that found in architectural acoustics, but in addition there is an effect called volume reverberation resulting from the presence of *scatterers* in the sea. It is thought that most of these scatterers are biological in nature. A *reverberation group* at the University of California, in collaboration with the Navy, has made extensive studies of this effect, but the results are not easy to interpret, since the *reverberation level* used in these studies is defined in a rather special manner. Perhaps the most significant finding was that the reverberation level had fallen to the ambient noise level for echo range in excess of 500 yards. It was also found that the reverberation level is proportional to the intensity and width of the pulse.

Under representative conditions, water noise, including reverberation noise, has a spectrum that decreases with frequency, and therefore has a low value at the high frequencies used for echo ranging. In addition, high frequencies bring about a narrower sound beam, and in deep water, surface and bottom reflections can be avoided by the use of such a beam, so that only the volume contribution of reverberation adds to the ambient noise.

12.4 Location of Targets in Azimuth

The popular conception of an echo ranging system has been created by comparing the sound beam to a searchlight. This is a good analogy if it is not carried too far. In the case of the searchlight, one either sees the target or does not. One either knows exactly where it is or has no idea at all. No sound beam can approach the narrowness of a searchlight beam, and as a result, when a signal is received in echo ranging with a directive beam, it is known that the target is within some solid angle, but this information is not so precise as is required. One might refine the information by swinging the axis of the beam through some angle, and noting the direction which gives the strongest echo signal, but this is time-consuming and inconvenient, and actually does not give an accurate indication. A device called *lobing* has been used in similar situations, in which the beam axis is continually alternated through a small angle about some average direction, and the echo strengths at the two extremes are compared, equal echo strengths signifying that the average training angle gives the direction of the target.

The *split transducer* utilizes the principle explained in binaural hearing, in which two ears, being some distance apart, will note a phase difference in a pure tone from a distant source unless the source is directly in front of the listener. We may consider the split transducer to be two separate transducers situated a small distance apart, each serving dually as transmitter and receiver of sound pulses. The two are driven synchronously during transmission, but in reception, the outputs are taken off separately. Thus the signal which strikes the transducer closer to the target leads that in the farther transducer by an electric angle equal to

$$\theta = \frac{2\pi d}{\lambda} \sin \phi \text{ radians}$$

where ϕ is the training angle, d is the distance between the centers of the transducers, λ is the wavelength of the sound in the water. It will be noted (Fig. 12.41) that $d \sin \phi$ is the additional distance traveled by the upper of the two

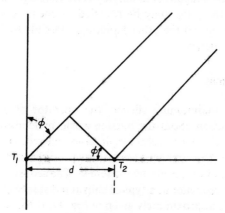

Fig. 12.41. The split transducer.

rays, which is the one reaching the farther transducer. Dividing by λ gives the distance in wavelengths, and multiplying by 2π converts to radians.

By rotating the split transducer until the phase angle between the two received waves is reduced to zero, it is possible to tell rather critically the direction of the target. By experience with binaural localization, it might be thought that only a rough indication of the target direction could be obtained in this way, but it must be remembered that a fairly pure tone is emitted during echo ranging, and circuits can be constructed that will make accurate comparisons of phase.

When the signal is first received with a split transducer, it is possible to tell whether the target direction is a positive or negative angle with respect to the training direction by noting the sign of the phase difference, and it becomes a simple problem in circuitry to tell the operator the direction in which he must turn to approach, rather than recede from, the direction of the target. By further refinement of circuitry, it is possible to build a *null-seeking* circuit which will automatically reduce the training angle to zero, thus giving an *automatic following* device.

Even though a split transducer is used, the accuracy of location in azimuth is still a function of the narrowness of the beam. This is an additional reason, therefore, why narrow beams are used in echo ranging. However, the narrower the beam the more restricted is the search field. Consequently, narrow-beam systems always have some provision for *scanning*. In general, scanning is accomplished by swinging the beam through a horizontal plane several times a minute. When the same problem arises in radar, beams of different directivities are often used, a fairly blunt beam for *searching*, and a narrow beam for *tracking*. In undersea location, on the other hand, the echo ranging system is more often supplemented by a *passive listening* system, which has a second advantage in addition to presenting a wider search field. Tactically, it is often dangerous to employ echo ranging, since the position of the craft emitting the pulse may be revealed to enemy craft in the vicinity. With passive listening, on the other hand, it is possible to detect enemy craft while maintaining silence.

12.5 Passive Listening

In addition to maintaining silence, the operator of a passive listening device gets information about the outside world by identification of sounds, which is totally lacking when echo ranging is employed. The most important sound produced in the water by a vessel, either on the surface or submerged, is usually the result of cavitation by the screw. The acoustic pressure produced in the water by the propeller of a typical ship at a distance of 1,000 yd, moving at medium speed, is approximately given in Fig. 12.51 for frequencies between 100 and 10,000 cycles. Machinery noises, of all types, have their unique characteristics, and experienced operators become surprisingly familiar with them. Cavitation and machinery noise spectra include the entire sonic range and the ultrasonic range up to about 30 kc.

Our study of absorption has shown that it increases rapidly with frequency. This fact makes it relatively certain that at long ranges an underwater sound will consist predominantly of low-frequency energy. On the other hand, water noise, except shrimp noise, has an energy distribution that falls off rapidly at higher frequencies. As a result of these two conflicting effects, high signal frequencies usually have better signal-to-noise ratios at close ranges, but the attenuation of the signal by absorption tends to cancel this advantage at distant ranges. As the listening ship approaches the sound source, the signal may first become recognizable anywhere in the spectrum, but it is most often in the range from 500 to 2,000 cycles. Ultrasonic frequencies may be rendered audible by the heterodyne method. For the listening function, therefore, it is desirable that the operator be able to hear the signal through a system having controlled frequency characteristics. For the tracking function, the system should, of course, be as directive as possible in azimuth.

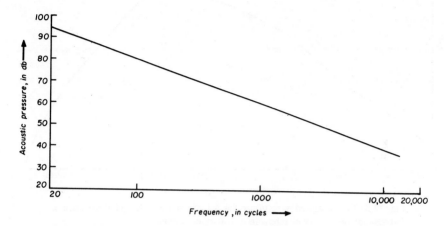

Fig. 12.51. Acoustic pressure in water, caused by propeller of freighter 1,000 yd away.

To fulfill requirements of passive listening, the JP system was developed by the U. S. Navy during World War II. To achieve the directivity desired in the hydrophone, a piston type would have been of unwieldy size. Therefore a *line hydrophone* was developed, consisting of a single tube in radial vibration. The tube used was 3 ft long and 2 in. in diameter. A baffle was used so that response would be obtained only in the forward direction. The "pancake" pattern of this transducer is not only as effective as directivity in both azimuth and elevation, but is actually preferred, since equal response in elevation enables the system to pick up noises more readily, whereas elevation data are of minor importance in undersea tactics.

The electric sensitivity of the system is approximately 10^{-8} v. With a hydrophone of the JP type, the system has an over-all sensitivity of about 20 db over that required to raise the water noise to audibility under average conditions. Further increases in sensitivity have not been found of value in listening systems, as the water noise is at present the limiting factor on the range of the system. Tests of large groups of operators have shown that for a signal to be recognized through the noise, the signal must be about equal to the noise level over a band of frequencies somewhere in the spectrum (cf. Art. 8.9). The width of such a band, known as the critical band width, varies somewhat with the position of the signal in the spectrum. To make the system operate at the point in the spectrum where the signal-to-noise ratio happens to be most favorable, several filters with different frequency characteristics are employed. A bass-boost filter aids in identifying such noise as heavy machinery vibration and banging chains, and is useful at long ranges. The higher pass filters are most useful at close ranges where the falling characteristic of the noise and the increased directivity with frequency can be used

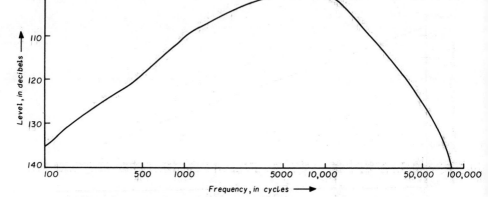

Fig. 12.52 (a). Frequency response for a hydrophone. Acoustic pressure = 1 dyne/cm² decibel level refers to 1 volt open circuit.

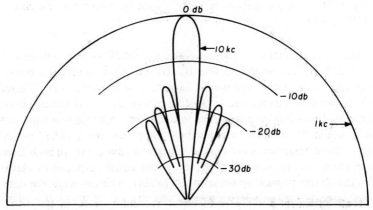

Fig. 12.52 (b). Directivity pattern of a hydrophone at different frequencies (1 and 10 kc).

with good advantage. Limiting the response will often eliminate the major part of the ambient noise energy, which is predominantly of low frequency. Also, reducing the band width reduces the noise power independent of differential frequency effects.

The frequency response and directivity characteristic of the hydrophone are shown in Fig. 12.52.

The ability of experienced operators to gather information by passive listening is little short of astonishing. They are able to pick out signals as much as 10 db below ambient noise level, in some instance to tell whether a ship is loaded or unloaded, and to detect the sharp turns of a ship in the water.

12.6 Underwater Sound Transducers

Underwater sound transducers employ either the piezoelectric or the magnetostrictive principle. Since we have already described the use of piezoelectric transducers to some extent, we shall analyze the magnetostrictive principle from the viewpoint of its application in underwater sound transducers.

If a rod of nickel is brought into a magnetic field parallel to its length, its length will be observed to decrease slightly, regardless of the direction of the magnetic field. This phenomenon is known as magnetostriction. The strain as a function of magnetic intensity is shown in Fig. 12.61. The magneto-

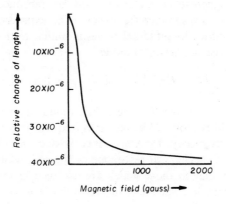

Fig. 12.61. Magnetostrictive strain in nickel.

strictive effect is reversible. If a previously magnetized rod of nickel is stretched, the magnetization decreases; if it is compressed in the direction of its length, the magnetization is increased. If the rod is used as the core of a solenoid, an alternating compressive force will give rise to an alternating emf in the solenoid.

For a reason that will become apparent, we shall be more interested in the magnitude of the magnetostrictive *force* than in the magnitude of the static strain, which is the ordinate of Fig. 12.61. Young's modulus for nickel is about 2.1×10^{12} dynes/cm². For a cross section of 3 cm² (approximately 1 cm radius) a strain of 30×10^{-6} (which is on the linear portion of the strain curve) would require a force of approximately 2×10^8 dynes. We may take this as an indication of the order of magnitude of the forces that may be produced by magnetostrictive action.

Let us now consider the force necessary to generate a 117 db pressure in water at a frequency of 24 kc with a piston of 30 cm radius, so that we can correlate the design of the transducer with the transmission problem of Art. 12.1. For simplicity, we may assume that the wave is effectively plane and therefore that the force which the piston must generate will be

$$F_{rms} = SP_{rms} = 0.707 \times 10^6 \times 900\pi \approx 2 \times 10^9 \text{ dynes}$$

Let us solve also for the amplitude of piston motion which will be required to generate this pressure at 24 kc.

$$F = vR_r = \omega AR_r$$

where v = velocity of vibration, A = amplitude of vibration, R_r = radiation resistance. Solving for A,

$$A = \frac{F}{\omega R_r} = \frac{2 \times 10^9}{2\pi \times 24 \times 10^3 \times 900\pi \times 1.5 \times 10^5}$$

$$\approx 30 \times 10^{-6} \text{ cm}$$

When the magnetostrictive effect is used for transducer action, the nickel tube is driven at its resonance frequency. The expression for the resonant frequency of a rod for longitudinal waves is similar to that for a string. It is given below for the fundamental mode.

$$f_0 = \frac{1}{2L}\sqrt{\frac{E}{\rho}}, \quad E = 2.1 \times 10^{12}, \quad \rho = 8.8, \quad f_0 = 24 \times 10^3$$

A substitution of the values for the elastic modulus and the density gives a length of about 10 cm for a 24 kc resonant frequency. Since the rod is driven at its resonant frequency, the impedance is due entirely to the radiation resistance and the mechanical resistance of the rod, which is small. Conditions are then similar to those which are assumed in solving for the initial efficiency of a horn loudspeaker. In fact, the efficiencies obtained with the magnetostrictive transducer in water are about the same as those obtained with the horn in air. We should note that the amplitude necessary for producing the desired pressure is well within the capabilities of a rod of 10 cm length, and that the force required is about 10 times that which can be produced in a single rod. However, several rods of equal length can be attached to the diaphragm and the individual magnetostrictive forces added.

An example of a magnetostrictive transducer used for echo ranging is shown in Fig. 12.62. In this transducer, 600 nickel tubes are attached to a steel diaphragm and driven by an electronic generator which has a power output of 600 w. The total length of the tube plus diaphragm thickness is chosen so that the transducer as a whole is resonant at the driving frequency. Since the efficiency is of the order of 50 per cent, this transducer is capable of generating an acoustic power output of about 300 w.

We have already mentioned that the magnetostrictive effect is reversible, and have described a magnetostrictive receiver in the preceding article. A simplified diagram of this receiver is shown in Fig. 12.62(b). However, one can construct a simpler and more sensitive transducer with piezoelectric elements. A hydrophone employing piezoelectric elements is shown in Fig. 12.63. The action is similar to that of the piezoelectric (crystal) microphone.

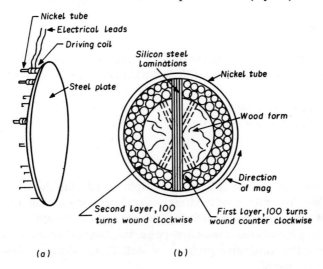

(a)   (b)

Fig. 12.62. Magnetostrictive transducers: (a) Piston type with bowling-pin directivity for echo ranging; (b) cross section of line-type magnetostrictive transducer which uses a long nickel tube for a "pancake" pattern of radiation.

However, there are some interesting details that are worthy of mention. In most piezoelectric materials, the application of voltage causes an increase in one dimension and a decrease in another, so that the net volume change is small. Conversely, if these piezoelectric elements are exposed to pressure along the length and simultaneously along the width, voltages of opposite polarity are produced, and often the two effects are almost equal, so that the sensitivity to *hydrostatic pressure* is small. In one piezoelectric substance, *lithium sulfate*, however, there is a net *volume change* on polarization, so that, conversely, the substance will be sensitive to hydrostatic pressure.

A second detail is the method by which the electric circuit is insulated from the short-circuiting action of the water while at the same time effective acoustic contact is maintained. The crystal stack is surrounded by castor oil, which

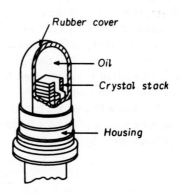

Fig. 12.63. Hydrophone with piezo-electric elements.

has about the same characteristic impedance as water, and the housing is constructed of a rubber especially developed to have a characteristic impedance close to that of water. This rubber is aptly called rho-c rubber.

References

R. J. Evans, "Echo Ranging Sonar," *Electronics*, August, 1946, pp. 88-93.
Lanier and Sawyer, "Sonar for Submarines," *Electronics*, April, 1946, pp. 99-103.
Kinsler and Frey, *Fundamentals of Acoustics*, Wiley, New York, 1950.
M. J. Sheehy, *J. Acous. Soc. Am.*, **22**, 24 (1950).

Problems

1. Find the particle velocity and displacement amplitude at 800 cycles ($\omega = 5,000$) for unit intensity (1 erg/sec/cm^2) in water and in air.

2. When a sound channel forms near the surface, the attenuation caused by spreading follows the inverse first-power law rather than the inverse square law. Solve the illustrative problem of Art. 12.1, supposing that a sound channel has formed.

3. Find the permissible value of acoustic pressure at a point 34 ft below the surface.

4. A circular piston is constructed as a split transducer, radiating a 24 kc signal. The piston has a radius of 30 cm. Find the phase difference between the two halves of the transducer resulting from a 3° error in training angle.

5. Young's modulus for nickel is 2.1×10^{12} dynes/cm^2 and the density is 8.8 g/cm^3. Find the speed of plane compressional waves in nickel. The fundamental frequency of a fixed-free bar is that for which the wavelength is 4 times the length of the bar. Find the length of a fixed-free nickel rod which is resonant at a frequency of 24 kc.

6. A nickel bar is impressed with a field of 4,000 gausses and is allowed to contract freely. It is then placed between two rigid planes separated by the exact length of the contracted bar. What stress will exist in the nickel when the field is removed?

7. For a free nickel bar, the magnetic induction-strain curve is approximately a parabola up to a frequency of 5,000 gausses, and the strain is given approximately by the equation

$$\frac{\partial \xi}{dx} = \text{Const } B^2$$

From the curve of magnetostrictive strain (Fig. 12.61), show that the value of the proportionality constant is approximately $- 1 \times 10^{-12}$ by noting the value of the strain at 2,000, 3,000, and 4,000 gausses.

8. If the internal magnetostrictive stress in a nickel rod is opposed by an external stress, the strain which takes place will be different from that shown in Fig. 12.61. Show that a more general relation for stress and strain in a magnetostrictive rod is given by the equation,

$$\frac{\partial \xi}{\partial x} = -\frac{F}{SY} + \text{Const } B^2$$

where F is the external force, and Y is Young's Modulus.

9. To prevent frequency doubling, a strong d-c polarizing field $(B_0 \gg B_1)$ is imposed on the nickel rod of a magnetostriction transducer, so that the instantaneous magnetic induction will be

$$B' = B_0 + B_1 \cos \omega t$$

where B_0 is the intensity of the polarizing field, B_1 is the peak value of the alternating component, B' is the total instantaneous field. The instantaneous strain may then be written,

$$\frac{\partial \xi'}{\partial x} = \left(\frac{\partial \xi}{\partial x}\right)_0 + \left(\frac{\partial \xi}{dx}\right)_1 \cos \omega t$$

Show that the equation of the fundamental components of the alternating magnetic induction, strain, and external force is

$$F_1 \cos \omega t = SY\left[-\left(\frac{\partial \xi}{\partial x}\right)_1 + 2\epsilon B_0 B_1\right] \cos \omega t$$

$$F_1 = SY\left[-\left(\frac{\partial \xi}{\partial x}\right)_1 + 2\epsilon B_0 B_1\right]$$

which can also be written,

$$B_1 = \frac{1}{2\epsilon B_0}\left[\frac{F_1}{SY} + \left(\frac{\partial \xi}{\partial x_1}\right)\right]$$

Here   is the magnetostriction strain constant. The last form of the equation shows that the magnetic force may be considered to be expended partially in overcoming the internal strain and partially in overcoming the external force F_1.

10. A nickel rod of cross-sectional area 10 cm² is fixed on one end, and the other end is exposed to a water column of infinite length. It is driven by an alternating magnetic intensity such that the peak value of the alternating magnetic induction is 400 gausses, which is superimposed on a d-c magnetic intensity of 4,000 gausses.

(a) Find the external force and the displacement amplitude A_0 in a rod with a 24 kc resonant frequency, if the driving frequency is 10 kc. *Hint:* remember that $F_1 = pcSwA_0$ and that the rod is stiffness-controlled at that frequency.

(b) Find the external force and the displacement at a frequency of 24 kc, which is the approximate resonant frequency, if it is assumed that the following simplified equation holds at the resonant frequency:

$$B_1 = \frac{1}{2\epsilon B_0} \cdot \frac{F}{SY}$$

Appendix 1

BESSEL FUNCTIONS

As an introduction to a discussion of Bessel functions, it is advisable to consider the general meaning of the term *function* in mathematics. The following is often used as defining the concept: If variable y depends on variable x such that the value of the variable x determines the value of the variable y, then y is said to be a function of x. In this case, x is the independent variable, and y is the dependent variable. A variable may be a function of two independent variables. Thus if the value of variables x and z, which are independent of each other, determines the value of the variable y, then y is said to be a function of x and z.

Functional relations may be defined in many ways: y may be given as an explicit polynominal function of x (or x and z); y may be given implicitly in terms of x by means of an algebraic equation connecting the two; y may be given in terms of x by means of a differential equation involving y, x, and derivatives of y with respect to x; the implicit relation between the two variables may also be expressed by an integral. Other forms of functional relation exist, but those given will suffice for this discussion of Bessel functions. It should be observed, however, that an infinite series will be considered a polynominal, so that the discussion of the expansion of functions by infinite series in Art. 1.5 will be very helpful as background for the present article.

As an example, the relation $y = \sin x$ may be equivalently expressed by the series

$$y = x - \frac{x^3}{3!} + \frac{x^5}{5!} - \cdots \tag{1}$$

and by the differential equation

$$\frac{\partial^2 y}{dx^2} + y = 0 \tag{2}$$

The series is sometimes said to be a *solution* of the differential equation, but the equation is equally good from the point of view of expressing the functional relation. Indeed, it expresses some of the characteristics of the relation better than the solution, e.g. the fact that the function is such that its second derivative is equal to the negative of its ordinate.

As an example of a functional relation expressed by an integral, we have

$$y = \int_0^x t^2 \, dt = \frac{x^3}{3}$$

390

Notice here that the independent variable appears in the limit and not in the integrand. This is sometimes expressed by saying that the value of an integral is a function of its limits (and, of course, the form of its integrand). Thus if the integrand were a cube instead of a square, a different functional relation would hold between x and y, namely, $y = x^4/4$. Thus in the integral

$$y = \int_0^x tz\, dt = \frac{x^{z+1}}{z+1}$$

y is a function of both x and z. However, it is *not* a function of the variable of integration t.

Sometimes the question arises as to the primary definition of a certain functional relation. Thus we may ask whether the series or the differential equation is the definition of the sine of x. If the series were taken as the definition, it could be shown that the differential equation follows from the prior definition. However, we take the view here that the two are equivalent definitions. Self-consistency is then the only property that we require among equivalent definitions of functions. This eliminates a great amount of difficult historical research as to the form that was first arrived at as the defining relation for a particular function. There are therefore different *representations* of the Bessel function. We shall be interested in three representations: the differential equation, the infinite series, and the integral. The form of the integral which we shall employ is generally called Hansen's representation. Many forms of integral representation exist, some of them more general in application than others. Hansen's is the most useful for most acoustic applications, and it is the one that is developed in the theory of the radiation from a piston. In each of the three cases, the Bessel function is a function of two variables. One of these variables is often taken as a parameter, rather than as a continuous variable, and is often restricted to positive integral values. This point should not be overemphasized, however, and since the value of the function depends on the values assigned to two quantities, it will be considered a function of two variables.

The differential equation which defines Bessel's function is

$$\frac{1}{x}\frac{d}{dx}\left(x\frac{dy}{dx}\right) + \left(1 - \frac{m^2}{x^2}\right)y = 0 \tag{3}$$

In this equation, y is obviously a function of x, but it is also a function of the value assigned to the parameter m, though in a different manner. Since this equation is of the second order, it must have two independent solutions. These solutions are called Bessel functions of the first and second kind. We shall restrict the discussion to the Bessel function of the first kind, and to eliminate continual qualifying remarks, shall refer to it as *the* Bessel function. From this viewpoint, the Bessel function is that relation between y, x, and m, which is a solution to the differential equation.

If m is made zero in the differential equation, the solution is obtained without undue difficulty by the series method. This method proceeds by assuming that y can be represented by a general power series in x (see Art. 1.5), finding the first and second derivatives under this assumption, and substituting them back into the differential equation. This gives a relation between the coefficients of the power series which must hold if the series is to be a solution of the equation. The series obtained with m set equal to zero is

$$y = 1 - \left(\frac{x}{2}\right)^2 + \frac{1}{2!2!}\left(\frac{x}{2}\right)^4 - \frac{1}{3!3!}\left(\frac{x}{2}\right)^6 + \cdots \tag{4}$$

The letter J is always used to express solutions to Bessel's equation. Since our solution above was obtained with m set equal to zero, a subscript is employed to indicate this fact. Thus we write

$$J_0 = 1 - \left(\frac{x}{2}\right)^2 + \frac{1}{2!2!}\left(\frac{x}{2}\right)^4 - \cdots \tag{5}$$

It is not much more difficult to solve the equation by the series method when other values of m are considered, particularly if they are integral values, and indeed the equation may be solved by allowing m to be an undetermined constant, and finding y as an expression involving both x and m. Such a solution is written, and the series for general m is

$$J_m(x) = \frac{(x/2)^m}{0!m!} - \frac{(x/2)^{m+2}}{1!(m+1)!} + \frac{(x/2)^{m+4}}{2!(m+2)!} - \frac{(x/2)^{m+6}}{3!(m+3)!} \tag{6}$$

(*Note:* $0! = 1$.)

Actually, the series above could be multiplied by any arbitrary constant and still be a solution of Bessel's equation, but the form above is arbitrarily defined as Bessel's function of the first kind and mth order. Often the term "of the first kind" is omitted.

Since series may be differentiated and integrated term by term (with certain qualifications that are not important here), the important relations given in Arts. 4.9 and 4.10, Eqs. (4.96) and (4.104) can be proved directly from the series representation.

Hansen found that the relation expressed by the series (6) could be compactly represented by means of an integral. We have already used this integral in Art. 4.9 as a representation of Bessel's function, and when it was introduced, it was remarked that it could be taken as a definition of the Bessel function. It is repeated for convenience. It is instructive to expand the integrand as a series, and integrate its term, comparing the result with the series representation of the Bessel function.

$$J_m(x) = \frac{1}{\pi} j^{-m} \int_0^\pi e^{jx \cos \varphi} \cos n\varphi \, d\varphi$$

Although the differential equation is given as a representation of the Bessel function, it is not adapted to computation. However, the series usually gives a close approximation to the numerical value of the function for any values of x and m, if only the first few terms are used.

Appendix 2

Table of Bessel Functions, Directivity Functions, and Impedance Functions

x	Bessel Functions		Directivity Functions		Piston Impedance Functions	
			Pressure	Intensity	$R_1(x)$	$X_1(x)$
	Zero Order $J_0(x)$	First Order $J_1(x)$	$(x = ka \sin \theta)$		$(x = 2ka)$	
			$\dfrac{2J_1(x)}{x}$	$\left[\dfrac{2J_1(x)}{x}\right]^2$	$1 - \dfrac{2J_1(x)}{x}$	$\dfrac{2K_1(x)}{x^2}$
0.0	1.0000	0.0000	1.0000	1.0000	0.0000	0.0000
0.1	0.9975	0.0499	0.9980	0.9960	0.0020	0.0424
0.2	0.9900	0.0995	0.9950	0.9900	0.0050	0.0847
0.3	0.9776	0.1483	0.9887	0.9775	0.0113	0.1272
0.4	0.9604	0.1960	0.9802	0.9608	0.0198	0.1680
0.5	0.9385	0.2423	0.9692	0.9393	0.0308	0.2120
0.6	0.9120	0.2867	0.9557	0.9134	0.0443	0.2486
0.7	0.8812	0.3290	0.9400	0.8836	0.0600	0.2968
0.8	0.8463	0.3688	0.9221	0.8503	0.0779	0.3253
0.9	0.8075	0.4059	0.9009	0.8117	0.0991	0.3816
1.0	0.7652	0.4401	0.8801	0.7746	0.1199	0.3969
1.1	0.7196	0.4709	0.8562	0.7331	0.1438	0.4296
1.2	0.6711	0.4983	0.8305	0.6897	0.1695	0.4624
1.3	0.6201	0.5220	0.8031	0.6450	0.1969	0.4915
1.4	0.5669	0.5419	0.7743	0.5995	0.2257	0.5207
1.5	0.5118	0.5579	0.7439	0.5533	0.2561	0.5460
1.6	0.4554	0.5699	0.7124	0.5075	0.2876	0.5713
1.7	0.3980	0.5778	0.6799	0.4619	0.3201	0.5924
1.8	0.3400	0.5815	0.6461	0.4174	0.3539	0.6134
1.9	0.2818	0.5811	0.6117	0.3740	0.3883	0.6301
2.0	0.2239	0.5767	0.5767	0.3326	0.4233	0.6468
2.2	0.1104	0.5560	0.5054	0.2554	0.4946	0.6711
2.4	+0.0025	0.5202	0.4335	0.1879	0.5665	0.6862
2.6	−0.0968	0.4708	0.3622	0.1326	0.6378	0.6925
2.8	−0.1850	0.4097	0.2927	0.0857	0.7073	0.6903
3.0	−0.2601	0.3391	0.2260	0.0511	0.7740	0.6800
3.2	−0.3202	0.2613	0.1633	0.0267	0.8367	0.6623
3.4	−0.3643	0.1792	0.1054	0.0111	0.8946	0.6381
3.6	−0.3918	0.0955	0.0530	0.0028	0.9470	0.6081
3.8	−0.4026	+0.0128	+0.0068	0.00005	0.9932	0.5733
4.0	−0.3971	−0.0660	−0.0330	0.0011	1.0330	0.5349
5.0	−0.1776	−0.3276	−0.1310	0.0172	1.1310	0.3232
6.0	+0.1507	−0.2767	−0.0922	0.0085	1.0922	0.1594
7.0	0.3001	−0.0047	−0.0013	0.00000	1.0013	0.0989
8.0	0.1716	+0.2346	+0.0587	0.0034	0.9413	0.1219
9.0	−0.0903	+0.2453	0.0545	0.0030	0.9455	0.1663
10.0	−0.2459	+0.0435	+0.0087	0.00008	0.9913	0.1784
11.0	−0.1712	−0.1768	−0.0321	0.0010	1.0321	0.1464
12.0	+0.0477	−0.2234	−0.0372	0.0014	1.0372	0.0973

Appendix 3

THE DYNAMIC MICROPHONE

For this discussion, reference must be made to Fig. 6.25(a), the construction diagram of the dynamic microphone. The mechanical diagram, 6.25(b), obtained for the microphone would be correct if the silk cloth which provides inertance and mechanical resistance were to communicate directly with the open air. However, the air, after passing through the silk cloth, enters the larger opening within the housing of the microphone, which shall be called

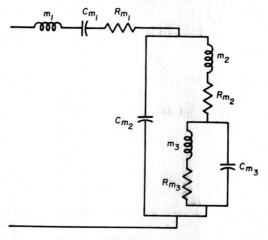

Fig. 3.1.

C_{m3}, and returns to the open air through the tube m_3-R_{m3}. Therefore the series element in the diagram of Fig. 6.25(b), consisting of m_2 and R_{m2}, should return to "ground" through a parallel element consisting of the large cavity compliance in one branch and the inertance and resistance of the tube in the other. This gives the mechanical circuit shown in Fig. 3.1.

This figure will be analyzed by neglecting the resistance, for the effect of resistance in general is to modify resonance effects, and the chief purpose of the discussion is to ascertain where the resonant frequencies of the circuit occur. For this purpose, the mechanical circuit will be converted into the electric circuit shown in Fig. 3.2. This is done as explained in Art. 6.2, by a conversion from series mechanical connections to parallel electric connections.

The major modification of this circuit with respect to the simpler electric circuit of Fig. 6.21(a) is to introduce a low-frequency resonance. Values of L_3 and C_3 are much larger than are L_2 and C_2. At low frequencies, the

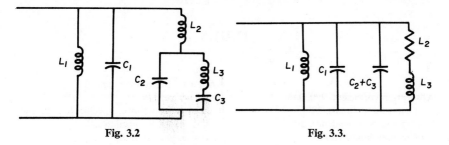

Fig. 3.2   Fig. 3.3.

inductive elements L_2 and L_3 have very low reactance, and the simpler circuit of Fig. 3.3 can be employed to predict the approximate performance of the circuit.

The only effect of the change is to introduce an effective capacitance of significant value in parallel with the effective capacitance due to the mechanical circuit. This results in a lowering of the first resonant frequency. Figure 3.4 indicates the gradual changes in the response produced by the addition of acoustic elements.

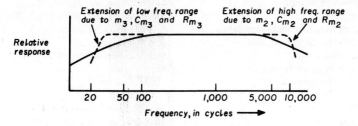

Fig. 3.4.

INDEX